TABLES

SIMPLIFIED DESIGN OF
REINFORCED CONCRETE

BOOKS BY HARRY PARKER

Simplified Design of Reinforced Concrete
    Second Edition

Simplified Design of Roof Trusses for Architects and Builders
    Second Edition

Simplified Design of Structural Steel
    Second Edition

Simplified Design of Structural Timber
    Second Edition

Simplified Engineering for Architects and Builders
    Third Edition

Simplified Mechanics and Strength of Materials
    Second Edition

Simplified Site Engineering for Architects and Builders
    By Harry Parker and John W. MacGuire

Kidder-Parker Architects' and Builders' Handbook
    By the late Frank E. Kidder and Harry Parker
    Eighteenth Edition

Materials and Methods of Architectural Construction
    By Harry Parker, the late Charles Merrick Gay, and John W. MacGuire
    Third Edition

New York · London · Sydney

JOHN WILEY & SONS, INC.

SIMPLIFIED DESIGN OF REINFORCED CONCRETE

SECOND EDITION

HARRY PARKER, M.S.

Emeritus Professor of Architectural Construction

School of Fine Arts

University of Pennsylvania

PREFACE TO SECOND EDITION

The first edition of *Simplified Design of Reinforced Concrete* was published in 1943. In the intervening years numerous changes in specification requirements, with respect to both concrete and the accompanying steel reinforcement, have made a complete revision necessary.

The purpose for which this book was originally written, as well as its scope and limitations, was stated in the preface to the first edition. Consequently, this preface is reprinted.

A major portion of this book consists of illustrative examples of the design of structural reinforced concrete members, accompanied by similar problems to be solved by the student. All these design examples and problems have been revised and expanded to agree with the current allowable stresses and specified design procedure. All the figures in the book are new, as are most of the tables. In accordance with current practice, reinforcing bar sizes are now identified by numbers instead of dimensions. In addition, the text now conforms with the American Standard abbreviations for engineering terms. The higher bond stresses permitted for deformed bars have, in many instances, made hooked ends unnecessary. The practice of using all straight reinforcing bars instead of a combination of both straight and bent bars in beams is explained and employed in illustrative design examples. Design examples conforming with recent code requirements relating to the spacing of web reinforcement for restrained beams that have no slab to provide T-beam action are also illustrated.

A new chapter on Prestressed Concrete has been added. Its purpose is to explain the theory of prestressing. An illustrative example shows by the design of a conventional reinforced concrete beam, and the same beam designed as prestressed concrete, why prestressing is advantageous in the economical use of materials.

I wish to thank Harlan Coornvelt, consulting engineer, for his kindness in examining this text. His criticism and practical suggestions have helped greatly to enhance the value of the book.

Whereas no particular unit stresses or specifications have been employed in discussions relating to the design of structural members, the latest printing of "Building Code Requirements for Reinforced Concrete" (ACI 318) of the American Concrete Institute has been used as a guide for procedure.

The *Reinforced Concrete Design Handbook*, published cooperatively by the American Concrete Institute, the Portland Cement Association, the Concrete Reinforcing Steel Institute, and the Rail Steel Bar Association, has been used as a valuable reference. I am indebted to the American Concrete Institute for their kindness in granting permission to reproduce certain tables and data from their publications. Without such cooperation this type of book could not have been written.

HARRY PARKER

High Hollow, Southampton, Pa.
January 1960

PREFACE TO FIRST EDITION

The preparation of this book has been prompted by the fact that many young men desirous of the ability to design elementary reinforced concrete structural members have been deprived of the usual preliminary training. The author has endeavored to simplify the subject matter for those having a minimum of preparation. Throughout the text will be found references to Section I of *Simplified Engineering for Architects and Builders.* * Familiarity with this brief treatment of the principles of mechanics is sufficient. Any textbook on mechanics will give the desired information. This particular book has been referred to as a convenience in having a direct reference. With these basic principles, and a high school knowledge of algebra, no other preparation is needed.

In preparing material for this book, the author has had in mind its use as a textbook as well as a book to be used for home study. Simple, concise explanations of the design of the most common structural elements have been given rather than discussions of the more involved problems. In addition to the usual design formulas sufficient theory underlying the principles of design is presented, in developing basic formulas, to ensure the student a thorough knowledge of the fundamentals involved.

A major portion of the book contains illustrative examples giving the solution of the design of structural members. Accompanying the examples are problems to be solved by the student.

The usual tables necessary in the design of reinforced concrete are included. No supplementary books, tables, or charts are required. Where practicable, safe load tables have been added, but

* In the Second Edition the reference book is *Simplified Mechanics and Strength of Materials.*

in each instance illustrative examples give the design steps showing the underlying principles by means of which the table was
prepared.

The titles of other volumes in this series of elementary books
relating to structural design have included the words "for Architects and Builders." The purpose of this has been to convey the
idea that the books are limited in scope and that they are not the
comprehensive and thorough treatises demanded by engineers. It
is found, however, that these books have a much wider use than
was anticipated. Because of this, it has seemed advisable to omit
the words "for Architects and Builders" from the title of the present volume even though it has been prepared with this particular
group in mind.

Grateful appreciation is extended to the Portland Cement Association and the American Concrete Institute for their kindness and
cooperation in granting permission to reproduce data and tables
from their publications.

The author has made no attempt to offer short-cuts or originality
in design. Instead, he has endeavored to present clearly and con-
cisely the present-day methods commonly used in the design of
reinforced concrete members. A thorough knowledge of the principles herein set forth should encourage the student and serve as
adequate preparation for advanced study.

HARRY PARKER

High Hollow, Southampton, Pa.
March 1943

SUGGESTIONS

The following suggestions are offered to those who wish to acquire a knowledge of the basic principles of the design of reinforced concrete as set forth in this book.

1. It is of the utmost importance that those who use this book be familiar with the elementary principles of mechanics. There are many excellent textbooks on the subject. To those who wish to refresh their memories, we suggest a study of Section I of *Simplified Engineering for Architects and Builders* or *Simplified Mechanics and Strength of Materials*. The subject is not difficult. It will be found that familiarity with the underlying principles will be of great assistance in the use of this book.

2. The subject matter herein presented has been arranged so that the various theories follow in a logical sequence. To use this book most advantageously, it is advisable to start at the beginning and master each chapter in the order in which it is presented.

3. Problems to be solved are given throughout the book. Make up and solve similar problems with specification data. Perhaps such problems may uncover some point that needs further study.

4. In solving problems, form the habit of writing the denomination of each quantity. The solution of an equation will be a number. It may be so many pounds, or is it pounds per square inch? Are the units foot-pounds or inch-pounds? Adding the names of the quantities signifies an exact knowledge of the quantity and frequently prevents subsequent errors.

5. The solution of a problem should include a drawing giving complete information by means of which a builder may construct the member exactly as it has been designed.

6. If, at present, you do not own a slide rule, get one (with a pamphlet of instructions) at the first opportunity. The ability to use it is readily acquired, and in a short time it will become indispensable.

7. Don't be hasty. Be thorough.

H. P.

CONTENTS

CHAPTER 3 · SHEAR AND BENDING MOMENTS IN BEAMS

CHAPTER 4 · FORMULAS FOR BENDING

CHAPTER 5 · SHEAR AND BOND STRESSES

CHAPTER 6 · DESIGN OF RECTANGULAR BEAMS

CHAPTER 7 · DESIGN OF T-BEAMS

CHAPTER 8 · BEAMS REINFORCED FOR COMPRESSION

CHAPTER 9 · REINFORCED CONCRETE FLOOR SYSTEMS

CHAPTER 10 · REINFORCED CONCRETE COLUMNS

CHAPTER 11 · FOUNDATIONS

CONTENTS

CHAPTER 12 · RETAINING WALLS

CHAPTER 13 · MISCELLANEOUS MEMBERS

CHAPTER 14 · PRESTRESSED CONCRETE

CHAPTER 1

MATERIALS

1–1. Concrete. Concrete is a conglomerate artificial stone. It is made by mixing a paste of cement and water with sand and crushed stone, gravel, or other inert material. The chemically active substance in the mixture is the cement which unites physically and chemically with the water and, upon hardening, binds the aggregates together to form a solid mass resembling stone.

A particular inherent property is that concrete may be made in any desired shape. The wet mixture is placed in wood or metal forms in which it hardens or sets. Properly proportioned concrete is a hard and durable material. It is strong in compression but brittle and almost useless in resisting tensile stresses. For structural members, in which stresses other than compression occur, steel reinforcement is added. Primarily, the steel is introduced to withstand the tensile stresses.

In members in which the stresses are almost entirely compressive, such as dams, piers, or certain types of footings, concrete may be used without adding reinforcement. This is known as *mass* or *plain concrete*. As a means of economy, large stones are sometimes placed in the concrete, thereby reducing the amount of sand and cement. The term *rubble aggregate* is applied to hard, durable stone with individual particles not weighing more than 100 lb. If the individual pieces exceed 100 lb in weight, the aggregate is termed *cyclopean aggregate*. Concrete in which reinforcement, other than that provided for shrinkage or temperature changes, is embedded in such a manner that the two materials act together in resisting forces is called *reinforced concrete*.

1–2. Water. The water used in making concrete should be clean and free from injurious amounts of oil, acid, alkali, organic matter, or other deleterious substances. Water containing 5% or more com-

1

mon salt should be avoided for use in concrete; sea water should never be used. Since only a certain amount of water can combine with the cement, an excess quantity of water dilutes the mixture and produces a concrete of reduced strength, watertightness, and durability. Thus it becomes imperative that particular attention be given to the proper proportioning of water and cement. See Art. 2–10.

1–3. Cement. Of all the cements, normal *portland cement* is by far the most extensively used in building construction. Briefly, it is made by mixing and then burning to incipient fusion two materials, one composed principally of lime, the other being a clayey or argil-laceous material containing silica, alumina, and iron. After burning, the clinker is finely pulverized. As compared with *natural cement*, portland cement sets slower but is much stronger and more uniform in quality. In specifying, it is customary to require that the portland cement conform to the latest standard specifications of the American Society for Testing Materials for portland cement.

High early strength portland cement has a decided advantage when it is desirable to obtain a high early strength, such as in concrete road making or in building construction during lower temperatures. In general, high early strength cement has approximately the same strength at the 3-day and 7-day periods that concrete made of normal portland cement produces at the 7-day and 28-day periods. Considerable heat is developed in its rapid gain in strength, and this tends to prevent the concrete from freezing under adverse weather conditions.

1–4. Sand. The materials held together by the paste formed of cement and water are the *aggregates*. The aggregates are inert materials: natural sand, crushed stone, pebbles, cinders, slag, etc. The material smaller than $\frac{3}{8}$ in. in diameter is called *fine aggregate*. The fine aggregate should consist of natural sand, or of inert materials with similar characteristics, having clean, hard, and durable grains, free from organic matter or loam. The size and grading of fine aggregate are determined by standard wire-cloth sieves. It is desirable to have a mixture of fine and coarse grains, as graded aggregate will produce a more compact, hence stronger, concrete. A common specification for grading fine aggregate requires that not less than 95 to 100% shall pass the No. 4 sieve and not more than 30% nor less than 10% shall pass the No. 50 sieve.

1–5. Crushed Stone. All material over $\frac{3}{8}$ in. in diameter is called *coarse aggregate.* This includes crushed stone, gravel, slag, or other inert materials. Like the fine aggregate, coarse aggregate should also range in size. In general, the sizes vary from $\frac{1}{4}$ to 3 in., the maximum size for reinforced concrete being 1 or $1\frac{1}{2}$ in. Some building codes limit the size of the coarse aggregate for reinforced concrete to three quarters of the minimum clear spacing between reinforcing bars and not larger than one fifth the narrowest dimension between the sides of the forms of the member for which the concrete is to be used. When concrete members are small, necessitating the close spacing of bars, the coarse aggregate is usually graded $\frac{1}{4}$ to $\frac{3}{4}$ in. Any crushed rock of durable and strong qualities or clean hard gravel may be used as coarse aggregate. Trap rock makes one of the best aggregates. Granite and hard limestone are likewise suitable, but certain sandstones are considered unfit for use. In proportioning fine to coarse aggregate, there are, of course, no fixed rules, but it is common practice to use for the coarse aggregate twice the volume of the fine aggregate or sand. For instance, a usual proportion is 2 of fine to 4 of coarse aggregate, written 2:4, $2\frac{1}{2}$:5 or 3:6. In general, good concrete should have the greatest possible density. This results partly from a careful grading of aggregate and rodding or vibrating the concrete when it is poured into the forms.

1–6. Cinders. Cinder concrete is sometimes used for reinforced floor and roof slabs of short spans and for fireproofing. As it is a porous material, it should never be used as a protection for steel in exposed positions nor below grade where moisture is present. Most engineers prefer cinders resulting from burning anthracite coal. Cinders should be hard, well burned, reasonably free from sulfides, unburned coal, and foreign matter.

1–7. Slag. Concrete made of blast-furnace slag makes a suitable lightweight concrete. Since the weight of crushed slag has wide variations, only material weighing 65 to 75 lb per cu ft should be used. When it is desired to use slag as a coarse aggregate, the sulfur content should be investigated, an excess quantity of sulfur being injurious to steel reinforcement.

1–8. Lightweight Aggregates. In addition to cinders and slag, several other lightweight aggregates are obtainable. Haydite, for example, is made by burning shale. Frequently a process of aeration is used to produce a porous lightweight aggregate. Such materials produce concrete of sufficient strength and, in comparison with stone concrete, reduce the dead loads appreciably. In general, lightweight aggregates should not exceed 70 lb per cu ft for fine aggregate and 55 lb per cu ft for coarse aggregate.

1–9. Admixtures. Substances added to concrete to improve its workability, accelerate its set, harden its surface, increase its waterproof qualities, etc., are known as *admixtures*. Many of the proprietary compounds contain hydrated lime, calcium chloride, and kaolin. Calcium chloride and calcium oxychloride are the admixtures generally used as accelerators. Care should be exercised in the use of admixtures, especially those of unknown composition. Although a manufacturer may claim superior qualities for his product, it is well to use only materials whose worth has been established by actual use.

1–10. Air-Entrained Concrete. Air-entraining portland cement is made by grinding small quantities of soaplike resinous or fatty materials with normal cement clinker. Sometimes, an air-entraining agent is added to the concrete in the mixer. This cement is used in making air-entrained concrete that increases the resistance to frost action. Air-entraining agents produce billions of microscopic air cells per cubic foot; they are distributed uniformly throughout the mass. These minute voids prevent the accumulation of water in larger voids, which would permit the water to expand, and spalling would result under frost action. Air-entrained concrete is used extensively in pavement and highway construction. It not only offers resistance to frost action and cycles of wetting and drying, or freezing and thawing, but it provides high immunity to surface scaling that results when certain chemicals are used to melt pavement ice. It has a high degree of workability and durability.

Air-entraining cements reduce, somewhat, the strength of concrete. Slightly richer mixes must be used to obtain the same strength concrete that results from using normal portland cement. See Table 2–1 for recommended water-cement ratios.

1–11. Reinforcement. Steel bars for reinforcement in concrete are made from billet steel and rail steel. The three grades of billet steel are structural, intermediate, and hard. Structural grade steel bars may be used with an allowable tensile unit stress of 18,000 psi. (The abbreviation psi is read "pounds per square inch.") Intermediate and hard grades of billet steel and rail steel may be stressed to 20,000 psi. Whereas rail steel is somewhat similar in physical qualities to hard steel, it is more brittle and more difficult to bend. The intermediate grade of billet steel is probably the most commonly used steel for reinforcement.

One of the fundamental assumptions upon which the design of reinforced concrete is based is that the concrete and reinforcement act together as a unit. If *plain bars* are used, the transmission of stresses depends upon the adhesion between the steel and concrete. To provide for a greater bond, reinforcing bars are made with lugs or corrugations and are known as *deformed bars*. These projections are for the purpose of providing a mechanical bond independent of the adhesion between the steel and concrete. Therefore, higher bond stresses are permitted when deformed bars are used. Round bars are now the standard in the United States. Bar #2 comes only in plain rounds.

Another type of reinforcement is *wire mesh*. It is used principally in slabs. The heavier wires, running from beam to beam, resist the tensile forces and are called the carrying wires, whereas the lighter wires cross the heavier wires, being secured by winding or welding. *Expanded metal* is also used for slab reinforcement. The use of wire mesh or expanded metal permits a uniform distribution of steel, whereas individual bars require more care in placing and frequently require metal supports with spacing rods to maintain a proper distribution.

Areas and perimeters of *standard sizes* of bars are shown in Table 1–1. No other sizes should be called for. The ten steel bars, with the exception of #2, are deformed. The shape and spacings of the small ridges on the surface of the bars must conform to the A.S.T.M. Designation A 305. These bars, frequently referred to as *improved deformed bars*, are so superior in bond value that hooking their ends adds very little strength. Notice, in Table 1–1, that in addition to areas and perimeters of individual members figures are given for combinations of 2, 3, and 4 bars. As an example of

TABLE 1–1. AREAS AND PERIMETERS OF ROUND BARS

Bar Desig- nation	Diameter, Inches		Number of Bars			
			1	2	3	4
#2	$\frac{1}{4}$ = 0.250	**Area**	**0.05**	**0.10**	**0.15**	**0.20**
		Perimeter	0.786	1.57	2.36	3.14
#3	$\frac{3}{8}$ = 0.375	**Area**	**0.11**	**0.22**	**0.33**	**0.44**
		Perimeter	1.178	2.36	3.53	4.71
#4	$\frac{1}{2}$ = 0.500	**Area**	**0.20**	**0.40**	**0.60**	**0.80**
		Perimeter	1.571	3.14	4.71	6.28
#5	$\frac{5}{8}$ = 0.625	**Area**	**0.31**	**0.62**	**0.93**	**1.24**
		Perimeter	1.963	3.93	5.89	7.85
#6	$\frac{3}{4}$ = 0.750	**Area**	**0.44**	**0.88**	**1.32**	**1.75**
		Perimeter	2.356	4.71	7.07	9.42
#7	$\frac{7}{8}$ = 0.875	**Area**	**0.60**	**1.20**	**1.80**	**2.41**
		Perimeter	2.749	5.50	8.25	11.00
#8	1 = 1.000	**Area**	**0.79**	**1.58**	**2.37**	**3.16**
		Perimeter	3.142	6.28	9.43	12.57
#9	1.128	**Area**	**1.00**	**2.00**	**3.00**	**4.00**
		Perimeter	3.544	7.09	10.63	14.18
#10	1.270	**Area**	**1.27**	**2.54**	**3.81**	**5.08**
		Perimeter	3.990	7.98	11.97	15.96
#11	1.410	**Area**	**1.56**	**3.12**	**4.68**	**6.24**
		Perimeter	4.430	8.86	13.29	17.72

The bar numbers are based on the nearest number of $\frac{1}{8}$ in. included in the nominal diameter of the bar. All bars are round.

Bar #2 comes in plain bars only.

Bars #9, #10, and #11 are round bars, equivalent in weight and nominal cross-sectional area to the old type 1 in., $1\frac{1}{8}$ in., and $1\frac{1}{4}$ in. square bars.

the convenience of such a table, suppose we have found that the area of tensile reinforcement required for a beam is 1.75 sq in. By referring to the table, we find without computations that 3-#7 or 4-#6 bars will give us this desired area.

1–12. Forms. The construction of wood or metal used to hold the concrete in place until it has hardened is called the *form*. The forms must be put together with exactness, holding to accurate dimensions. Formwork should be rigid and strong enough to support the weight of the concrete without deformation or appreciable deflection. In addition, formwork should be tight enough to prevent the seepage of water and so designed as to permit ready removal.

Timber used for formwork is usually spruce or pine surfaced on the side coming in contact with the concrete. Frequently the timber is oiled. This fills the pores of the wood, results in smoother concrete surfaces, and permits the planks to be removed more readily. The boards should be tongued and grooved, or plywood or Prestwood should be employed. Steel forms are used extensively. They have the decided advantage of being more substantial if they are to be reused. Steel invariably gives smoother surfaces in the concrete, though it is almost impossible to avoid showing the joints. For ribbed floors, metal pans and domes are used extensively, and columns, circular in cross section, invariably are made with metal forms. For ornamental concrete work the forms are generally made of plaster or glue.

Since the formwork for a concrete structure constitutes a considerable item in the cost of the completed structure, particular care should be exercised in its design. It is desirable to maintain a repetition of identical units so that the forms may be removed and reused at other locations with a minimum amount of labor.

There are no exact rules concerning the length of time the forms should remain in place. Obviously they should not be removed until the concrete is strong enough to support its own weight in addition to any loads that may be placed on it. Sometimes the side forms of beams are removed before the bottom forms. When this is done, posts or shoring are placed under the bottoms of the members to give additional support. This is called *re-posting*. The time for stripping depends upon the type of member, the character of the concrete, and the weather conditions. The minimum length of time for walls is 2 days and for beams and columns, 7 to 11 days. A rule of thumb is to retain the bottom forms 2 days for each inch of thickness of concrete. The time for stripping must conform with the governing building code requirements, and the temperatures during the curing period should be recorded and given due consideration. For practical purposes we may assume that concrete attains its desired strength at the end of 28 days.

CHAPTER 2

PROPORTIONING AND MIXING

2–1. Requirements for Concrete. Since concrete is a mixture in which a paste made of portland cement and water binds together fine and coarse particles of inert materials, known as aggregates, it is readily seen that by varying the proportions of the ingredients innumerable combinations are possible. These various combinations result in concrete of different qualities. When the cement has hydrated, the plastic mass changes to a material resembling stone. This period of hardening is called *curing*, in which three things are required: time, favorable temperatures, and the continued presence of water.

To fulfill requirements, it is essential that the hardened concrete have, above all else, *strength* and *durability*. In order that the concrete in its plastic form may be readily placed in the forms, another essential quality is *workability*. Where watertightness is required, concrete must be *dense* and *uniform* in quality. Hence it is seen that in determining the various proportions of the mixture the designer must have in mind the purpose for which the concrete is to be used and the exposure to which it will be subjected. When these requirements have been filled, the following factors regulate the quality of the concrete: suitable materials, correct proportions, proper methods of mixing and placing, and adequate protection during curing.

2–2. Strength. In view of the many tests to which concrete has been subjected, it is quite possible to predict in advance the strength that given proportions of ingredients will produce in hardened concrete. In its plastic condition concrete, of course, cannot be tested for strength, and the customary procedure is to take samples as the concrete is mixed. After curing, the samples are subjected to compressive tests. In addition to compressive

9

stresses, concrete must resist diagonal tension and the bonding stresses that are present where the reinforcing steel comes in contact with the concrete. We can, of course, test concrete for all of these individual stresses, but the compressive test gives a fair indication of the other qualities. Since this test is relatively simple to make, compressive tests on concrete samples are the ones most frequently made. As an indication of the strength of concrete, we refer to it as 2000- or 3000 psi concrete. In our formulas this is represented by the term f'_c. It represents the ultimate compressive stress in pounds per square inch at the end of 28 days of curing.

2–3. Durability. The use of reinforced concrete for structural members of buildings has increased with amazing rapidity so that today it is universally employed. Although older structures invariably proved to have adequate strength for the imposed loads, there are many instances in which insufficient attention was given to the *durability* of the concrete. As used in building construction, concrete may have various *degrees of exposure*. For instance, columns and girders on the exterior of a structure are subjected to atmospheric conditions to which interior members are not exposed. Again, walls and piers subjected to alternate wetting and drying, or freezing and thaws, must necessarily be made of concrete designed to withstand such conditions. Thus it is seen that the designer of a reinforced concrete structure must, in determining the proper mix, bear in mind the degree of exposure as well as the strength of the concrete.

2–4. Workability. In addition to the above qualifications, concrete in its plastic condition must have a consistency that will permit it to be placed readily in the forms. This quality is known as *workability*. Different classes of work require different degrees of plasticity. The shape, width, and depth of forms and spaces between reinforcement are all factors that determine the required degree of workability. It might appear that varying the amount of water in the mix would readily permit any desired consistency. In former years this procedure of producing workable concrete frequently resulted in a mixture having an excess amount of water, thereby producing, on hardening, a porous concrete of lower strength than desired. As a result of innumerable tests and past experience, it has been found that the quantity of water in relation to the quantity of cement is a vital factor in determining the strength of concrete, and, this desired ratio having been established, the degree of plasticity is best obtained by regulating the proportions of the cement and water paste with the aggregate.

2–5. Mixing. To produce a first quality concrete, the use of a mixing machine is essential. Thorough mixing not only tends to produce a concrete of uniform quality, but longer periods of mixing also increase the strength of the concrete, and a greater degree of workability is effected.

Many types of portable mixers are obtainable today. Their capacities range from 3 cu ft to 4 cu yd. The strength and quality of the concrete depend principally upon the length of time the concrete remains in the mixer rather than upon the speed of rotation. Concrete should never be mixed less than 1 min, and a longer period is desirable when conditions permit. When concrete of superior quality is desired for extreme exposure conditions or for watertightness, longer periods of mixing will be advantageous.

Central-mixed or ready-mixed concrete is used whenever it is available. Certificates indicating the composition of each truck load insure compliance with specifications relating to strength.

2–6. Segregation. The consistency of concrete should be such that a mass of uniform quality will result when it has been deposited in the forms. It is well to remember that concrete in its plastic condition is in reality a paste in which the aggregates are mixed. Care should be exercised to prevent the particles of sand and stone from being separated from this paste, for such separation produces an inferior concrete. Factors that must be considered in preventing segregation of aggregates are transporting the concrete from the mixing machine to the forms, dropping the concrete from too great a height, and tamping or spading. Dropping the concrete more than 3 ft into the forms tends to permit the larger aggregate to work its way to a lower level, thus preventing a uniform quality.

Great care must be taken to see that the plastic concrete flows properly into all corners and angles of the forms and that the reinforcement is completely surrounded with concrete. When concrete is placed in the forms by means of chutes, it is important that long flows be avoided, since there is a possibility that the large aggregate will separate from the other materials in the mix. If the use of long chutes is unavoidable, the concrete should be deposited into a hopper from which it is taken before being placed in the forms. The purpose of this procedure is to remix the materials, thereby correcting any segregation.

Another cause of segregation is an excess amount of tamping, vibrating, or puddling in the forms. To avoid honeycombing, a common procedure is to spade the concrete where it comes in contact with the forms. In accomplishing this it is advisable not to spade too vigorously, thus preventing the materials from becoming separated.

2–7. Laitance. When an excess amount of water is used, the concrete upon curing will have a milky layer composed of cement and fine aggregate on the upper surface of the mass. This is called *laitance*. Upon evaporation of the excess water, this layer becomes weak, porous, and readily disintegrated and permits water to pass through under slight pressure. The removal of this thin layer before pouring more concrete is of little benefit, for several inches of inferior concrete remain below. It is quite possible that the concrete at the bottom of the placing may be hard and dense. If the presence of laitance is detected, several inches below the uppermost surface should be removed if a durable and strong concrete is desired. Therefore, to avoid laitance, use only a concrete of a proper consistency and water-cement ratio. This will prevent a watery layer from accumulating on the upper surface.

2–8. Curing. Regardless of the care taken in proportioning, mixing, and placing, first-quality concrete can be obtained only when due consideration and provision are made for curing. The hardening of concrete is due to the chemical reaction between the water and cement. This hardening continues indefinitely as long as moisture is present and the temperatures are favorable. The initial set does not begin until two or three hours after the concrete has been mixed. During this interval moisture evaporates, particularly on the exposed surfaces, and unless provision is made to prevent the loss of moisture the concrete will craze. A typical specification requires that the concrete be so protected that there is no loss of moisture from the surface for a period of 7 days when normal portland cement is used and 3 days when the cement is of high early strength.

To prevent the loss of moisture during curing, several methods may be employed. When hard enough to walk on, slabs may be covered with burlap kept continuously wet or with a suitable building paper with the edges pasted down. Another method is to cover the slabs with a 1-in. layer of wet sand or sawdust. Frequently, a 6-in. layer of wet straw or hay is placed on the slabs. Another method sometimes resorted to is the continuous sprinkling of the exposed surfaces with water. The early removal of forms permits undue evaporation, hence the forms should be allowed to remain for as long a period as is practicable. In addition to strength and durability, controlled curing is one of the best precautions in making a watertight concrete.

The period of protection against evaporation of moisture varies with the type of structure and climatic conditions. Thin sections or concrete placed during hot weather require an increased period of protection.

2-9. Temperature. Low temperatures during the period of curing produce concrete of lower strength than concrete cured at 72°F. Freezing of concrete before it has cured should never be permitted, for the resulting concrete is of poor quality and indeterminate strength.

Although special precautions are required, concrete work may be continued during severe weather conditions. To keep the concrete above freezing, the materials may be heated before mixing or the concrete may be protected with suitable covers or kept in heated enclosures. If the weather is only moderately cold, heating the water used for mixing may be a sufficient precaution. For more severe weather, it may be necessary to heat both water and aggregates. The materials should never have a temperature exceeding 90°F when deposited.

One common method of protecting concrete is to cover it with a thick layer of straw and tarpaulins. Canvas enclosures heated by steam give excellent protection, since desirable temperatures may be maintained and the concrete is protected against drying out. If salamanders are used, care should be exercised to see that moisture is not evaporated from the concrete.

2-10. Water-Cement Ratio. We may think of concrete as a paste made of water and cement thoroughly mixed with fine and coarse aggregate. When the paste hardens, the particles of sand and crushed stone are tightly bound together to form a solid stonelike mass. The quality of the paste is determined by the proportions of water and cement. Likewise, the strength, resistance to weather, and watertightness of the hardened concrete are also controlled by this water-cement ratio. This ratio is expressed as a number indicating the number of gallons of water to a 94-lb sack of cement.

It should be remembered that the plastic concrete should always be workable. It should be neither too dry nor too wet. If it is too dry, it is difficult to place in the forms, it resists packing around the reinforcement, and the result is honeycombing. If the concrete is too wet, segregation of the ingredients results. To produce a workable concrete, more water must be used than is required to combine chemically with the cement. Hence a certain amount of water is distributed within the paste, which, upon evaporation, leaves minute voids. Thus it is seen that the water-cement ratio determines the density of the cement paste, which, in turn, determines the strength, durability, and watertightness of the hardened concrete.

It is important that the concrete used in a building operation be of uniform strength and density; therefore it becomes necessary to maintain the water-cement ratio carefully. Tests made in laboratories show that, within reasonable limits, the less water per sack of cement, the greater will be the strength of the concrete. Remember, however, that concrete must be *workable*, that is, it must have a consistency that will permit its being readily placed in the forms. When the desired water-cement ratio has been established in accordance with the exposure to which the concrete will be subjected and the strength desired, the best combinations of aggregates are then selected to produce an economical and workable concrete. Remember that for given materials the strength of the concrete is determined primarily by the ratio of the volume of water to the volume of cement, *provided the mix is of a workable plasticity*. The water-cement ratios given in Table 2–1 are to be used as a guide for mixing concrete of various strengths.

2–11. Proportioning. The first step in determining the proportions of the various ingredients in concrete is to establish the water-cement ratio. As stated above, this depends primarily upon the exposure to which the concrete will be subjected and the strength desired   The next step is to decide upon the most economical com-

TABLE 2–1. PERMISSIBLE WATER-CEMENT RATIOS FOR CONCRETE *

Specified Minimum Compressive Strength at 28 Days, psi	Maximum Permissible Water-Cement Ratio, U.S. Gallons per 94-Lb Sack of Cement †	
	Non-Air-Entrained Concrete	Air-Entrained Concrete
2000	8	$7\frac{1}{4}$
2500	$7\frac{1}{4}$	$6\frac{1}{4}$
3000	$6\frac{1}{2}$	$5\frac{1}{4}$
3500	$5\frac{3}{4}$	$4\frac{1}{2}$
4000	5	4

* Reproduced from *Building Code Requirements for Reinforced Concrete* by permission of the American Concrete Institute.

† Including free surface moisture on aggregates.

bination of fine and coarse aggregates that will result in a concrete having a plasticity that is workable.

The general theory in establishing the proportions of the fine and coarse aggregates is that the voids in the coarse aggregate should be filled with the cement paste and fine aggregate. The voids in coarse aggregate depend upon the kind of material and its size. In general, the voids average slightly less than one half the volume and it is customary to use about one half as much sand as the volume of crushed stone. We express the proportions in this sequence: cement, sand, and coarse aggregate. For instance, the mix may be 1:2:4, $1:2\frac{1}{2}:5$, 1:3:6. Very often the fine and coarse aggregates are given as one figure, and a mix of 1:2:4 may be expressed as 1:6. The reason for this is that the sand should not always be one half the volume of the crushed stone, for it may prove to be more economical to use a $1:2\frac{1}{2}:3\frac{1}{2}$ mix. This, however, is another way of expressing a 1:6 proportion. Sand containing an average amount of moisture will bulk about 20%, and this fact should always be kept in mind in determining the proportions to be used. The sum of fine and coarse aggregates in proportion to the cement paste depends upon the consistency required. In general, stiffer mixes are more economical with respect to the cost of materials, but if the mix is unusually dry the cost of placing it in the forms is increased and care must be taken to avoid honeycombing. When the proportion of fine aggregate is increased, a smoother working concrete results, but this generally requires more cement paste and may not be economical. Table 2–2 lists recommended proportions of coarse aggregate to volume of concrete, depending on the fineness of the sand. The smaller ratio corresponds to sand of greater fineness.

TABLE 2–2. RECOMMENDED PROPORTIONS OF COARSE AGGREGATE
TO VOLUME OF CONCRETE

Maximum Size of Coarse Aggregate in Inches	Ratio of Coarse Aggregate to Volume of Concrete	
	Minimum	Maximum
$\frac{3}{8}$	0.40	0.46
$\frac{3}{4}$	0.59	0.65
1 and over	0.64	0.70

Probably the commonest mix for average job conditions is 1 of cement to 5 of combined aggregates with a water-cement ratio of $6\frac{1}{2}$. The 1:5 mix may be $1:1\frac{3}{4}:3\frac{1}{4}$ or $1:2:3$. Specimens thus made will produce a concrete having an ultimate compressive strength of about 3000 psi.

If a concrete of greater strength is desired, or if the degree of exposure is severer, the water-cement ratio should be reduced to produce a denser concrete.

When the concrete structure is of sufficient magnitude to warrant the expense involved, another method of determining proportions may be used. Certain data are given the contractor in the specifications, such as class of work, required strength, maximum water-cement ratio, maximum sizes of aggregates, and slump range. The contractor must, of course, use a concrete that is plastic and workable. Within the specified limitations, a series of reliable tests is made of various proportions, and a water-cement strength curve is established. This method of trial batches, based on the water-cement ratio, permits the contractor to produce most economically a concrete having the required qualities. Having determined the water-cement ratio in accordance with the desired strength and resistance to exposure, he then selects the most suitable combination of aggregates that will produce the required degree of workability.

2–12. Surface Water in Aggregates. In any estimation of the amount of water to be used in mixing concrete, in accordance with the water-cement ratio theory, the surface water carried by the aggregates must be included. Table 2–3 gives approximate quantities carried by average aggregates. At building operations all aggre-

TABLE 2–3. APPROXIMATE QUANTITY OF SURFACE WATER
CARRIED BY AVERAGE AGGREGATES

Very wet sand	$\frac{3}{4}$ to 1 gal per cu ft
Moderately wet sand	about $\frac{1}{2}$ gal per cu ft
Moist sand	about $\frac{1}{4}$ gal per cu ft
Moist gravel or crushed rock	about $\frac{1}{4}$ gal per cu ft

gates carry a certain degree of moisture, and the coarser the aggregate, the less surface water it will carry. In addition to making provision for this surface water, remember that moderately wet sand increases about 20% in bulk.

2–13. Degrees of Exposure. In establishing the mix to be used for concrete, it is important that, in addition to the required strength, the degree of exposure to which the concrete will be subjected be given due consideration. The water-cement ratio is the basis on which the selection is made. All concrete exposed to the action of the weather should have a water-content not in excess of 6 gal per sack of cement. In the earlier reinforced concrete structures too little thought was given to durability, with the result that there are many instances of undue disintegration that might have been avoided. Table 2–4 is presented as a guide in selecting the proper water-cement ratio for concrete having different degrees of exposure. Note that surface water carried by the aggregates must be included as a part of the mixing water.

2–14. Watertightness. The quality of watertightness in concrete is of extreme importance. First of all, certain structures, such as tanks or basement walls and floors below grade, must be watertight to prevent the passage of water from one side to the other. There

TABLE 2–4.   MAXIMUM PERMISSIBLE WATER-CEMENT RATIOS (GALLON PER BAG) FOR DIFFERENT TYPES OF STRUCTURES AND DEGREES OF EXPOSURE

Type of Structure	Severe wide range in temperature, or frequent alternations of freezing and thawing (air-entrained concrete only)			Mild temperature rarely below freezing, or rainy, or arid		
	In air	At the water line or within the range of fluctuating water level or spray		In air	At the water line or within the range of fluctuating water level or spray	
		In fresh water	In sea water or in contact with sulfates †		In fresh water	In sea water or in contact with sulfates †
Thin sections, such as railings, curbs, sills, ledges, ornamental or architectural concrete, reinforced piles, pipe, and all sections with less than 1 in. concrete cover over reinforcing	5.5	5.0	4.5 ‡	6	5.5	4.5 ‡
Moderate sections, such as retaining walls, abutments, piers, girders, beams	6.0	5.5	5.0 ‡	§	6.0	5.0 ‡
Exterior portions of heavy (mass) sections	6.5	5.5	5.0 ‡	§	6.0	5.0 ‡
Concrete deposited by tremie under water	—	5.0	5.0	—	5.0	5.0
Concrete slabs laid on the ground	6.0	—	—	§	—	—
Concrete protected from the weather, interiors of buildings, concrete below ground	§	—	—	§	—	—
Concrete which will later be protected by enclosure or backfill but which may be exposed to freezing and thawing for several years before such protection is offered	6.0	—	—	§	—	—

* Air-entrained concrete should be used under all conditions involving severe exposure and may be used under mild exposure conditions to improve workability of the mixture.
† Soil or ground water containing sulfate concentrations of more than 0.2%.
‡ When sulfate resisting cement is used, maximum water-cement ratio may be increased by 0.5 gal per bag.
§ Water-cement ratio should be selected on basis of strength and workability requirements.
Reproduced by permission of the American Concrete Institute from *Recommended Practice for Selecting Proportions for Concrete* (A.C.I. 613-54).

is, however, another important reason for making watertight concrete. Disintegration of concrete may be physical or chemical, and deterioration of exposed concrete is due largely to the penetration of moisture.

Several factors enter into the construction of watertight concrete. Obviously the aggregates must be nonporous, durable, and well-graded materials. The concrete must be dense; that is, the water-cement ratio must be as low as possible, and it must be borne in mind that the mix must be workable and that the particles of aggregate must be completely bound together in the cement paste. It is customary to retain the ingredients in the mixing machine for a somewhat longer period if a complete incorporation of cement paste and aggregates is to be obtained. More precautions than usual should be taken in the placing of the concrete. This demands careful spading or vibration so that the reinforcement is completely encased and a uniform and dense exposed surface results.

The mix for 3000-psi concrete may vary with job conditions but should never be leaner than 1:2:3. A ratio of 6 gal of water per sack of cement will produce a watertight concrete for average conditions if the other precautions are observed. A water-cement ratio of $6\frac{1}{2}$ should be considered a maximum for 3000-lb concrete. In producing a watertight concrete the water-cement ratio should be strictly followed and the mass should be of a uniform quality throughout.

The importance of proper curing of concrete, if it is to be watertight, cannot be overestimated. This is particularly true in the early stages of hardening. The exposed surfaces must be kept continuously damp so that a hard, dense surface will result to prevent checking and dusting.

2–15. Tests. As noted in Art. 2–11, if the operation is of sufficient magnitude, concrete made of various proportions should be tested several weeks before the actual construction of the building. The usual procedure is to test several combinations, using at least four different water-cement ratios. The results of the tests are then plotted and the most economical mix chosen that will produce a concrete of the desired density and strength. It is customary to continue the testing of the concrete during construction, particularly if there are changing weather conditions.

One of the simplest tests for determining a suitable mix with fixed proportions of water and cement is to make samples of small batches. Various combinations are mixed with a trowel, and an experienced workman may make adjustments in the proportions and readily obtain a concrete of the desired proportions. By its appearance certain qualities are at once shown. A mixture containing insufficient cement-sand mortar to fill completely the voids between the coarse aggregate produces a concrete that is difficult to work and results in honeycombed surfaces. If the mixture contains too much cement-sand mortar in proportion to the coarse aggregate, the mix will be uneconomical, since the yield of concrete will be low, the concrete will probably be porous, and segregation will result when placing.

The two commonest tests of concrete are the slump test for determining the degree of plasticity and the compression tests on cylinders of cured concrete to establish its strength.

2–16. Slump Test. The term *consistency*, as applied to freshly mixed concrete, refers to its state of fluidity. If the concrete is "plastic," it may be readily molded but changes form slowly when the form or mold is removed. A concrete is said to be *workable* if it is readily placed in the forms for which it is intended. For instance, a concrete may be workable in large open forms but not workable in small forms containing numerous reinforcing bars.

The slump test affords a ready means of determining the consistency of the freshly mixed concrete. It is not necessarily a measure of workability and should not be used to compare mixes of wholly different proportions or kinds of aggregates. To make a slump test is a simple matter. The equipment consists of a piece of sheet metal having the shape of a truncated cone, 12 in. in height, a base diameter of 8 in., and a top diameter of 4 in. Both top and bottom are left open. Handles are attached to the outside of the mold. Freshly mixed concrete is placed in the mold in three layers, each being rodded separately twenty-five times with a $\frac{5}{8}$-in. diameter rod. When the mold is filled and rodded, the top is leveled off, and the mold is lifted at once. Immediately, the slumping action of the concrete is measured by taking the difference in height between the top of the mold and the top of the slumped mass of concrete. See Fig. 2–1. If the concrete settles 3 in., we say the particular sample has a 3-in. slump. Thus the degree of consistency of the concrete is ascertained. Table 2–5 gives recommended slumps for concrete to be used in various types of structures.

2–17. Compression Test. The test given to concrete for strength is the compression test. The specimens to be tested are cylindrical

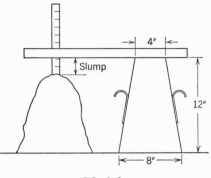

FIG. 2-1

TABLE 2-5. RECOMMENDED SLUMPS FOR VARIOUS TYPES OF CONSTRUCTION

Types of Construction	Slump, Inches *	
	Maximum	Minimum
Reinforced foundation walls and footings	5	2
Plain footings, caissons, and substructure walls	4	1
Slabs, beams, and reinforced walls	6	3
Building columns	6	3
Pavements	3	2
Heavy mass construction	3	1

* When high-frequency vibrators are used, the values given should be reduced about one third.

Reproduced by permission of the American Concrete Institute from *Recommended Practice for Selecting Proportions for Concrete* (A.C.I. 613-54).

in shape and have a length twice the diameter. The standard is 6 in. in diameter and 12 in. in height when the coarse aggregate does not exceed 2 in. in size. If the coarse aggregate is larger than 2 in., the cylinder should have a diameter at least three times the maximum nominal size of the aggregate.

The mold used in making the cylinders is of some nonabsorbent material such as metal or waxed cardboard. It is placed on a smooth plane surface, $\frac{1}{4}$-in. plate glass or $\frac{1}{2}$-in. planed metal. Freshly made concrete is then placed into the mold in three separate layers, each about one third the volume of the mold. Each layer is rodded separately with twenty-five strokes of a $\frac{5}{8}$-in. rod, 24 in. in length, bullet-pointed at the lower end. After the top layer has been rodded, the surface is leveled with a trowel and covered with glass or planed metal. After 2 to 4 hours, when the concrete has ceased settling, the specimens are capped with a thin layer of neat-cement paste and covered with glass or metal. It is customary to keep the specimens at the site of the operation for 24 hours. After this, they are taken to the laboratory and cured in a moist atmosphere at 70°F. Tests are usually made at 7- and 28-day periods. In making specimens extreme care should be taken to see that the ends are plane parallel surfaces, for irregularities in this respect will give faulty results when the specimens are tested. After the specimen is placed in the testing machine, a compressive load is applied until the specimen fails. The load causing failure is recorded, and this load divided by the cross-sectional area of the cylinder gives the ultimate compressive unit stress, usually expressed in psi.

We express the grade or kind of concrete as its ultimate compressive strength, in psi, at the 28-day period. In our formulas used in designing concrete structural members the term denoting this strength is f'_c. Probably the most commonly used concrete for structural members is the 3000-psi grade. Bear in mind that this is its *ultimate* strength. The allowable working stresses are given as fractions of the ultimate compressive strength. For instance, the allowable extreme compressive fiber stress of 3000-psi concrete, for members in bending, is $0.45 f'_c$, or $0.45 \times 3000 = 1350$ psi. See Table 4-2. Two other kinds of concrete frequently used are the 2500-psi and 3750-psi grades.

2-18. Modulus of Elasticity. The modulus of elasticity * of a material is its unit stress divided by its unit deformation. We may think of the modulus of elasticity of a material as a number which represents its degrees of stiffness. As an example, the modulus of elasticity of southern yellow pine is 1,760,000 psi. For steel used for reinforcement in concrete it is considered to be 30,000,000 psi. One may readily understand that steel is stiffer than wood, and this characteristic is represented by their moduli of elasticity. We can understand, also, that concretes of various strengths have different degrees of stiffness and that they will have different amounts of

---

* See Art. 54, *Simplified Mechanics and Strength of Materials*, by Harry Parker, John Wiley and Sons, New York, 1951.

deformation for equal stresses. That is to say, they have different moduli of elasticity. Table 2–6 lists these moduli of elasticity for concretes of different strengths.

TABLE 2–6. MODULUS OF ELASTICITY OF CONCRETE

f'_c Ultimate Compressive Strength at 28-Day Period in Pounds per Square Inch	E_c Modulus of Elasticity of Concrete in Pounds per Square Inch	$n = \dfrac{E_s}{E_c}$ $n = \dfrac{30,000}{f'_c}$
1500	1,500,000	20
2000	2,000,000	15
2500	2,500,000	12
3000	3,000,000	10
3750	3,750,000	8

In computations for the design of reinforced concrete it is important that we know the ratio of the modulus of elasticity of steel to that of the concrete we are using. The term expressing this ratio is n and $n = \dfrac{E_s}{E_c}$, in which E_s is the modulus of elasticity of steel and E_c the modulus of elasticity of concrete. Hence, for 3000-psi concrete, $E_c = 3,000,000$ psi and $n = \dfrac{30,000,000}{3,000,000} = 10$. For concrete of any strength, $n = \dfrac{30,000}{f'_c}$. This applies to concrete having stone or gravel aggregate. Concrete made of lightweight aggregate has a lower modulus of elasticity than stone concrete. This fact must be given consideration in computing deflections.

2–19. Plastic Flow. All building materials deform without an increase in loads when the internal stresses exceed the elastic limit. In loaded concrete members there is also a tendency to change size or shape with the lapse of time; this deformation is called *plastic flow*. Unlike most materials, concrete lacks a degree of proportionality with respect to stress and deformation, and the phenomena of plastic flow and shrinkage are somewhat similar. Because of plastic flow, the deflection of concrete beams cannot be computed by the common formulas used for other materials.

CHAPTER 3

SHEAR AND
BENDING MOMENTS IN BEAMS

3–1. Members in Bending. The *stress* in a member is the internal resistance in the fibers that results from an exterior force or forces. Consider, for example, a short timber post, 10 x 10 in. in cross section, subjected to an axial compressive load of 80,000 lb. Assuming that the stresses in the post are uniformly distributed, the unit compressive stress in the member will be $f = \dfrac{P}{A}$,* or $f = \dfrac{80,000}{100} =$ 800 psi. This illustrates the fundamental relation between loads, areas, and unit stresses for members subjected to direct stresses.

Next consider a simple timber beam, 16 ft 0 in. in length, having a concentrated load of 4000 lb at the center of the span. If we are asked to compute the size of the beam to support this load, we must first determine the maximum bending moment. The procedure is not so elementary as that for the post in which the stresses are equally distributed over the cross section. To begin with, the tendency to fail by flexure, which is another term for bending, is not the same at all sections in the length of the beam. It varies from zero at the supports to a maximum magnitude directly under the load. See Fig. 3–4(*b*). The maximum bending moment for this particular beam is $M = \dfrac{PL}{4}$, or $M = 4000 \times 16 \times \dfrac{12}{4} = 192,000$ in-lb. This is read "192,000 inch-pounds." To find the required section modulus, assuming the allowable extreme fiber stress to be

---

* See Art. 45, *Simplified Mechanics and Strength of Materials*, by Harry Parker, John Wiley and Sons, New York, 1951.

800 psi, we use the flexure formula $\dfrac{M}{f} = S$, * or $\dfrac{192,000}{800} = 240$ in^3.
A 10 x 12 in. beam provides this section modulus and therefore is adequate.

The problem just illustrated refers to a homogeneous beam, a beam composed of a single material. If we visualize the shape the beam tends to assume, we note that the upper surface is concave. See Fig. 3–1(d). Obviously, the fibers in the upper portion of the

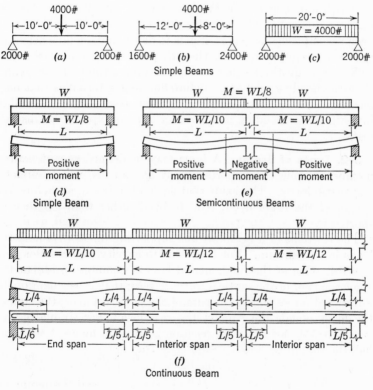

FIG. 3–1

beam are in compression, whereas those below the neutral axis or central plane are in tension and tend to elongate. The stresses in

* See Arts. 90 and 92, *Simplified Mechanics and Strength of Materials.*

the fibers are not equally distributed over the cross section; they have maximum values at the upper and lower surfaces and diminish in magnitude as they approach the neutral axis.

Since concrete is a material capable of resisting relatively large compressive forces but having a tensile strength so low that it is neglected in computations, the basic theory of a reinforced concrete beam is to place steel rods in those parts of the beam at which tensile stresses are developed. Thus the concrete resists the compressive stresses and the steel withstands the tensile stresses. To design a beam, one of the first steps is to compute the greatest bending moment to which the beam will be subjected. This having been accomplished, the next step is to determine the dimensions of the cross section of the beam that will provide concrete and steel in sufficient quantities to offer a resisting moment equal to or greater than the bending moment. Before developing formulas that may be used in the design of reinforced concrete beams, it will be well to investigate the bending moments for various types of beams and loads.

3–2. Types of Beams. A *beam* may be defined as a structural member, resting on supports usually at its ends, which supports transverse loads. The loads that act on the beam, as well as the weight of the beam itself, tend to bend rather than lengthen or shorten it.

The *reactions* of a beam are the supporting forces that hold the loads in equilibrium. For loads due to gravity, the reactions are upward. One of the fundamental laws of equilibrium is that the algebraic sum of the vertical forces is zero; that is, the sum of the downward forces equals the sum of the upward forces; the sum of the loads equals the sum of the reactions. For simple beams, symmetrically loaded, each reaction is equal in magnitude to one half the sum of the loads. See Fig. 3–1(*a*) and (*c*).

A *simple beam* is a beam having a single span with a support at each end, there being no restraint at the supports. See Fig. 3–1(*a*), (*b*), (*c*), and (*d*).

A beam that is supported at one end only, or that portion of a beam projecting beyond one of its supports, is known as a *cantilever beam*. A beam projecting from a wall is a typical example of a cantilever. See Fig. 3–4(*e*) and (*f*).

A *continuous beam* is a beam resting on more than two supports.

See Fig. 3–1(*f*). The term *semicontinuous beam* is frequently used in reinforced concrete. It refers to a beam having two spans with little or no restraint at the two extreme ends of the beam. See Fig. 3–1(*e*). The *end span* of a continuous beam, where little or no restraint is provided at the end support, is referred to as a semicontinuous beam. See Fig. 3–1(*f*). With respect to continuous beams, the terms "end span" and "semicontinuous" are used synonymously as are also the terms "interior span" and "fully continuous." The dotted diagonal lines in this figure show the positions of the bends in the reinforcement when bent bars are used.

The end of a beam is said to be *fixed* when it is rigidly connected or *restrained* against rotation. Figure 3–2(*b*) represents a beam simply supported (no restraint) at the wall end and fixed or fully restrained at the connection to the column.

A *girder* is the term applied to a beam that supports one or more smaller beams.

3–3. Vertical Shear. Two important quantities that must be considered in the design of beams are the *vertical shear* and the *bending moment*.

We may define vertical shear as the tendency for one part of a beam to move vertically with respect to an adjacent part. Its magnitude at any point in the length of a beam is the algebraic sum of the vertical forces on either side of the section, the vertical forces being the reactions, or upward forces, and the loads, which are downward forces. A rather easy rule to remember is: *The magnitude of the vertical shear at any section of a beam is equal to the reactions minus the loads to the left of the section.* Since the magnitude of the shear is forces minus forces, the shear is expressed in units of force, generally pounds. For simple beams unsymmetrically loaded, it is seen that the value of the maximum shear is equal to the greater reaction. Figure 3–1(*b*) indicates a concentrated load of 4000 lb at 12 ft 0 in. from the left support and 8 ft 0 in. from the right support. R_1 and R_2, the left and right reactions, are, respectively, 1600 lb and 2400 lb. Hence the maximum vertical shear is 2400 lb.

For simple beams symmetrically loaded, the reactions are equal, and each is equal to one half the sum of the loads. Figure 3–1(*a*) and (*c*) represent simple beams each of which has a load of 4000 lb.

The reactions for both beams are each 2000 lb, hence the maximum shear in each beam is 2000 lb.

Consider the continuous beam having a uniformly distributed load represented in Fig. 3–1(f). There is a difference in magnitude in the bending moment at the left support and the first interior support; these two reactions are not equal. For the load on the end span, it is considered to be sufficiently accurate to assume that the left support is $0.4W$ and the first interior support, $0.6W$. For these values, W represents the total load on each span. Very often we use the letter w to represent the uniformly distributed load in pounds per linear foot and the letter l to represent the length of the span in feet. If these letters are used, W, the total load on the span $= wl$, and the first two reactions are $0.4wl$ and $0.6wl$ for the load on the end span. Then the first interior reaction will be $0.6wl + 0.5wl$ (from the second span) $= 1.1wl$. See Fig 3–3. The other interior supports have the value of $0.5wl + 0.5wl$ or $1.0wl$.

The letter used to designate the total vertical shear is V, and the magnitude is generally expressed in units of pounds. The *shearing unit stress* is represented by the letter v, the units usually being pounds per square inch (psi).

3–4. Bending Moments in Simple Beams. We may define a *moment* as the tendency of a force to cause rotation about a certain point or axis. It is usually expressed as so many foot-pounds or inch-pounds, since it is the result of multiplying a force by a distance.

The *bending moment* at any section of a beam is equal to the algebraic sum of the moments of the forces on either side of the section. For example, consider the forces to the left. Then a simple rule to remember is: *The value of the bending moment at any section of a beam is equal to the moments of the reactions minus the moments of the loads to the left of the section.* From this it is seen that the magnitude of the tendency of the external forces to cause bending in a beam varies throughout the length of the member. In order to design a beam, it is necessary to compute the greatest value. It is called the maximum bending moment and is represented by the letter M.

Consider the simple beam having a length of 20 ft 0 in. with a concentrated load of 4000 lb at the center of the span, Fig. 3–1 (a). The value of the maximum bending moment for this type of beam and

loading is $M = \dfrac{Pl}{4}$, Fig. 3–4(b). Therefore, $M = 4000 \times 20 \times \dfrac{12}{4}$
$= 240,000$ in-lb.

If the load of 4000 lb is placed at 12 ft 0 in. from the left reaction, Fig. 3–1(b), R_1 and R_2, the left and right reactions,* are, respectively, 1600 lb and 2400 lb. The maximum bending moment occurs under the concentrated load, and, if we apply the above rule, $M = 1600 \times 12 \times 12 = 230,400$ in-lb.

Again, assume the 4000-lb load to be uniformly distributed over the entire length of the beam, Fig. 3–1(c). The value of the maximum bending moment for this loading is $M = \dfrac{Wl}{8}$, Fig. 3–4(a). Hence $M = 4000 \times 20 \times \dfrac{12}{8} = 120,000$ in-lb.

These three illustrative problems refer to *simple* beams. In each case note that the span length and load are the same, the difference being in the manner or position of loading. Of the three, the greatest bending moment occurs in the first problem, the concentrated load being placed at the center of the span. Note that there is no restraint at the supports of these beams and, as will be seen, the bending moment is positive in each instance. Most of the steel beams in practice are figured as simple beams based on the assumption that the connections at the supports provide so little restraint that it may be ignored. On the other hand, most of the beams and slabs of reinforced concrete are either continuous beams or are supported at the ends in a manner that produces a certain degree of restraint, thereby producing a negative bending moment.

The span length, l, of reinforced concrete members that are not built integrally with their supports should be taken as the clear span plus the depth of the slab or beam but should not exceed the distance between centers of supports.

3–5. Positive and Negative Bending Moments. When a simple beam bends, the uppermost surface becomes concave and there is a tendency for the beam to assume the shape indicated in Fig. 3–1(d). It is obvious that the fibers in the upper portion of the beam are somewhat shortened; they are in compression. Similarly, the fibers below the neutral surface are lengthened and the stresses are tensile.

* See Art. 42, *Simplified Mechanics and Strength of Materials*.

A *positive bending moment* exists when the fibers in the upper portion of a beam are compressive. Sometimes we say a positive bending moment occurs when the curve assumed by the bent beam is concave upward.

Consider next the semicontinuous beam shown in Fig. 3–1(*e*). Note that the extreme ends of the beams are free from restraint. When this beam bends, it tends to take the shape as indicated below the loading. Now this is unlike the simple beam shown in Fig. 3–1(*d*), for it is seen that above the interior support the upper surface of the beam is concave *downward;* that is, the fibers in the upper portion of the beam are in tension. Wherever this condition exists the bending moment is *negative.* It is the exact opposite of a positive bending moment. On examining the bending-shape diagram, it is seen that the outer portions of this particular beam have positive bending moments. For continuous beams, Fig. 3–1(*f*), the bending-shape diagram indicates that positive bending moments occur between the supports and that the bending moments are negative for certain distances above the interior supports.

The section of a beam at which the bending moment changes from positive to negative is called the *inflection point.* As has been explained, the resistance to tension in concrete is ignored in design computations, and the longitudinal steel reinforcement is assumed to take all the tensile stresses. With this in mind, we are careful to place the reinforcement in those parts of the beam at which the tensile stresses occur. For positive moments, the steel, then, is placed in the lower part of the beam, whereas at those parts of the beam at which negative moments occur the reinforcement must be placed in the upper part. To accomplish this, two methods may be employed:

1. The reinforcing bars not required for the positive moment are bent up at or near the inflection points and extended at the top of the beam across the supports into the adjacent spans.

2. In this method there are no bent bars. Separate straight bars are placed in the top of the beams over the supports and extended to their required lengths. Other straight bars are placed in the bottom of the beams where the bending moments are positive. This results in a slightly greater weight of reinforcement but has the advantage of easier fabrication and placing. In addition, in

using this method it is easier to substitute for bars misplaced on the job, forgotten in the shipment, or cut or bent incorrectly.

The exact position of the inflection point depends upon the positions and magnitudes of the loads as well as the end conditions of the beams. For continuous beams having equal spans and uniformly distributed loads, it is considered to be sufficiently accurate to consider the inflection point to be at one fifth the clear span between faces of supports. See Fig. 3–1(f). If there is no restraint at the outer ends of a beam, there is no bending moment. To provide for diagonal tension stresses, however, a portion of the steel reinforcement may be bent up. If there is "medium restraint" [see Fig. 3–2(e)], the negative moment is considered to be $WL/16$ and the bend in the reinforcement is made at one sixth the clear span between faces of support.

3–6. Degrees of Restraint. Unlike steel construction, the concrete for many reinforced concrete members is placed at one time, thereby forming a monolithic construction resulting in a rigid frame. A simple beam with no restraint at the ends, and having a uniformly distributed load, has a maximum positive bending moment of $WL/8$, in which W is the total uniformly distributed load and L is the span of the beam. There are no negative moments at the supports. An example to illustrate this condition is a concrete beam resting on brick walls at its ends. See Fig. 3–2(a). The shear and moment diagrams for this beam are shown in Fig. 3–4(a).

If both ends of a beam, having a uniformly distributed load, are rigidly restrained at the ends, as illustrated in Fig. 3–2(f), the theoretical positive moment is $WL/24$ and each of the negative moments at the supports are $WL/12$. Theoretical values of the moments for various end conditions are shown in Fig. 3–2(a), (b), (c), (d), (e), and (f).

Figure 3–2(g) shows the distribution of shear and moment values for a continuous beam. Note that the spans are equal and that the load is uniformly distributed. The outer ends of the beam are simply supported with no restraint. Bear in mind that these are theoretical values based on the foregoing data. If, as is usually the case, a certain degree of restraint occurs at the end supports, these values are modified. It should be remembered, also, that the theoretical values given are based on the assumption of a uniformly

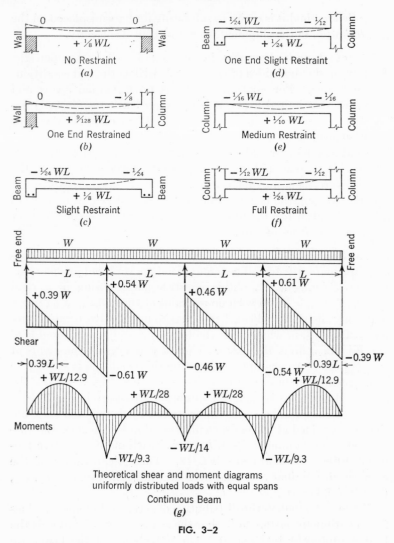

No Restraint
(a)

One End Slight Restraint
(d)

One End Restrained
(b)

Medium Restraint
(e)

Slight Restraint
(c)

Full Restraint
(f)

Theoretical shear and moment diagrams
uniformly distributed loads with equal spans
Continuous Beam
(g)

FIG. 3-2

distributed load. The design load W is made up of both live and
dead loads and, although the dead load may be computed accurately, the live load seldom, if ever, is exactly the same as that
given in the design data. It is probably never exactly distributed
uniformly over the length of the beam. For this reason, as well as

because of other indeterminate factors, minute accuracy in the design of reinforced concrete members is unnecessary.

3–7. Bending Moment Factors. All structural members of reinforced concrete should be designed to resist bending moments as determined by the principle of continuity. It is permitted, however, in the case of approximately equal spans with loads uniformly distributed, when the live load does not exceed three times the dead load, to use the bending moment values given in Fig. 3–3.

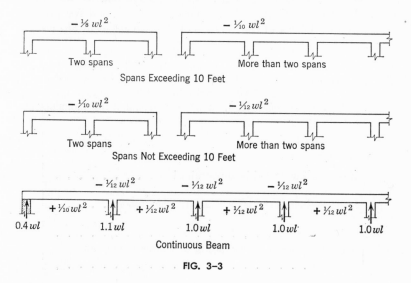

FIG. 3–3

These moment factors are given as coefficients of WL when W is the total uniformly distributed load and L is the length of the span. If the distributed load is given as w pounds per linear foot, then the total load is wL and the moment factors are coefficients of wL^2. It should be noted that no distinction is made between L and l; each represents the span length. The values shown in Fig. 3–3 are average intermediate values of the theoretical moment factors and are conservative.

It is customary, therefore, for continuous beams of three or more equal spans, carrying uniformly distributed loads, to use the values of $WL/12$ for both the positive and negative moments for the interior spans. For the end span, the positive moment may be taken as $WL/10$, and the negative moment over the first interior support may be assumed to be $WL/12$. For semicontinuous beams, that is, beams of two spans, the maximum positive moment is $WL/10$, and $WL/8$ is the maximum negative moment. These moment factors are more conservative than the theoretical values. They are values commonly used, and they will be used throughout this book.

The following excerpt is taken from *Building Code Requirements for Reinforced Concrete* (A.C.I., 318–56), published by the American Concrete Institute. Note that l' = clear span for positive moment and shear and the average of the two adjacent clear spans for negative moment.

In the case of two or more approximately equal spans (the larger of two adjacent spans not exceeding the shorter by more than 20 per cent) with loads uniformly distributed, where the unit live load does not exceed three times the unit dead load, design for the following moments and shears is satisfactory:

Positive moment
    End spans

      If discontinuous end is unrestrained . . . . $\dfrac{1}{11} wl'^2$

      If discontinuous end is integral with the support . . . . . $\dfrac{1}{14} wl'^2$

    Interior spans . . . . $\dfrac{1}{16} wl'^2$

Negative moment at exterior face of first interior support

    Two spans . . . . $\dfrac{1}{9} wl'^2$

    More than two spans . . . . $\dfrac{1}{10} wl'^2$

Negative moment at other faces of interior supports . . . . . $\dfrac{1}{11} wl'^2$

Negative moment at face of all supports for, (a) slabs with spans not exceeding 10 ft, and (b) beams and girders where ratio of sum of column stiffnesses to beam stiffness exceeds eight at

    each end of the span . . . . $\dfrac{1}{12} wl'^2$

Negative moment at interior faces of exterior supports for members built integrally with their supports

    Where the support is a spandrel beam or girder . . . . . . $\dfrac{1}{24} wl'^2$

    Where the support is a column . . . . $\dfrac{1}{16} wl'^2$

Shear in end members at first interior support . . . . $1.15 \dfrac{wl'}{2}$

Shear at all other supports . . . . $\dfrac{wl'}{2}$

3–8. Bending Moments for Concentrated Loads. The moment factors discussed in the previous article have related to beams having uniformly distributed loads. Girders are beams that support smaller beams, and therefore the girder is a beam having concentrated loads in addition to the uniformly distributed load due to the weight of girder itself.

Figure 3–4 shows the shear and moment distribution as well as the maximum values for simple and cantilever beams with various conditions of loading. Figure 3–4(b), (c), and (d) illustrate loading of beams with concentrated loads at the center and at the $\frac{1}{3}$ and $\frac{1}{4}$ points. Note that these are *simple* beams and that the values of the maximum bending moment are, respectively, $PL/4$, $PL/3$, and $PL/2$.

To find the maximum bending moment for beams having concentrated loads *when the members are continuous beams*, it is considered sufficiently accurate to compute the maximum moment on the assumption that the member is a simple beam and then multiply this moment by a reducing factor. The reducing factor is $\frac{8}{12}$ if the end condition is fully continuous and $\frac{8}{10}$ if it is semicontinuous.

As an example, suppose we have a girder of three spans, each span being 24 ft 0 in. from center to center of supports. Each span has loads of 20,000 lb concentrated at the third points.

First consider the center span. If we assume that this span acts as a simple beam, the maximum bending moment formula is $M = \dfrac{PL}{3}$, Fig. 3–4(c). Then,

$$M = \frac{20{,}000 \times 24 \times 12}{3} = 1{,}920{,}000 \text{ in-lb}$$

However, since this span has end conditions corresponding to a fully continuous beam, we reduce this moment by multiplying by $\frac{8}{12}$, or $M = 1{,}920{,}000 \times \frac{8}{12} = 1{,}280{,}000$ in-lb, the maximum bending moment for the beam with fully continuous end conditions.

Now let us consider an end span. Again assuming the span to be

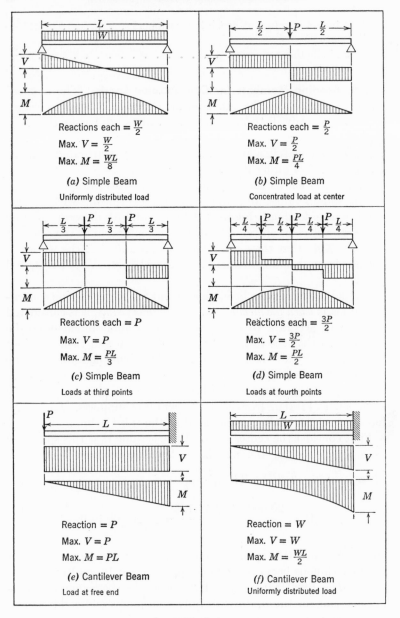

Reactions each $= \dfrac{W}{2}$

Max. $V = \dfrac{W}{2}$

Max. $M = \dfrac{WL}{8}$

(a) Simple Beam

Uniformly distributed load

Reactions each $= \dfrac{P}{2}$

Max. $V = \dfrac{P}{2}$

Max. $M = \dfrac{PL}{4}$

(b) Simple Beam

Concentrated load at center

Reactions each $= P$

Max. $V = P$

Max. $M = \dfrac{PL}{3}$

(c) Simple Beam

Loads at third points

Reactions each $= \dfrac{3P}{2}$

Max. $V = \dfrac{3P}{2}$

Max. $M = \dfrac{PL}{2}$

(d) Simple Beam

Loads at fourth points

Reaction $= P$

Max. $V = P$

Max. $M = PL$

(e) Cantilever Beam

Load at free end

Reaction $= W$

Max. $V = W$

Max. $M = \dfrac{WL}{2}$

(f) Cantilever Beam

Uniformly distributed load

FIG. 3–4

a simple beam, $M = \dfrac{PL}{3}$, or the maximum bending moment is

$$M = \frac{20,000 \times 24 \times 12}{3} = 1,920,000 \text{ in-lb}$$

This span, however, has end conditions corresponding to a semi-continuous beam, and therefore we reduce the above moment by multiplying by $\frac{8}{10}$. Hence $M = 1,920,000 \times \frac{8}{10} = 1,536,000$ in-lb, the maximum bending moment for the end span which is semi-continuous.

FORMULAS FOR BENDING

4-1. Theory of Bending. Before developing formulas to be used in the design of reinforced concrete beams, it is of the utmost importance that the basic theory of bending be understood. Two terms, *bending moment* and *resisting moment*, are used constantly in such discussions and they must be thoroughly understood.

Figure 4-1(a) represents a simple beam loaded with two concentrated loads. The reactions at the left and right ends are, respec-

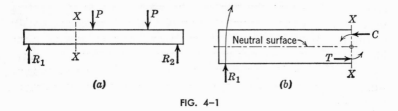

(a)   **(b)**

FIG. 4-1

tively, R_1 and R_2. In accordance with laws of equilibrium, the algebraic sum of the vertical forces equals zero, the algebraic sum of the horizontal forces equals zero, and the algebraic sum of the moments of the forces equals zero. These three laws are expressed in this manner, $\Sigma V = 0$, $\Sigma H = 0$, and $\Sigma M = 0$. For the present we shall be concerned only with the law relating to moments.

Consider now a portion of the left side of the beam, from the reaction up to the imaginary section X-X. An enlarged drawing of this part of the beam is shown in Fig. 4-1(b). The *neutral surface* is an imaginary plane in a beam above which the stresses in the fibers are compressive and below which they are in tension. Let C and T represent, respectively, the resultants of the compressive and tensile stresses in the section taken at X-X. The neutral surface at a section of the beam is an imaginary line called the *neutral axis,* and in Fig. 4–1(*b*) it is indicated by a point on the neutral surface. Now, with this point in mind, let us consider the *moments* of the forces.

As shown in the diagram, the only external force for this portion of the beam is R_1. With respect to the neutral axis, this external force tends to cause a clockwise rotation and is so indicated by the arrow. The moment of the external force with respect to the section is the *bending moment.* Since the beam is in equilibrium, there is no rotation, for the internal stresses, *C* and *T*, tend to cause rotation in a counterclockwise or opposite direction. Note the arrows on *C* and *T* indicating this tendency to rotate. We may say the sum of the moments of all the stresses in the fibers of the cross section produces a *resisting moment,* since this moment resists the bending moment.

The *bending moment* at any section of a beam is the algebraic sum of the moments of the *external* forces, whereas the resisting moment is the sum of the moments of the *internal* stresses in the section. To satisfy equilibrium, the magnitudes of the bending moment and resisting moment must be equal. Attention is called to the fact that the left side of the beam has been taken for this illustration. But, remember, if the forces on the right side of the section had been considered, the magnitude of the bending moment would have been the same, hence the same resisting moment would have resulted.

To design a beam for a given span and loading, all that is necessary, with respect to bending, is to compute the maximum bending moment and then select a beam having a cross section, at the point of maximum bending moment, of such dimensions and of such material as to produce a resisting moment equal in magnitude to the bending moment.

4–2. Resisting Moment of a Homogeneous Beam. Figure 4–2(*a*) represents the left portion of a rectangular homogeneous beam cut at section *X–X.* To develop a formula expressing the relation between the bending moment and the resisting moment, the following terms are used:

b = width of the beam, in inches.
d = depth of the beam, in inches.
f_c = the unit compressive stress on the fibers at the uppermost surface of the cross section, in pounds per square inch.

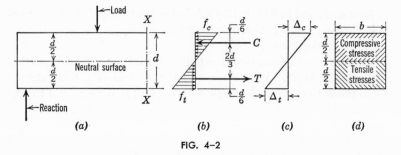

FIG. 4–2

f_t = the unit tensile stress on the fibers at the lower surface of the cross section, in pounds per square inch.

C = the resultant of all the compressive stresses, in pounds.

T = the resultant of all the tensile stresses, in pounds.

M = the bending moment at section X–X, in inch-pounds.

Figure 4–2(b) shows the distribution of the stresses in the cross section. The stresses on the fibers at the neutral surface are zero and increase in magnitude to maximum values at the upper and lower surfaces. These stresses are directly proportional to their distances from the neutral surface; that is to say, if the unit stress on the fibers at 1 in. from the neutral surface is 100 psi, the stress on the fibers at 2 in. is twice this value, or 200 psi, and at the distance $d/2$ from the neutral surface they will be $\left(100 \times \dfrac{d}{2}\right)$ psi. Since the stresses increase directly from zero to a value of f_c, the *average* unit compressive stress is $f_c/2$. The area of the cross section in compression is $b \times \dfrac{d}{2}$, and therefore the sum of all the compressive stresses is $\dfrac{f_c}{2} \times b \times \dfrac{d}{2}$ and is shown in Fig. 4–2(b) by the line C. We call C the resultant of all the compressive forces, the *resultant* being a single force that produces the same effect as a number of forces acting together. In a similar manner, $T = \dfrac{f_t}{2} \times b \times \dfrac{d}{2}$.

A *mechanical couple* is the term applied to two equal parallel forces acting in opposite directions not having the same line of action. The two forces, C and T, constitute a mechanical couple.

They tend to cause rotation. The *moment of a mechanical couple* is the magnitude of one of the forces multiplied by the normal distance between their lines of action. Note in Fig. 4–2(*b*) that the stresses in the fibers above the neutral surface increase from zero to f_c, the diagram of distribution being a triangle. The resultant of the compressive forces passes through the centroid of the triangle and, since the centroid of a triangle lies at a point one third the distance from the base to the apex, the resultant of the compressive forces lies at a distance $d/6$ from the upper surface of the beam. Hence the distance between the two resultant forces, C and T, is $2d/3$. The *resisting moment* is the sum of the moments of all the stresses in the cross section. Now, since one force of the mechanical couple is $\dfrac{f_c}{2} \times b \times \dfrac{d}{2}$ and the lever arm of the couple is $2d/3$, the resisting moment must be $\dfrac{f_c}{2} \times b \times \dfrac{d}{2} \times \dfrac{2d}{3}$, or $\dfrac{f_c b d^2}{6}$. From Art. 4–1 it is seen that the bending moment and resisting moment must be equal, hence $M = \dfrac{f_c b d^2}{6}$ or $\dfrac{M}{f_c} = \dfrac{b d^2}{6}$, which actually is the flexure formula * for homogeneous rectangular beams. Since f_c and f_t are equal, we may write $\dfrac{M}{f} = \dfrac{b d^2}{6}$, in which f is the unit stress on the fiber at the greatest distance from the neutral surface.

To illustrate how readily this formula may be used in the design of homogeneous beams let us try the following problem.

Example: A timber beam has a span of 16 ft 0 in. and a uniformly distributed load of 7000 lb. If we assume that the allowable extreme fiber stress of the timber is 1200 psi, what should be the dimensions of the beam with respect to bending?

SOLUTION: $M = \dfrac{Wl}{8}$. See Fig. 3–4(*a*). Then,

$$M = \frac{7000 \times 16 \times 12}{8} = 168{,}000 \text{ in-lb}$$

---

* See Art. 90, *Simplified Mechanics and Strength of Materials*, by Harry Parker, John Wiley and Sons, 1951.

the maximum bending moment.   The flexure formula given above is

$$\frac{M}{f} = \frac{bd^2}{6} \quad \text{or} \quad \frac{168,000}{1200} = \frac{bd^2}{6} \quad \text{or} \quad 140 = \frac{bd^2}{6}$$

If we assume that the width of the beam is 6 in., $140 = 6 \times \dfrac{d^2}{6}$, or $d^2 = 140$, and $d = 11.8$ in.   A beam 6 x 12 in. in cross section is acceptable if these are the actual dimensions.   In practice, however, there is a difference between nominal and actual sizes.   A table * giving the section moduli of rectangular beams shows that an 8 x 12 in. beam has actual dimensions of $7\frac{1}{2}$ x $11\frac{1}{2}$ in. and a section modulus, $bd^2/6$, of 165.31 in.^{3}, and therefore is acceptable, as it is in excess of the required 140 in.^{3}.

Bear in mind that this illustrative problem deals with a homogeneous beam, a beam composed of only one material.   Reinforced concrete beams, however, consist of concrete and steel.   The derivation of design formulas for these beams presents other problems.   In the first place, the position of the neutral surface is not midway between the upper and lower surfaces; its location must be computed.   As will be seen, there are other factors that must be considered, but the basic principle is the same.   The bending moment and resisting moment are equal in magnitude, and our problem is to develop expressions for the resisting moments of both the concrete and steel.

4–3. Theoretical Assumptions.   Owing to the fact that concrete offers little resistance to tension, steel reinforcing rods are placed in those parts of members at which tensile stresses are developed. Formulas used in design are based on the theory that the compressive stresses are resisted by the concrete and that the steel reinforcement resists all tensile stresses.   Unlike the homogeneous beams discussed in Art. 4–2, the position of the neutral surface depends upon the unit tensile and compressive stresses and n, the ratio of the modulus of elasticity of steel to the modulus of elasticity of the concrete.   See Art. 2–18.

In a book of this scope it is not feasible to develop all the many formulas that are used in the design of reinforced concrete mem-

---

* See Table 13, *Simplified Mechanics and Strength of Materials.*

bers. As a matter of fact, certain formulas in use are empirical. In any event, a designer of reinforced concrete must use the formulas laid down in the governing building code. Such formulas are far from being uniform.

In order to have a thorough knowledge of the principles involved in the design of beams, it is advisable that certain of the most commonly used formulas be investigated. The various steps in their development having been accepted, the use and limitations of the formulas are retained, although the exact procedure in developing the formulas may be forgotten.

To develop the formulas used in the design of reinforced concrete, certain fundamental assumptions are used as a basis. Briefly, they are as follows:

1. A plane cross section of a beam before bending remains a plane section after bending. This is another way of saying that the deformations of the fibers are directly proportional to their distances from the neutral surface.

2. Perfect adhesion exists between the concrete and the steel reinforcement. Deformations of the materials do not break the bond between them.

3. The tensile resistance of concrete is ignored, and the steel reinforcement is depended upon to resist all tensile stresses.

4–4. Notation Used in Reinforced Concrete Beam Formulas. The following notation is used in formulas for reinforced concrete members in bending:

Δ_c and Δ_s = deformations per unit of length of concrete and steel, respectively, as indicated in Fig. 4–3(a).

E_s = modulus of elasticity of steel, in pounds per square inch, 30,000,000 psi.

E_c = modulus of elasticity of concrete in compression, in pounds per square inch, the magnitude depending on the quality of the concrete.

n = ratio of modulus of elasticity of steel to that of concrete = E_s/E_c.

f_c = compressive unit stress on the concrete at the surface most remote from the neutral surface, in pounds per square inch.

f_s = tensile unit stress in the longitudinal reinforcement, in pounds per square inch.

b = the width of the rectangular beam, in inches.

d = the depth from the compression face of the beam to the center of the longitudinal steel reinforcement, in inches. This is known as *the effective depth*.

k = ratio of distance of the neutral axis of the cross section from extreme fibers in compression to the effective depth of the beam.

kd = the distance from the neutral axis of the cross section to the extreme fibers in compression, in inches.

j = ratio of the distance between the resultant of the compressive stresses and center of tensile stresses to d, the effective depth of the beam.

jd = the distance between the resultant of the compressive stresses and the center of the tensile stresses. It is the lever arm of the resisting couple, in inches.

A_s = the area of the cross section of the longitudinal steel reinforcement, in square inches.

p = the ratio of the area of the cross section of the longitudinal steel reinforcement to the effective area of the concrete beam, $p = \dfrac{A_s}{bd}$.

M_c = the resisting moment of the compressive stresses in the concrete, in inch-pounds.

M_s = the resisting moment of the tensile stresses in the longitudinal steel reinforcement, in inch-pounds.

M = the bending moment resulting from external forces, in inch-pounds.

C = the sum of the horizontal compressive stresses in the concrete, in pounds.

T = the sum of the horizontal tensile stresses in the longitudinal steel reinforcement, in pounds.

4–5. Derivation of Flexure Formulas for Rectangular Reinforced Concrete Beams. In accordance with the theoretical assumptions noted in Art. 4–3, the deformations of the fibers are directly proportional to their distances from the neutral axis of the cross section, as indicated in the deformation diagram, Fig. 4–3(a). Likewise, the

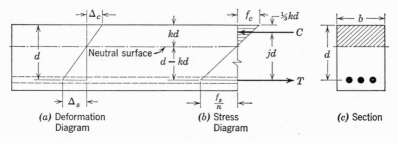

(a) Deformation
Diagram

(b) Stress
Diagram

(c) Section

FIG. 4–3

stresses in the fibers are proportional to their deformations and also are directly proportional to their distances from the neutral axis. By definition,

$$E, \text{ modulus of elasticity} = \frac{\text{unit stress}}{\text{unit deformation}}$$

Therefore,

$$E_s = \frac{f_s}{\Delta_s} \quad \text{and} \quad E_c = \frac{f_c}{\Delta_c}$$

Transposing,

$$\Delta_s = \frac{f_s}{E_s} \quad \text{and} \quad \Delta_c = \frac{f_c}{E_c}$$

Since the deformations are directly proportional to their distances from the neutral axis,

$$\frac{f_c/E_c}{f_s/E_s} = \frac{kd}{d - kd}$$

or

$$\frac{f_c E_s}{f_s E_c} = \frac{k}{1 - k} \tag{a}$$

Substituting in (a) the value $n = \dfrac{E_s}{E_c}$,

$$\frac{n f_c}{f_s} = \frac{k}{1 - k} \quad \text{or} \quad \frac{f_c}{f_s} = \frac{k}{n(1 - k)} \tag{b}$$

from which

$$f_c = \frac{f_s k}{n(1 - k)} \qquad (1)$$

and

$$f_s = \frac{n f_c (1 - k)}{k} \qquad (2)$$

From (2)

$$k = \frac{n f_c (1 - k)}{f_s} \qquad \text{or} \qquad k = \frac{n - nk}{f_s/f_c}$$

or

$$k = \frac{n}{n + f_s/f_c} \qquad (3)$$

Consider the resisting moment, M_c, with respect to the compressive stresses in the concrete; the stresses vary in magnitude from zero to f_c, hence the average unit stress is $\frac{1}{2}f_c$. The area of concrete in compression is bkd. Therefore, C, the sum of the compressive stresses, is $\frac{1}{2}f_c bkd$. The lever arm of the mechanical couple is jd. Therefore, the resisting moment

$$M_c = \frac{1}{2}f_c jkbd^2 \qquad (c)$$

Next consider M_s, the resisting moment with respect to the tensile stresses in the steel reinforcement. The unit tensile stress is f_s, the area of the steel is A_s and therefore T, the sum of all the tensile stresses, is $A_s f_s$. Again the lever arm of the couple is jd, and the resisting moment,

$$M_s = A_s f_s jd$$

But

$$A_s = pbd$$

therefore,

$$M_s = A_s f_s jd \qquad \text{or} \qquad M_s = p f_s jbd^2 \qquad (d)$$

The resisting moments are, of course, equal in magnitude, hence we may equate (c) and (d), or

$$p f_s jbd^2 = \frac{1}{2}f_c jkbd^2$$

from which,

$$2p f_s = f_c k \qquad \text{or} \qquad \frac{f_c}{f_s} = \frac{2p}{k} \qquad (e)$$

If the values of $\dfrac{f_c}{f_s}$, in (b) and (e), are placed equal to each other,

$$\frac{k}{n(1-k)} = \frac{2p}{k}$$

$$k^2 = 2pn(1-k) \quad \text{or} \quad k^2 + 2pnk = 2pn$$

Completing the square and solving for k,

$$k = \sqrt{2pn + (pn)^2} - pn \tag{4}$$

The resultant of the compressive stresses in the concrete is $\frac{1}{3}kd$ from the uppermost fiber, and since the distance between the sum of the compressive stresses and the sum of the tensile stresses is jd, as shown in Fig. 4–3(b),

$$jd = d - \frac{kd}{3} \quad \text{or} \quad j = 1 - \frac{k}{3} \tag{5}$$

Since the magnitudes of the bending moment and resisting moment must be equal, equation (c) may be written

$$M = \frac{1}{2}f_c jkbd^2 \quad \text{or} \quad d^2 = \frac{M}{\frac{1}{2}f_c jkb}$$

and

$$d = \sqrt{\frac{M}{\frac{1}{2}f_c jkb}}$$

As a matter of convenience, let $K = \frac{1}{2}f_c jk$, then

$$d = \sqrt{\frac{M}{Kb}} \tag{6}$$

The bending moment, M, may also be substituted for the resisting moment, M_s, in (d). Then,

$$M = A_s f_s jd$$

and

$$A_s = \frac{M}{f_s jd} \tag{7}$$

By definition,

$$p = \frac{A_s}{bd}$$

Therefore,

$$A_s = pbd \tag{8}$$

Equation (e) gives

$$2pf_s = f_c k$$

Transposing,

$$p = \frac{kf_c}{2f_s} \tag{9}$$

4–6. Summary of Flexure Formulas for Beams. The various formulas developed in the previous article apply to rectangular reinforced concrete beams with respect to flexure or bending. They may be used in the design of slabs as well, since, in reality, a slab is a beam of considerable width as compared to its depth. The terms or notation used in the formulas are those commonly used and are listed in Art. 4–4.

As a matter of convenience, the important formulas are summarized as follows. No other flexure formulas are needed for the design of rectangular beams for bending stresses.

$$f_c = \frac{f_s k}{n(1 - k)} \tag{1}$$

$$f_s = \frac{nf_c(1 - k)}{k} \tag{2}$$

$$k = \frac{n}{n + (f_s/f_c)} \tag{3}$$

$$k = \sqrt{2pn + (pn)^2} - pn \tag{4}$$

$$j = 1 - \frac{k}{3} \tag{5}$$

$$d = \sqrt{\frac{M}{\frac{1}{2}f_c jkb}} \quad \text{or} \quad d = \sqrt{\frac{M}{Kb}} \tag{6}$$

$$A_s = \frac{M}{f_s jd} \tag{7}$$

$$A_s = pbd \tag{8}$$

$$p = \frac{kf_c}{2f_s} \tag{9}$$

4–7. Types of Beam Problems. Before discussing the use of the various formulas, a brief explanation is necessary. There are in general two distinct types of problems to be solved in connection with beams, depending on the given data.

The first and most important type of problem is *design*. Nearly all the discussions in this text are devoted to design problems. For such problems, f_c and f_s, the allowable unit stresses of the concrete and steel, as well as n, the ratio of the moduli of elasticity, are given. The maximum bending moment is computed, and, with these values as data, design problems consist of determining the dimensions of the members including the steel reinforcement.

The other type of problem is that of *investigation*. In these problems all dimensions of the members are known, and the problem is one of determining the unit fiber stresses developed due to a given loading.

Certain formulas do not apply to both design and investigation. For example, formula (3) can be used in design only, since f_s and f_c are given as data. This formula is not applicable to investigation problems, for in such problems the fiber stresses are unknown.

4–8. Application of Beam Formulas. It is important that certain terms in the beam formulas be thoroughly understood. By referring to Fig. 4–3, note that d, the effective depth, is a linear dimension, a number of inches. This is also true of b, the width of the beam. The letters k and j, however, are coefficients, whereas kd and jd are linear dimensions. A_s is the total area of the steel reinforcement in the beam, regardless of the number of bars, and is given in square inches.

To illustrate how certain formulas may be used in the design of a reinforced concrete beam for flexure, let us try a problem.

Example. A beam whose end conditions are fully continuous has a clear span between faces of supports of 20 ft 0 in. The total uniformly distributed load, including the weight of the beam, is 30,000 lb. Let it be required to determine the width, depth, and longitudinal steel reinforcement. Note particularly that this beam is to be designed for flexure only. Other reinforcement, stirrups, may be required to resist shearing stresses, but computations for this type of reinforcement are discussed in Chapter 5.

Specification data:

$$f_s = 20,000 \text{ psi}$$

$$f_c = 1350 \text{ psi}$$

$$n = 10$$

SOLUTION: To find the coefficient k, use the formula

$$k = \frac{n}{n + (f_s/f_c)} \qquad \text{Formula (3), Art. 4–5}$$

Substituting,

$$k = \frac{10}{10 + (20,000/1350)} \qquad \text{or} \qquad k = 0.403$$

The coefficient j may be found by the formula

$$j = 1 - \frac{k}{3} \qquad \text{Formula (5), Art. 4–5}$$

Substituting the value of k, just found,

$$j = 1 - \frac{0.403}{3} = 1 - 0.134 = 0.866$$

The percentage of longitudinal steel reinforcement is found by use of equation

$$p = \frac{kf_c}{2f_s} \qquad \text{Formula (9), Art. 4–5}$$

Substituting the known values,

$$p = \frac{0.403 \times 1350}{2 \times 20,000} = 0.0136$$

The value of the maximum bending moment for a beam having a uniformly distributed load with the end conditions fully continuous is

$$M = \frac{Wl}{12} \qquad \text{(See Art. 3–7)}$$

Then

$$M = \frac{30,000 \times 20 \times 12}{12} = 600,000 \text{ in-lb}$$

The formula to determine d, the effective depth, is

$$d = \sqrt{\frac{M}{\frac{1}{2}f_c jkb}} \qquad \text{Formula (6), Art. 4–5}$$

Assume b, the width of the beam, to be 10 in., then substituting in (6),

$$d = \sqrt{\frac{600,000}{\frac{1}{2} \times 1350 \times 0.866 \times 0.403 \times 10}} = \sqrt{255} = 15.9 \text{ in.}$$

the effective depth. From Fig. 4–3 note that d is the distance from the center of the longitudinal steel reinforcement to the uppermost surface in compression. If we assume that one half the diameter of the bars is 0.5 in. and that 1.5 in. of concrete will be used below the bars for fireproofing, the total depth will be $15.9 + 0.5 + 1.5 = 17.9$ in. Accept a total depth of 18 in., thus making the effective depth $d = 18 - 2 = 16$ in.

To determine the area of the tensile reinforcing bars,

$$A_s = \frac{M}{f_s jd} \qquad \text{Formula (7), Art. 4–5}$$

Substituting the known values,

$$A_s = \frac{600,000}{20,000 \times 0.866 \times 16} = 2.16 \text{ sq in.}$$

the total area of the longitudinal steel.

Referring to Table 1–1, we find that 3-#8 bars have an area of 2.37 sq in. and therefore are acceptable.

If the effective depth 15.9 in. had been used instead of 16 in., we could have used formula (8), $A_s = pbd$ or $A_s = 0.0136 \times 10 \times 15.9 = 2.16$ sq in. This equation is used for *balanced reinforcement*, discussed in Art. 4–11.

These computations do not complete the design of the beam. Notice, however, what we have accomplished. The width of the beam was assumed to be 10 in. and, with this assumption, d, the effective depth, 15.9 in., was determined by equation (6). In addition to the cross-sectional dimensions of the beam, we have found that 2.16 sq in. of longitudinal steel reinforcement is required. The steps necessary for completing the design of the beam include computing the bond stress to see that it does not exceed the allowable, investigating the shearing stresses to determine whether or not web reinforcement is necessary, and, finally, the construction of a diagram giving all dimensions showing position, bends, hooks, lengths, etc., of the reinforcing members.

Problem 4–8–A. A fully continuous beam has a clear span of 24 ft 0 in. and a uniformly distributed load, including the weight of the beam, of 1200 lb per linear ft. Determine the width, depth, and longitudinal steel reinforcement. Specification data:

$$f_s = 20,000 \text{ psi}$$

$$f_c = 1125 \text{ psi}$$

$$n = 12$$

Problem 4–8–B. If $f_s = 20,000$ psi, $f_c = 1688$ psi, and $n = 8$, compute the values of the formula coefficients k, j, and p.

4–9. Coefficients for Beam Formulas. The computations given in Art. 4–8 for determining the values of the formula factors are somewhat tedious. As a matter of fact, they are quite unnecessary, for they may be found directly by referring to Table 4–1. This table gives formula coefficients for the three grades of concrete most frequently used: $n = 12$ when $f'_c = 2500$ psi, $n = 10$ when $f'_c = 3000$ psi, and $n = 8$ when $f'_c = 3750$ psi. The term f'_c indicates the ultimate compressive stress at the 28-day curing period. Perhaps the most commonly used grade of concrete is that having $f'_c = 3000$ psi, for which $n = 10$, the allowable unit stresses for steel and concrete being, respectively, $f_s = 20,000$ psi and $f_c = 1350$ psi. These stresses were used in the example given in Art. 4–8. Check the values of the coefficients found by computations with those given in Table 4–1. The allowable extreme fiber stress in the concrete, f_c, is generally given by building code specifications as $0.45f'_c$. Hence, for the foregoing grades of concrete, the usual allowable concrete stresses are $f_c = 1125$ psi, 1350 psi, and 1688 psi. In certain older building codes $f_c = 0.40f'_c$, hence $f_c = 1000$ psi, 1200 psi, and 1500 psi. The value of f_s, the allowable tensile unit stress for the longitudinal steel, is either 18,000 or 20,000 psi, depending on the building code requirements.

4–10. Resisting Moment for Concrete Stresses. As has been explained, the resisting moment of the stresses in a cross section

TABLE 4-1. FORMULA COEFFICIENTS FOR RECTANGULAR BEAM SECTIONS

$n = 12$ $(f'_c = 2500 \text{ psi})$

f_s	f_c	K	k	j	p
18,000	875	141	0.368	0.877	0.0089
	950	161	0.388	0.871	0.0102
	1000	173	0.400	0.867	0.0111
	1125	207	0.429	0.857	0.0134
20,000	875	133	0.344	0.885	0.0075
	950	152	0.363	0.879	0.0086
	1000	164	0.375	0.875	0.0094
	1125	196	0.403	0.866	0.0113

$n = 10$ $(f'_c = 3000 \text{ psi})$

f_s	f_c	K	k	j	p
18,000	1050	169	0.368	0.877	0.0107
	1125	189	0.385	0.872	0.0120
	1200	208	0.400	0.867	0.0133
	1350	248	0.429	0.857	0.0161
20,000	1050	160	0.344	0.885	0.0090
	1125	178	0.360	0.880	0.0101
	1200	197	0.375	0.875	0.0113
	1350	236	0.403	0.866	0.0136

$n = 8$ $(f'_c = 3750 \text{ psi})$

f_s	f_c	K	k	j	p
18,000	1300	209	0.366	0.878	0.0132
	1400	234	0.384	0.872	0.0149
	1500	260	0.400	0.867	0.0167
	1688	309	0.428	0.857	0.0200
20,000	1300	197	0.342	0.886	0.0111
	1400	221	0.359	0.880	0.0126
	1500	246	0.375	0.875	0.0141
	1688	294	0.403	0.866	0.0170

is equal in magnitude to the bending moment. Therefore, we may equate the resisting moment of the concrete stresses given in equation (c), Art. 4–5, to M, the bending moment, or $M = \frac{1}{2}f_c jkbd^2$.

For convenience, let us combine the terms $\frac{1}{2}f_c jk$ and represent the quantity by K. Then

$$M = Kbd^2$$

or

$$d = \sqrt{\frac{M}{Kb}}$$

This is formula (6) in Art. 4–5, and, in this form, it is of great convenience in determining the effective depth of rectangular sections.

For $f_s = 20{,}000$ psi, $f_c = 1350$ psi, and $n = 10$, we find, by referring to Table 4–1, that $j = 0.866$ and $k = 0.403$. Hence, $K = \frac{1}{2} \times 1350 \times 0.866 \times 0.403 = 236$, or we may write equation (6), $d = \sqrt{\dfrac{M}{236b}}$.

Note that the value of K for various unit stresses is given in Table 4–1 and need not be computed each time.

To illustrate how readily the formula $d = \sqrt{\dfrac{M}{Kb}}$ may be used, suppose we are to determine the effective depth of a beam having a maximum bending moment of 900,000 in-lb. ($f_s = 20{,}000$ psi, $f_c = 1350$ psi, and $n = 10$.) Assume that the width of the beam, b, is 12 in.

Referring to Table 4–1, we find that $K = 236$. Then

$$d = \sqrt{\frac{M}{Kb}} \quad \text{or} \quad d = \sqrt{\frac{900{,}000}{236 \times 12}} = \sqrt{318} = 17.8 \text{ in.}$$

If we had assumed a width of 10 in., $b = 10$ and, substituting,

$$d = \sqrt{\frac{900{,}000}{236 \times 10}} = \sqrt{380} = 19.5 \text{ in.}$$

How simple!

Problem 4–10–A. A beam has a maximum bending moment of 1,200,000 in-lb. By use of formula (6), Art. 4–5, compute its effective depth, assuming the width to be 12 in. Specification data:

$$f_s = 20,000 \text{ psi}$$

$$f_c = 1125 \text{ psi}$$

$$n = 12$$

Problem 4–10–B. Assume that the width of a reinforced concrete beam is 8 in. Compute its effective depth if the maximum bending moment is 600,000 in-lb. Specification data:

$$f_s = 20,000 \text{ psi}$$

$$f_c = 1688 \text{ psi}$$

$$n = 8$$

4–11. Balanced Reinforcement. The term *balanced reinforcement* (or balanced beam) refers to a reinforced concrete beam in which the cross-sectional areas of concrete and steel are such that each develops its full allowable stress simultaneously. Equations $A_s = \dfrac{M}{f_s jd}$ and $A_s = pbd$, identified as (7) and (8), respectively, Art. 4–5, are both to be used for computing the area of the longitudinal steel reinforcement. The use of equation (6), $d = \sqrt{\dfrac{M}{Kb}}$, determines d, the effective depth, and provides for f_c and f_s being stressed to their allowable working values. Having established d, equation (8), $A_s = pbd$, gives quickly the area of the longitudinal steel. The use of this formula also is based on balanced reinforcement. When, however, d is a dimension other than that found by use of equation (6), equation (7), $A_s = \dfrac{M}{f_s jd}$, establishes the required steel area based on the actual bending moment and a predetermined unit stress for the steel. To illustrate, consider the following problem.

Example. A reinforced concrete beam has a maximum bending moment of 900,000 in-lb. Data:

$$f_s = 20,000 \text{ psi}$$

$$f_c = 1350 \text{ psi}$$

$$n = 10$$

Assuming that the width, b, is 10 in., determine the area of the longitudinal steel reinforcement.

SOLUTION. Referring to Table 4–1, $p = 0.0136$, $j = 0.866$, and $K = 236$. Then

$$d = \sqrt{\frac{M}{Kb}} \qquad \text{Equation (6), Art. 4–5}$$

Substituting,

$$d = \sqrt{\frac{900,000}{236 \times 10}} = \sqrt{380} = 19.5 \text{ in.}$$

the minimum effective depth. Since this formula is based on balanced reinforcement, to find A_s we can use

$$A_s = pbd \qquad \text{Equation (8), Art. 4–5}$$

Substituting,

$$A_s = 0.0136 \times 10 \times 19.5 = 2.65 \text{ sq in.}$$

the steel area.

If the exact value of d as found from equation (6) is maintained, we might have used

$$A_s = \frac{M}{f_s j d} \qquad \text{Equation (7), Art. 4–5}$$

Substituting,

$$A_s = \frac{900,000}{20,000 \times 0.866 \times 19.5} = 2.65 \text{ sq in.}$$

Note that this is the same steel area found by the use of equation (8).

Let us suppose that an adjacent beam has a shorter span resulting in a maximum bending moment of only 300,000 in-lb and that the same dimensions of the beam are to be maintained. The use of equation (8) would give a steel area of 2.65 sq in., obviously more steel than would be necessary to provide a unit stress of 20,000 psi.

This is where we may use equation (7), for in this formula the steel area is determined in accordance with the bending moment and a steel unit stress of 20,000 psi. Therefore,

$$A_s = \frac{M}{f_s j d} \qquad \text{or} \qquad A_s = \frac{300,000}{20,000 \times 0.866 \times 19.5} = 0.887 \text{ sq in.}$$

Thus it is seen that the use of equation (7) is appropriate when the areas of concrete and steel do not provide a balanced beam, a condition that occurs frequently when the depth of the beam is increased over that theoretically required so that the total depth of the beam will be in full inches, not fractions. Note, however, that most building codes require certain minimum steel areas. This is explained in the following article.

Problem 4–11–A. A beam has a maximum bending moment of 1,000,000 in-lb. Assuming the width to be 12 in., determine the effective depth and area of the longitudinal steel reinforcement. Specification data:

$$f_s = 18,000 \text{ psi}$$

$$f_c = 1125 \text{ psi}$$

$$n = 12$$

4–12. Minimum Reinforcement. In practice, the depths of certain beams are often increased considerably over that which is theoretically required. This increase may be for architectural reasons or for economy in re-using forms. Most building codes specify a required minimum area of tensile reinforcement regardless of the area required by computations. These areas are

for slabs, minimum $A_s = 0.0025bd$

for beams, minimum $A_s = 0.005bd$

In the example given in Art. 4–11 the steel area required for a bending moment of 300,000 in-lb was 0.887 sq in. The minimum area of tensile reinforcement, however, for a beam 10 in. in width with an effective depth of 19.5 in. is $0.005bd$, or $0.005 \times 10 \times 19.5 = 0.975$ sq in. Consequently, the longitudinal tensile reinforcement must have an area of at least 0.975 sq in. regardless of that required by equation (7).

Problem 4–12–A. A simple beam has a width of 12 in. and an effective depth of 22 in. Compute the minimum area of the longitudinal tensile reinforcement permitted if the maximum bending moment is 400,000 in-lb. Specification data:

$$f_s = 20,000 \text{ psi}$$

$$f_c = 1350 \text{ psi}$$

$$n = 10$$

4–13. The Transformed Section. From Fig. 4–3(a) it is seen that the steel and concrete have equal deformations at equal distances from the neutral surface. However, since the steel is n times stiffer than the concrete, it requires n times as much stress to deform the steel a given distance as would be required to produce the same deformation in the concrete. Because of this fact, the theory of the *transformed section* has been evolved. The transformed section is an imaginary cross section of a beam in which the steel is replaced by a hypothetical concrete area that is n times the area of the steel. This imaginary concrete area has the same modulus of elasticity as the concrete in compression above the neutral axis, and, in addition, we assume that it is capable of resisting tension. See Fig. 4–4(b). By the use of this imaginary or transformed section, we can apply the customary methods used for homogeneous beams in deriving formulas to be used for reinforced concrete.

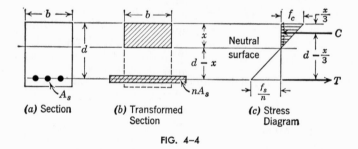

FIG. 4–4

The term *statical moment* refers to an area multiplied by the distance from its centroid to a given point or axis. The neutral axis of a cross section passes through the centroid of the section, hence the statical moment of the compression area is equal to the statical moment of the tension area about the neutral axis. Let us call x the distance from the upper surface of a rectangular beam to the neutral axis. See Fig. 4–4(b). This is the distance kd in Fig. 4–3. Then, as the area in compression is bx and the distance of its centroid to the neutral axis is $\frac{1}{2}x$, the moment of this area, with respect to the neutral axis, is $bx \times \frac{1}{2}x$. Similarly, the area of the imaginary tension area is nA_s and its lever arm is $d - x$. Therefore, the moment of the tension area is $nA_s \times (d - x)$. Since the two moments are equal, we may write

$$bx \times \tfrac{1}{2}x = nA_s \times (d - x)$$

This equation enables us to compute the distance x, which of course is kd, when b, d, A_s, and n are known. It should be noted that this distance is not dependent on the fiber stresses or the bending moment. The use of the transformed section is of particular value in the *investigation* of beams, that is, the determination of the unit stresses when the actual dimensions of the beam are known.

4–14. Investigation of Beams. The commonest engineering problem met with by architects and engineers is the *design* of structural members, the determination of their dimensions. Another problem, however, is to determine the unit stresses in members of given dimensions under a specific loading. Problems of this type are known as *investigation*. They consist principally in testing the safety of a given member by determining the actual unit stresses and comparing them with the allowable. Such problems are readily solved by the use of the transformed section.

Example. A beam has a width of 10 in. and an effective depth of 22 in., with 2 sq in. of longitudinal steel reinforcement. See Fig. 4–5(*a*). If $n = 15$ and the maximum bending moment is 500,000 in-lb, compute f_c and f_s, the maximum fiber stresses in the concrete and steel.

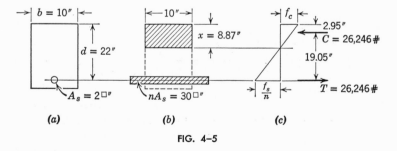

FIG. 4–5

SOLUTION. The first step in the solution of this problem is to determine x, the distance of the neutral axis from the upper surface of the beam. As explained in the previous article,

$$bx \times \tfrac{1}{2}x = nA_s(d - x) \qquad \text{(See Fig. 4–4)}$$

Substituting the known values,

$$10x \times \tfrac{1}{2}x = 15 \times 2 \times (22 - x)$$

or

$$5x^2 + 30x = 660 \qquad \text{or} \qquad x^2 + 6x = 132$$

Completing the square,

$$x^2 + 6x + 9 = 132 + 9$$

or

$$x + 3 = 11.87$$

and

$$x = 8.87 \text{ in.}$$

Then the lever arm of the couple is $d - \dfrac{x}{3}$ or

$$d - \frac{x}{3} = 22 - \frac{8.87}{3} = 19.05 \text{ in.} \qquad \text{[See Fig. 4–5(c)]}$$

The resisting moment of the compressive stresses $= C \times 19.05$. The resisting moment of the tensile stresses $= T \times 19.05$. But the resisting moment and the bending moment are equal and by data $M = 500,000$ in-lb. Therefore,

$$500,000 = C \times 19.05 \qquad \text{or} \qquad C = 26,246 \text{ lb}$$

and

$$500,000 = T \times 19.05 \qquad \text{or} \qquad T = 26,246 \text{ lb}$$

The compressive stresses are

$$C = 26,246 = \tfrac{1}{2}f_c \times 10 \times 8.87 \qquad \text{or} \qquad f_c = 591 \text{ psi}$$

The tensile stresses are

$$T = 26,246 = 2 \times f_s \qquad \text{or} \qquad f_s = 13,123 \text{ psi}$$

Problem 4–14–A. A simple reinforced concrete beam has a width of 10 in., an effective depth of 20 in., and a maximum bending moment of 600,000 in-lb. The tensile reinforcement consists of four #6 bars. Compute the maximum compressive unit stress in the concrete and the maximum tensile unit stress in the longitudinal tensile reinforcement. Specification data: $n = 10$

4–15. Allowable Unit Stresses in Concrete and Steel. The allowable unit stresses for concrete are given as percentages of f'_c, the ultimate compressive stress at the 28-day period. These percentages vary in different building codes. Table 4–2 gives allowable unit stresses in concrete, and Table 4–3 gives the maximum

TABLE 4–2.   ALLOWABLE UNIT STRESSES IN CONCRETE

			Allowable Unit Stresses					
Description		For Any Strength of Concrete in Accordance with Section 302 of A.C.I. Code $n = \dfrac{30{,}000}{f'_c}$	Maximum Value, psi	For Strength of Concrete Shown Below				
				$f'_c = 2000$ psi $n = 15$	$f'_c = 2500$ psi $n = 12$	$f'_c = 3000$ psi $n = 10$	$f'_c = 3750$ psi $n = 8$	$f'_c = 5000$ psi $n = 6$
Flexure: f_c								
Extreme fiber stress in compression	f_c	$0.45f'_c$		900	1125	1350	1688	2250
Extreme fiber stress in tension in plain concrete footings	f_c	$0.03f'_c$		60	75	90	113	150
Shear: v (as a measure of diagonal tension)								
Beams with no web reinforcement	v_c	$0.03f'_c$	90	60	75	90	90	90
Beams with longitudinal bars and with either stirrups or properly located bent bars	v	$0.08f'_c$	240	160	200	240	240	240
Beams with longitudinal bars and a combination of stirrups and bent bars (the latter bent up suitably to carry at least $0.04f'_c$)	v	$0.12f'_c$	360	240	300	360	360	360
Footings	v_c	$0.03f'_c$	75	60	75	75	75	75
Bond: u								
Deformed bars								
Top bars *	u	$0.07f'_c$	245	140	175	210	245	245
In two-way footings (except top bars)	u	$0.08f'_c$	280	160	200	240	280	280
All others	u	$0.10f'_c$	350	200	250	300	350	350
Plain bars (must be hooked)								
Top bars	u	$0.03f'_c$	105	60	75	90	105	105
In two-way footings (except top bars)	u	$0.036f'_c$	126	72	90	108	126	126
All others	u	$0.045f'_c$	158	90	113	135	158	158
Bearing: f_c								
On full area	f_c	$0.25f'_c$		500	625	750	938	1250
On one third area or less †	f_c	$0.375f'_c$		750	938	1125	1405	1875

* Top bars, in reference to bond, are horizontal bars so placed that more than 12 in. of concrete is cast in the member below the bar.

† This increase shall be permitted only when the least distance between the edges of the loaded and unloaded areas is a minimum of one fourth of the parallel side dimension of the loaded area. The allowable bearing stress on a reasonably concentric area greater than one third but less than the full area shall be interpolated between the values given.

Reproduced, by permission of the American Concrete Institute, from *Building Code Requirements for Reinforced Concrete* (A.C.I. 318-56).

unit stresses to be used in reinforcing steel. Both Tables 4–2 and 4–3 are taken from data given in the *Building Code Requirements for Reinforced Concrete* (A.C.I. 318–56).

TABLE 4–3. ALLOWABLE UNIT STRESSES IN REINFORCEMENT *

Steel for concrete reinforcement shall not be stressed in excess of the following limits:

Tension
f_s = tensile unit stress in longitudinal reinforcement and
f_v = tensile unit stress in web reinforcement.
20,000 psi for rail-steel concrete reinforcement bars, billet-steel concrete reinforcement bars (of intermediate and hard grades), axle-steel concrete reinforcement bars (of intermediate and hard grades) and cold-drawn steel wire for concrete reinforcement.
18,000 psi for billet-steel concrete reinforcement bars (of structural grade) and axle-steel concrete reinforcement bars (of structural grade).

Tension in One-Way Slabs of Not More Than 12-ft. Span
f_s = tensile unit stress in main reinforcement.
For the main reinforcement, $\frac{3}{8}$ in. or less in diameter, in one-way slabs, 50% of the minimum yield point specified in the Standard Specifications of the American Society for Testing Materials for the particular kind and grade of reinforcement used, but in no case to exceed 30,000 psi.

Compression, Vertical Column Reinforcement
f_s = nominal working stress in vertical column reinforcement.
Forty % of the minimum yield point specified in the Standard Specifications of the American Society for Testing Materials for the particular kind and grade of reinforcement used, but in no case to exceed 30,000 psi.
f_r = allowable unit stress in the metal core of composite and combination columns:

structural steel sections	16,000 psi
cast-iron sections	10,000 psi

* Reproduced, by permission of the American Concrete Institute, from *Building Code Requirements for Reinforced Concrete* (A.C.I. 318-56).

A designer of reinforced concrete must, of course, consult the local building regulations to determine the allowable stresses to be used. Unfortunately, they are not uniform throughout the country. As an instance, some older codes permit an allowable extreme fiber stress in compression in concrete of $0.4f'_c$, whereas Table 4–2 gives this stress to be $0.45f'_c$. For 3000 psi concrete, these allowable stresses are, respectively, 1200 psi and 1350 psi. In the illustrative examples and problems throughout this book no attempt has been made to have the unit stresses conform to any one code; various unit stresses are used. Since a value of $0.45f'_c$ (1350 psi for 3000 psi concrete) is used so frequently, it is used in many of the following examples.

CHAPTER 5

SHEAR AND BOND STRESSES

5–1. Diagonal Tension. In a simple beam subjected to bending the fibers above the neutral surface are in compression while tensile stresses occur in the fibers below this surface. In addition to these obvious stresses, there are also inclined tensile stresses. If a concrete beam is reinforced with longitudinal steel only, these diagonal stresses tend to produce cracks, as indicated in Fig. 5–1(a). These

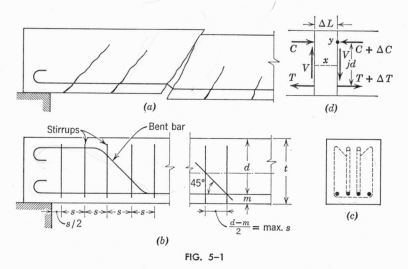

FIG. 5–1

cracks are vertical at the center of the span and become more inclined as they approach the supports where they slope at an angle of about 45°. The stresses that cause these cracks are known as *diagonal tension*. To prevent failure due to diagonal tension, additional reinforcing bars are added. Sloping bars placed at right angles to the direction of these cracks would be one method of reinforcing for diagonal tension, but, although this is sometimes done, it is not the most economical method. The usual procedure is to add #3 or #4 bars, bent in the shape of the letter U, in vertical positions at those places in the beam at which the diagonal tension stresses require their use. When the stresses are sufficiently large, W-shaped bars are used. These bent reinforcing bars are called *stirrups*. They should always have hooks at the ends to provide anchorage to resist the tensile stresses. A U-shaped stirrup is indicated in Fig. 5–1(c).

The theory for providing vertical stirrups to resist diagonal tension is based on the assumption that the stirrups resist the vertical component of the diagonal tension and the longitudinal reinforcement resists the horizontal component. Diagonal tension is a combination of vertical and horizontal shear. For practical considerations, *the intensity of the vertical shear is considered to be a measure of the intensity of the diagonal tension*. Because of this assumption we use the term *shear*, whereas we know that the stress is actually diagonal tension.

If the shearing unit stress in a beam exceeds $0.08f'_c$, stirrups alone are not adequate for shear reinforcement. Inclined bars, perpendicular to the potential cracks [see Fig. 5–1(a)] must be used with particular care taken to locate them in their proper positions. Longitudinal tensile bars may be bent up at a point at which they are no longer needed to resist tensile bending stresses, and the bent portion of such bars serve as reinforcement for shear. In general, it is preferable to keep shearing stresses below the limit that would require the use of inclined bars.

Reinforcement used to resist shearing stresses is known as *web reinforcement*. *Ties* are frequently used for web reinforcement in place of stirrups. A tie is generally made of #3 bars, but it completely encircles the longitudinal tensile steel instead of being U-shaped with hooked ends.

5–2. Shearing Unit Stress. In designing a reinforced concrete beam it is customary to determine first the effective depth and then the area of the longitudinal tensile reinforcement. Having done this, we next determine whether or not stirrups are required. We know that concrete is capable of resisting a limited amount of shear; hence we determine the value of the shearing unit stress, and its magnitude indicates whether or not web reinforcement is necessary.

Let V = the total vertical shear at the section considered, usually the maximum value at the supports, in pounds,

v = the shearing unit stress at the section, in pounds per square inch,

b = the width of the beam, in inches,

d = the effective depth of the beam, in inches,

jd = distance between the resultant compressive and tensile stresses, in inches,

j = $\frac{7}{8}$ or 0.875, the value customarily used in computations for shear.

To determine the magnitude of the shearing unit stress, consider an infinitely short length, ΔL, of a beam, as indicated in Fig. 5-1(d). This small portion of the beam is in equilibrium under the compression, tension, and shearing stresses as shown. We assume that the length ΔL is so small that the value of the external shear V is about the same on each side of the section. In accordance with one of the laws of equilibrium, we know that the algebraic sum of the moments of all the forces about any point in the section is zero. Therefore, taking the point y as a center of moments,

$$(V \times \Delta L) - (\Delta T \times jd) = 0 \qquad \text{or} \qquad V\Delta L = \Delta Tjd$$

The horizontal shear, ΔT, is resisted by a horizontal plane x, the dimensions of which are ΔL and b. Therefore, if v is the shearing unit stress

$$\Delta T = v \, \Delta Lb$$

Substituting this value of ΔT in the above equation,

$$V \, \Delta L = v \, \Delta Lbjd$$

or

$$V = vjbd \qquad \text{or} \qquad v = \frac{V}{jbd} \qquad (10)$$

Since, in computations for shear, $j = 0.875$ which may be expressed as the fraction $\frac{7}{8}$, formula (10) may be written

$$v = \frac{V}{0.875bd} \qquad \text{or} \qquad v = \frac{8V}{7bd}$$

This is the formula used to determine the shearing unit stress based on the assumption that the shear is a measure of the diagonal tension.

Example. A beam having a width of 10 in. and an effective depth of 24 in. has a total uniformly distributed load of 50,000 lb, including the weight of the beam. Let it be required to compute the maximum shearing unit stress.

SOLUTION. The total uniformly distributed load on the beam is 50,000 lb; hence each reaction $= \frac{1}{2} \times 50,000 = 25,000$ lb. Therefore, $V = 25,000$ lb, the value of the maximum vertical shear. See Art. 3–3 and Fig. 3–4(a). By data, $b = 10$, $d = 24$, and $j = 0.875$, the value used in computations for shear.

By formula (10),

$$v = \frac{V}{jbd}$$

Substituting the known values,

$$v = \frac{25,000}{0.875 \times 10 \times 24} = 119 \text{ psi}$$

the value of the maximum shearing unit stress. Since 25,000 lb is the value of the *maximum* vertical shear, it is at the face of the supports of the beam. Hence v, just found, is the unit stress *at the face of the supports.* For this beam, the value of V, the shear, decreases as we approach the center of the span where it has a zero value. See Fig. 3–4(a). Thus, we see that the value v depends on the position at which V is taken.

The concrete alone can resist a limited amount of shear, which we know actually to be diagonal tension. In Table 4–2 the magnitudes of the allowable shearing stresses for concrete are given as percentages of f'_c and depend upon the type of shear reinforcement. In the table this value is represented by v_c. For beams with no web reinforcement, $v_c = 0.03 f'_c$. For 3000-psi concrete, $v_c = 0.03 \times 3000 = 90$ psi. When the maximum shearing unit stress exceeds the values permitted in Table 4–2, or the values given in the governing building regulations, stirrups or ties must be added. Such additional steel is known as *web reinforcement.* In the above example $v = 119$ psi and therefore web reinforcement is required.

Problem 5–2–A. The total uniformly distributed load on a fully continuous beam is 35,000 lb. The width of the beam is 10 in. and the effective depth is 21 in. Compute the maximum shearing unit stress.

Problem 5–2–B. A simple reinforced concrete beam has a width of 8 in. and an effective depth of 14 in. The uniformly distributed load on the beam, including its own weight, is 15,400 lb. If 2500 psi concrete is to be used, is web reinforcement required?

5–3. Portion of Beam Requiring Web Reinforcement. If v, the actual shearing unit stress, is in excess of v_c, the shearing unit stress permitted on the concrete, web reinforcement is required. The commonest type of web reinforcement consists of vertical stirrups, #3 or #4 bars bent in the shape of the letters U or W. Having used formula (10), Art. 5–2, to determine v, we refer to Table 4–2 to see whether or not v exceeds the allowable v_c. If it does, web reinforcement is required and the next step is to determine the portions of the beam in which the stirrups must be placed.

For a uniformly distributed load on a beam with equal reactions, the shear diagram has the shape of two triangles. See Fig. 3–4(a). The magnitude of the shear is maximum at the supports and diminishes in value as we approach the center of the span, at which point it has a zero value. Thus it is seen that if the concrete alone is capable of resisting a certain amount of shear, stirrups will be required only in that length of the beam adjacent to the supports where the value of the shear exceeds v_c, the shear to be resisted by the concrete.

To determine the length of the beam in which stirrups are required, let

v = the maximum shearing unit stress, in pounds per square inch,

v_c = the allowable shearing unit stress permitted on the concrete as given in Table 4–2, in pounds per square inch,

$v' = v - v_c$ = the excess shear to be resisted by the stirrups, in pounds per square inch,

L = the span of the beam, in feet,

a = the length of the beam from the supports in which stirrups are required, in feet.

Figure 5–2(a) shows the left-hand side of the shear diagram for a simple beam with equal reactions and a uniformly distributed load. By similar triangles, the following relation is found,

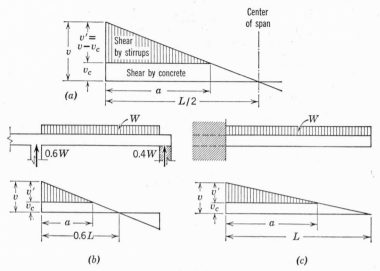

FIG. 5-2

$$\frac{L}{2} : \left(\frac{L}{2} - a\right) = v : v_c$$

or

$$\frac{L}{2} \times v_c = \left(\frac{L}{2} \times v\right) - av$$

from which

$$a = \frac{L/2(v - v_c)}{v} \qquad \text{(a)}$$

Substituting the value v' for $v - v_c$ in equation (a),

$$a = \frac{L}{2}\left(\frac{v'}{v}\right) \qquad \text{(11)}$$

This is the formula to be used in determining the distance from the supports in which stirrups are required for web reinforcement. Note that it applies only to beams having uniformly distributed loads and whose reactions are equal in magnitude.

Equation (11) may be used for any beam supporting a uniformly distributed load over its entire length if, instead of $L/2$, we substitute the distance from the point of maximum shear to the point of zero shear. Figure 5–2(b) shows the shear diagram for a semicontinuous beam, a beam fixed at one end and simply supported at the other. One reaction is greater than the other, as indicated. For this condition we may use equation (11) by substituting $0.6L$ in place of $L/2$. Figure 5–2(c) shows the shear diagram for a cantilever beam. In this instance we use equation (11) by substituting L for $L/2$.

The A.C.I. code contains another specification requirement relating to the length of beam in which web reinforcement is required. When continuous or restrained beams *do not have a slab so cast as to provide T-beam action*, the following provisions shall apply: web reinforcement shall be provided from the support to a point beyond the extreme position of the point of inflection, a distance equal to either $\frac{1}{16}$ of the clear span or the depth of the member, whichever is greater, even though the shearing unit stress does not exceed v_c. Such reinforcement shall be designed to carry at least two thirds of the total shear at the section. Sufficient web reinforcement shall be provided to carry at least two thirds of the total shear at a section in which there is negative reinforcement.

Example. A simple reinforced concrete beam having a span of 18 ft 0 in. has a uniformly distributed load of 55,000 lb. The width of the beam is 10 in. and the effective depth is 21 in. If v_c is limited to 90 psi, determine whether or not stirrups are required and, if so, the distance from the supports in which they are to be placed.

SOLUTION. To determine the value of v, the maximum shearing unit stress, we shall use equation (10), Art. 5–2.

$$v = \frac{V}{jbd} \tag{10}$$

Since the total uniformly distributed load is 55,000 lb, the maximum shear $V = \dfrac{55,000}{2} = 27,500$ lb [see Fig. 3–4(a)], $j = 0.875$, the approximation used in computing shear, $b = 10$ in., and $d = 21$ in.

Then substituting these values in equation (10),

$$v = \frac{27,500}{0.875 \times 10 \times 21} = 150 \text{ psi}$$

This value being in excess of 90 psi, the allowable concrete stress, web reinforcement is required.

To find the distance from the supports in which the stirrups are to be placed, use equation (11)

$$a = \frac{L}{2}\left(\frac{v'}{v}\right) \tag{11}$$

$v' = v - v_c$ or $v' = 150 - 90 = 60$ psi, $L = 18$ ft 0 in., and $v = 150$ psi. Substituting these values in equation (11),

$$a = \frac{18}{2}\left(\frac{60}{150}\right) = 3.6 \text{ ft}$$

the distance from the supports in which the stirrups will be placed and beyond which the shearing stresses can be carried by the concrete without the aid of web reinforcement.

Equation (11) applies only to beams having uniformly distributed loads. For beams loaded irregularly or unsymmetrically, it is sometimes necessary to construct a shear diagram. By means of this diagram, the value of the shear at various sections of the beam is established, and, by use of equation (10), Art. 5–2, we can determine the portions of the beam that require web reinforcement.

Figure 3–4(b), (c), and (d) gives shear diagrams for beams with concentrated loads at the center, the third and fourth points of the span. These types of loading are common for girders supporting smaller beams. We should remember that the weight of the beam alone produces shearing stresses. In the diagrams shown, however, the weight of the beam has been ignored. The beam weight is usually quite small in comparison to the loads exerted by the beam concentrations. As an illustration for the investigation of web reinforcement in a girder subjected to concentrated loads, consider the following problem.

Example. A girder having a span of 18 ft 0 in. has two loads of 24,000 lb each concentrated at the third points of the span. The beam has a width of 12 in. and an effective depth of 22 in. If v_c is limited to 75 psi, investigate the necessity of web reinforcement.

SOLUTION. By referring to Fig. 3–4(c), we note that the value of the shear is equal to P lb between the supports and the concentrated loads. We see also that the shear has a zero value between the two loads. Since each reaction is equal in magnitude to one of the two equal loads, the value of the maximum shear is P lb. Thus it would appear that stirrups may be needed between the supports and the loads but not between the loads at the middle third of the beam. To show that there need be no guesswork, let us consider the weight of the beam to be 300 lb per linear ft and construct an accurate shear diagram.* See Fig. 5–3.

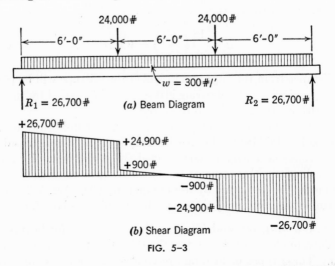

(a) Beam Diagram

(b) Shear Diagram

FIG. 5–3

The total load on the beam is $24,000 + 24,000 + (18 \times 300) = 53,400$ lb. The beam being loaded symmetrically, each reaction is equal to $\frac{1}{2} \times 53,400$ lb, or 26,700 lb. Therefore, the maximum shear is at the supports and $V = 26,700$ lb. The shear immediately to the left of the first 24,000 lb load is $26,700 - (6 \times 300) = 24,900$ lb. Just to the right of this load, $V = 26,700 - [(6 \times 300) + 24,000] = 900$ lb. These values are plotted and the shear diagram takes the shape as shown in Fig. 5–3(b).

The value of the maximum shear $V = 26,700$ lb, and, by equation (10), $v = \dfrac{V}{jbd}$, the maximum shearing stress is

* See Art. 67, *Simplified Mechanics and Strength of Materials*, by Harry Parker, John Wiley and Sons, New York, 1951, for the construction of shear diagrams.

$$v = \frac{26,700}{0.875 \times 12 \times 22} = 115 \text{ psi}$$

This value being in excess of 75 psi, the limiting stress permitted on the concrete, stirrups must be introduced to provide for the excess stress.

Immediately to the right of the first concentrated load, $V = 900$ lb. By use of equation (10),

$$v = \frac{900}{0.875 \times 12 \times 22} = 3.9 \text{ psi}$$

This shearing unit stress being well below 75 psi, the allowable, we find that no stirrups are required between the two concentrated loads. This is apparent in Fig. 3–4(c), but in this diagram no consideration is given to the weight of the beam. Thus, by computing the shear values at various points in the beam, we find that web reinforcement, stirrups, will be required between the supports and the concentrated loads and that no stirrups are needed in the middle third of the beam.

Problem 5–3–A. A simple beam whose clear span is 20 ft 0 in. has a uniformly distributed load, including its own weight, of 60,000 lb. The effective depth is 24 in., and the width is 12 in. If v_c is limited to 90 psi, is web reinforcement required? If so, determine the distance from the supports in which the stirrups are to be placed.

5–4. Spacing of Stirrups. Web reinforcement is usually provided by vertical stirrups. Sloping bars placed at right angles to the direction taken by the diagonal tension cracks are sometimes used, as noted in Art. 5–1.

As has been explained, the greatest bending moment for a symmetrically loaded simple beam occurs at the center of the span and diminishes in magnitude as we approach the supports. It is possible to bend up one or more of the longitudinal tensile reinforcing bars when they are no longer required to resist the bending moment. An even number of bars is generally employed for the main tensile reinforcement, and one half of them are bent up. The point of bending is the *inflection point*,* for continuous beams generally accepted to be at one fifth the span from the supports. The bend of these main tensile reinforcing bars is usually between 30

---

* See Art. 81, *Simplified Mechanics and Strength of Materials.*

and 45°, with the horizontal, an angle of 45° being the commonest. The inclined portions of these bent bars, if they are properly located, may be considered as effective in resisting diagonal tension. When the web reinforcement consists of a single bent bar or of a single group of bent bars, the required area of such bars is computed by the formula $A_v = \dfrac{V'}{f_v \sin \alpha}$, in which A_v = the area of the web reinforcement, V' = the excess of total shear over that permitted on the concrete, f_v = the tensile unit stress in the web reinforcement, and α = angle of inclination of the bent bars.

It is required that web reinforcement shall be so spaced that every 45° line (representing a potential crack) extending from the mid-depth of the beam to the longitudinal tensile bars shall be crossed by at least one line of reinforcement.

By referring to Fig. 5–1(b), it is seen that the distance marked $\dfrac{d - m}{2}$ is the maximum allowable spacing in accordance with the foregoing requirement. By employing the letters shown in the figure, $s_{max} = \dfrac{t}{2} - m$. But $t = d + m$, and, substituting this value of t, $s_{max} = \dfrac{d + m}{2} - m$ and $s_{max} = \dfrac{d - m}{2}$, the maximum allowable spacing of the stirrups.

The vertical stirrups employed for web reinforcement usually consist of #3 or #4 bars bent in the shape of the letters U or W. Stirrups should encircle the main tensile reinforcement, and hooks bent around a pin having a diameter not less than five times the diameter of the stirrup bar should be made at the ends. It should be remembered that these bars are in tension and the hooks must be provided to insure an adequate bond.

When bent longitudinal reinforcement serves as web reinforcement, hooks should be made at the ends or the bars should be carried well past the supports in order to prevent slipping of bars in the concrete.

The purpose of the stirrups is to resist diagonal tension stresses, and, as has been pointed out, the vertical shear may be considered as a measure of the vertical component of the diagonal tension. Both the concrete and steel stirrups resist the shear. Some codes require that a definite proportion, one third, for instance, of the vertical shear be carried by the concrete and the remaining two thirds by the steel. Another assumption is that the concrete resists v_c, the allowable stress given in specifications, and the stirrups take the remainder.

A_v is the symbol used to indicate the total cross-sectional area of one stirrup. A #3 bar has an area of 0.11 sq in., and, if the stirrup is U-shaped, $A_v = 2 \times 0.11$ or 0.22 sq in. If the stirrup is W-shaped, there are four legs, and $A_v = 4 \times 0.11 = 0.44$ sq in. Similarly a #4 bar has an area of 0.2 sq in., and for a U-shaped stirrup $A_v = 2 \times 0.2 = 0.4$ sq in. For a #4 W-shaped stirrup, $A_v = 4 \times 0.2 = 0.8$ sq in.

To determine a formula to be used in finding the spacing of stirrups, the following notation is used:

$A_v =$ the total cross-sectional area of the legs of one stirrup, in square inches.

$f_v =$ the allowable tensile unit stress in stirrups, in pounds per square inch. This stress is usually 18,000 or 20,000 psi, depending on the building code.

$v =$ the shearing unit stress, in pounds per square inch.

$v_c =$ the shearing unit stress permitted on the concrete, in pounds per square inch.

$v' = v - v_c =$ the excess shear *to be resisted by the stirrups*, in pounds per square inch.

$b =$ width of the beam, in inches.

$s =$ the spacing of the stirrups, in inches.

If b is the width of the beam, s the spacing of the stirrups, and v' the shearing unit stress to be taken by the stirrups, the stirrup stress is $v'bs$.

Since A_v is the cross-sectional area of a stirrup and f_v, the allowable tensile unit stress, $A_vf_v =$ the total stirrup stress. Then

$$A_vf_v = v'bs$$

and

$$s = \frac{A_vf_v}{v'b} \tag{12}$$

Thus, by selecting a stirrup of a definite cross section and shape, the use of this equation determines the proper spacing of the stirrups. It is customary to place the first stirrup at $s/2$ from the face of the support. Remember, however, that $\dfrac{d-m}{2}$ is the maximum allowable spacing of the stirrups.

Example. A beam 12 in. wide, having an effective depth of 20 in. and a total depth of 22 in., has a span of 20 ft 0 in. and a uniformly distributed load of 3000 lb per linear ft, including the weight of the beam. Assuming v_c to be limited to 75 psi and that #3 U-stirrups are to be used with 20,000 psi as the allowable stirrup unit stress, determine the spacing of the stirrups.

SOLUTION. Total load = $3000 \times 20 = 60,000$ lb.

As the beam is symmetrically loaded, each reaction and therefore the maximum shear $V = 60,000 \times \frac{1}{2} = 30,000$ lb. The maximum shearing unit stress is

$$v = \frac{V}{jbd} \qquad \text{Formula (10), Art. 5–2}$$

or

$$v = \frac{30,000}{0.875 \times 12 \times 20} = 142 \text{ psi}$$

Since 142 psi exceeds 75 psi, web reinforcement is required.

$$v' = v - v_c \qquad \text{or} \qquad v' = 142 - 75 = 67 \text{ psi}$$

The distance from the supports in which stirrups are required is found by the formula

$$a = \frac{L}{2}\left(\frac{v'}{v}\right) \qquad \text{Formula (11), Art. 5–3}$$

or

$$a = \frac{20}{2}\left(\frac{67}{142}\right) = 4.7 \text{ ft}$$

The cross-sectional area of a #3 bar is 0.11 sq in., Table 1–1. As a U-stirrup has two legs, $A_v = 2 \times 0.11$. Therefore, the spacing of the stirrups may be found by use of the formula

$$s = \frac{A_v f_v}{v' b} \qquad (12)$$

or

$$s = \frac{2 \times 0.11 \times 20,000}{67 \times 12} = 5.5 \text{ in.}$$

It is customary to avoid fractions of inches in designating the stirrup spacing; therefore 5 in. will be considered as the spacing, and the first stirrup will be placed 2 in. from the support.

As is indicated in Fig. 5–4(a), twelve stirrups will be required at each end of the beam, making a total of twenty-four, the spacing to be as shown.

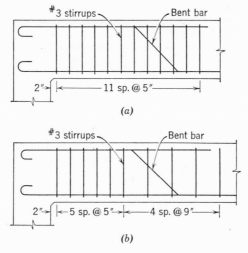

FIG. 5–4

Beams of constant cross section with uniformly distributed loads have shearing stresses that decrease in a straight line from a maximum value at the supports to the point of zero shear. See Fig. 3–4(a). In this example the stirrup spacing, 5 in., was determined by the maximum shearing unit stress, 142 psi. Note that this is the value *at the face of the support.* If the value of v is taken at any other point in the length of the beam, values of v and v' would be smaller, and thus s, the stirrup spacing, would be greater. Theoretically, the stirrup spacing increases from its value at the face of the support to its maximum allowable value, in this instance,
$$\frac{d - m}{2} = \frac{20 - 2}{2}, \text{ or 9 in.}$$
To find this increase in stirrup spacing, many designers use the following convenient method. Divide the length of beam in which stirrups are required (length a) into any convenient lengths, 2 ft

for instance, and determine the values of v' for each length. Figure 5–5 represents the 4.7-ft length of beam requiring stirrups with the maximum value of v', 67 psi, at the support. There are two lengths of 2 ft each and a remainder of 0.7 ft. By similar triangles,

$$v'_2 = \frac{67 \times 2.7}{4.7} = 39 \text{ psi} \qquad s_2 = \frac{2 \times 0.11 \times 20,000}{39 \times 12} = 9.4 \text{ in.}$$

$$v'_4 = \frac{67 \times 0.7}{4.7} = 10 \text{ psi} \qquad s_4 = \frac{2 \times 0.11 \times 20,000}{10 \times 12} = 36.6 \text{ in.}$$

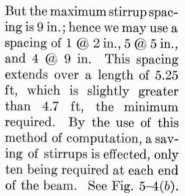

FIG. 5–5

But the maximum stirrup spacing is 9 in.; hence we may use a spacing of 1 @ 2 in., 5 @ 5 in., and 4 @ 9 in. This spacing extends over a length of 5.25 ft, which is slightly greater than 4.7 ft, the minimum required. By the use of this method of computation, a saving of stirrups is effected, only ten being required at each end of the beam. See Fig. 5–4(b).

The previous example dealt with a beam having a uniformly distributed load. Next let us consider a beam subjected to concentrated loads.

Example. A simple beam having a span of 21 ft 0 in. has two loads of 25,000 lb each concentrated at the third points. This is a typical loading of a girder supporting two beams at equal distances from the supports. The beam is 10 in. in width and has an effective depth of 30 in. Let us assume that v_c is limited to 75 psi and that #3 U-stirrups are to be used with $f_v = 18,000$ psi. Determine the spacing of the stirrups.

SOLUTION. Assume that the total depth of the beam is 32 in. Then, if we consider concrete to weigh 150 lb per cu ft, the weight of the beam per linear foot is $\frac{10 \times 32}{144} \times 150 = 333$ lb, say 330 lb. The total load on the beam $= 25,000 + 25,000 + (21 \times 330) = 56,930$ lb. The beam being symmetrically loaded, each reaction

It is customary to avoid fractions of inches in designating the stirrup spacing; therefore 5 in. will be considered as the spacing, and the first stirrup will be placed 2 in. from the support.

As is indicated in Fig. 5–4(a), twelve stirrups will be required at each end of the beam, making a total of twenty-four, the spacing to be as shown.

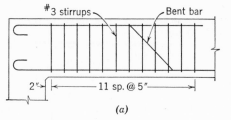

(a)

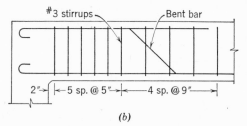

(b)

FIG. 5–4

Beams of constant cross section with uniformly distributed loads have shearing stresses that decrease in a straight line from a maximum value at the supports to the point of zero shear. See Fig. 3–4(a). In this example the stirrup spacing, 5 in., was determined by the maximum shearing unit stress, 142 psi. Note that this is the value *at the face of the support*. If the value of v is taken at any other point in the length of the beam, values of v and v' would be smaller, and thus s, the stirrup spacing, would be greater. Theoretically, the stirrup spacing increases from its value at the face of the support to its maximum allowable value, in this instance,

$$\frac{d - m}{2} = \frac{20 - 2}{2}, \text{ or 9 in.}$$

To find this increase in stirrup spacing, many designers use the following convenient method. Divide the length of beam in which stirrups are required (length a) into any convenient lengths, 2 ft for instance, and determine the values of v' for each length. Figure 5–5 represents the 4.7-ft length of beam requiring stirrups with the maximum value of v', 67 psi, at the support. There are two lengths of 2 ft each and a remainder of 0.7 ft. By similar triangles,

$$v'_2 = \frac{67 \times 2.7}{4.7} = 39 \text{ psi} \qquad s_2 = \frac{2 \times 0.11 \times 20{,}000}{39 \times 12} = 9.4 \text{ in.}$$

$$v'_4 = \frac{67 \times 0.7}{4.7} = 10 \text{ psi} \qquad s_4 = \frac{2 \times 0.11 \times 20{,}000}{10 \times 12} = 36.6 \text{ in.}$$

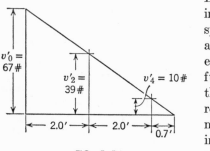

FIG. 5–5

But the maximum stirrup spacing is 9 in.; hence we may use a spacing of 1 @ 2 in., 5 @ 5 in., and 4 @ 9 in. This spacing extends over a length of 5.25 ft, which is slightly greater than 4.7 ft, the minimum required. By the use of this method of computation, a saving of stirrups is effected, only ten being required at each end of the beam. See Fig. 5–4(b).

The previous example dealt with a beam having a uniformly distributed load. Next let us consider a beam subjected to concentrated loads.

Example. A simple beam having a span of 21 ft 0 in. has two loads of 25,000 lb each concentrated at the third points. This is a typical loading of a girder supporting two beams at equal distances from the supports. The beam is 10 in. in width and has an effective depth of 30 in. Let us assume that v_c is limited to 75 psi and that #3 U-stirrups are to be used with $f_v = 18{,}000$ psi. Determine the spacing of the stirrups.

SOLUTION. Assume that the total depth of the beam is 32 in. Then, if we consider concrete to weigh 150 lb per cu ft, the weight of the beam per linear foot is $\dfrac{10 \times 32}{144} \times 150 = 333$ lb, say 330 lb. The total load on the beam $= 25{,}000 + 25{,}000 + (21 \times 330) = 56{,}930$ lb. The beam being symmetrically loaded, each reaction and therefore the maximum shear $V = 56,930 \times \frac{1}{2} = 28,465$ lb. The maximum shearing unit stress is found by the formula

$$v = \frac{V}{jbd}$$ Formula (10), Art. 5–2

or

$$v = \frac{28,465}{0.875 \times 10 \times 30} = 109 \text{ psi}$$

$$v' = v - v_c \quad \text{or} \quad v' = 109 - 75 = 34 \text{ psi}$$

Ignoring the weight of the beam, the value of the maximum vertical shear is uniform and extends from the supports up to the concentrated loads. See Fig. 3–4(c) and the second example under Art. 5–3. The vertical shear has a zero value between the two concentrated loads. Thus stirrups will be required between the supports and the concentrated loads but probably not at the middle third of the beam. Note particularly that formula (11), Art. 5–3, does not apply, since it is applicable only to uniformly distributed loads.

A U-stirrup has two legs and, as the area of a #3 bar is 0.11 sq in., $A_v = 2 \times 0.11$ sq in.

The stirrup spacing is found by the formula

$$s = \frac{A_v f_v}{v'b}$$ (12)

or

$$s = \frac{2 \times 0.11 \times 18,000}{34 \times 10} = 11.7 \text{ in., the stirrup spacing}$$

The maximum stirrup spacing is $(d - m)/2$ or $\dfrac{30 - 2}{2} = 14$ in.

Thus the stirrup spacing will be accepted as 11 in., the stirrups to be spaced uniformly up to the concentrated load, as shown in Fig. 5–6.

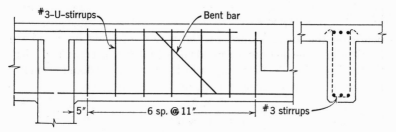

FIG. 5–6

Immediately to the right of the concentrated load the value of the shear $V = 1155$ lb, and, by use of formula (10), $v = 4.4$ psi. Since this value of v is less than 75 psi, stirrups are not needed between the concentrated loads. Note that Fig. 5–6 indicates the web reinforcement in one end of the beam; an equal number of stirrups is used in the other end.

Problem 5–4–A. For the beam given in Problem 5–3–A, compute the stirrup spacing, using #3 U-shaped stirrups with $f_v = 20,000$ psi.

5–5. Stirrup Spacing by Use of Charts. Formula (12), Art. 5–4, used to determine s, the spacing of stirrups, contains the symbol v'. This is the value of the excess shear that is to be resisted by the stirrups. To find v', we subtract v_c from v, that is, $v' = v - v_c$. In the first illustrative example in Art. 5–4 v was taken as the *maximum* shearing unit stress. It was the value taken at the point of maximum vertical shear at the supports. The value of v, and consequently v', becomes smaller as the distance from the support increases; therefore the stirrup spacing becomes greater.

For the first example under Art. 5–4, it would be more exact to have asked for the *end* spacing, for actually that is the spacing that was determined. However, the use of this spacing in the portions of the beam requiring web reinforcement is common practice and, as is seen, errs on the side of safety.

A convenient method of determining stirrup spacing for uniformly distributed loads is afforded by use of the chart shown in Fig. 5–7.

To use this chart find the unit shear, $v = \dfrac{V}{bjd}$. Then find $v' = v - v_c$ and distance a, over which stirrups are required, $= \dfrac{L}{2}\left(\dfrac{v'}{v}\right)$. Compute $\dfrac{v' \times b}{B \times A_v \times f_v}$. In this quantity B is a number that depends on the angle formed by the web reinforcing bars and the longitudinal tensile reinforcement; it is 1 for vertical stirrups. Note that values of $A_v \times f_v$ are given in the upper right-hand corner of the chart. Place a straight edge on the chart connecting the calculated values of a and $\dfrac{v' \times b}{B \times A_v \times f_v}$, and read off the spacing of stirrups where their respective heavy lines cross the straight edge.

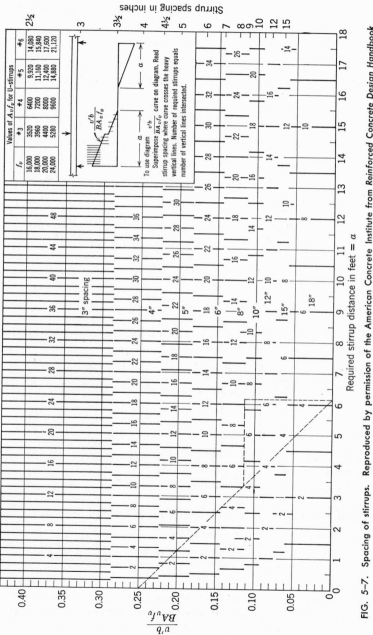

FIG. 5-7. Spacing of stirrups. Reproduced by permission of the American Concrete Institute from *Reinforced Concrete Design Handbook*

In case the spacing is greater than the maximum allowable spacing
of $\dfrac{d-m}{2}$, use the last spacing permitted, until distance a is reached.

For example: $L = 28$ ft, $b = 14$ in., $d = 22.5$ in., $m = 2.5$ in.,
$V = 44{,}100$ lb, and $v_c = 90$ psi. The load on the beam is uniformly distributed. Required is the number and spacing of #3
U-stirrups in each end of the beam. Let $f_v = 18{,}000$ psi.

$$v = \frac{44{,}100}{0.875 \times 14 \times 22.5} = 160 \text{ psi}$$

$$v' = 160 - 90 = 70 \text{ psi}$$

$$\frac{bv'}{BA_v f_v} = \frac{14 \times 70}{1 \times 0.22 \times 18{,}000} = 0.248$$

$$a = \frac{28}{2}\left(\frac{70}{160}\right) = 6.12 \text{ ft}$$

Maximum allowable spacing $= \dfrac{22.5 - 2.5}{2} = 10$ in.

From the chart, $s = 3$ @ 4 in., 2 @ 6 in., 2 @ 8 in., 4 @ 10 in.
See Fig. 5–8.

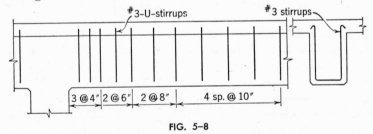

FIG. 5–8

Number of stirrups in each end of beam $= 11$.
If formula (12), Art. 5–4, is used,

$$s = \frac{A_v f_v}{v'b} = \frac{2 \times 0.11 \times 18{,}000}{70 \times 14} = 4.05 \text{ in.}$$

This is the end spacing of the stirrups determined by the value of
$v' = 70$ at the point where the shearing unit stress is maximum.

By using equation (12), Art. 5–4, let us find the spacing at some other point in the length of the beam, for instance, at 3 ft 0 in. from the support.

Each reaction = 44,100 lb; therefore 44,100 × 2 = 88,200 lb = W, the total load on the beam. The load per linear foot then equals 88,200 ÷ 28 = 3150 lb.

V (at 3 ft 0 in. from the support) = 44,100 − (3 × 3150)

$$= 34,650 \text{ lb}$$

$$v = \frac{V}{jbd} = \frac{34,650}{0.875 \times 14 \times 22.5} = 126 \text{ psi}$$

$$v' = 126 - 90 = 36 \text{ psi}$$

$$s = \frac{A_v f_v}{bv'} \quad \text{or} \quad s = \frac{2 \times 0.11 \times 18,000}{14 \times 36} = 7.85 \text{ in.,} \quad \text{say 8 in.}$$

the stirrup spacing at 3 ft 0 in. from the support.

Other points might be taken and the spacing at these points computed in a similar manner. The use of the chart, Fig. 5–7, however, makes this unnecessary, for an economical spacing of stirrups is readily found by the use of the straight edge as described.

5–6. Bond Stresses. One of the fundamental assumptions upon which the theory of reinforced concrete beams is based is that there is perfect adhesion between the concrete and the steel reinforcement and that the concrete and steel stretch together without the bond between them being broken. The tendency for the reinforcement to slip in the concrete is always present. The bond between the surface of the steel and the concrete is due to the initial shrinkage of the concrete in setting and the friction between the two materials. Bars rolled with lugs or projections are known as *deformed bars*, their purpose being to develop a mechanical bond between the concrete and steel.

The allowable bond stresses in beams and slabs generally given in specifications is $0.045f'_c$ for plain bars and $0.10f'_c$ for deformed bars, except for top bars and bars in certain types of footings, f'_c being the ultimate compressive stress of concrete at the 28-day period. Then for 3000-psi concrete u, the allowable bond stress, is 135 psi and 300 psi for plain and deformed bars, respectively. See Table 4–2.

The usual procedure in designing is to determine the number and size of bars in accordance with the bending moment. This having been done, the bond stress at the critical section is computed to determine whether plain or deformed bars are required. Deformed bars are used almost exclusively. If the bond stress is found to be greater than the allowable, it may be necessary to use a greater number of smaller bars, thereby producing an equivalent cross-sectional area but offering a greater surface to resist bond stresses.

To develop a formula to be used in computing the bond stress, the following notation is used:

u = the bond stress per unit of surface area of the bar, in pounds per square inch.

V = the total vertical shear, in pounds. This is usually the maximum value, taken at the face of supports.

j = 0.875, the value generally used for shear and bond computations.

d = the effective depth of the beam, in inches.

Σ_0 = the sum of the perimeters of all the horizontal tensile reinforcing bars at the section considered, in inches.

Referring to Fig. 5–1(d) and writing an equation of moments about point y,

$$V \times \Delta L = \Delta T \times jd \qquad \text{(See Art. 5–2)}$$

Note that ΔT is the force tending to pull the short length of reinforcement out of the concrete. The surface area of the reinforcement offering a resistance to bond is the total perimeter of the reinforcement multiplied by the length, or $\Sigma_0 \times \Delta L$. If u is the bond stress per unit of area, $\Sigma_0 \times \Delta L \times u$ is the force resisting the tendency of the reinforcement to pull out of the concrete. Then

$$\Delta T = \Sigma_0 \times \Delta L \times u$$

Substituting the value of ΔT in the previous equation,

$$V \times \Delta L = \Sigma_0 \times \Delta L \times u \times jd$$

or

$$u = \frac{V}{\Sigma_0 jd} \qquad (13)$$

Since, from formula (10), Art. 5–2, $V = vjbd$, formula (13) may be written

$$u = \frac{vb}{\Sigma_0}$$

In computing the bond stress this form of equation (13) may be used conveniently if the value of v has been previously computed.

Example. A continuous beam having a width of 12 in. and an effective depth of 28 in. has 4-#8 bars for the tensile longitudinal reinforcement at the top of the beam over the supports. The total vertical shear at the supports $V = 50,000$ lb. If $f'_c = 2500$ psi, compute the bond unit stress. Referring to Table 4–2, we note that the allowable bond unit stress for deformed top bars is 175 psi when $f'_c = 2500$ psi.

SOLUTION. A #8 bar has a perimeter of 3.14 in. (Table 1–1); therefore the sum of the perimeters $\Sigma_0 = 4 \times 3.14$. Then, substituting the known quantities in the equation

$$u = \frac{V}{\Sigma_0 jd} \tag{13}$$

$$u = \frac{50,000}{(4 \times 3.14) \times 0.875 \times 28} = 163 \text{ psi}$$

the unit bond stress.

Suppose in designing the beam we had previously computed the value of v in determining the web reinforcement. The formula used would be

$$v = \frac{V}{jbd} \qquad \text{Formula (10), Art. 5–2}$$

Then

$$v = \frac{50,000}{0.875 \times 12 \times 28} = 170 \text{ psi}$$

By use of the formula $u = \dfrac{vb}{\Sigma_0}$

$$u = \frac{170 \times 12}{4 \times 3.14} = 163 \text{ psi}$$

the same result, of course, found above by formula (13).

Since 163 psi is not in excess of 175 psi, the allowable bond unit stress for deformed top bars, the 4-#8 bars are acceptable. But, if u had been greater than 175 psi, bars with a greater Σ_0, but with at least a total cross-sectional area of (4×3.14) sq in., would have been required.

Suppose that u had been found to be 190 psi. Then the minimum required Σ_0 would be

$$\Sigma_0 = 4 \times 3.14 \times \frac{190}{175} = 13.62 \text{ in.}$$

but the required area of the bars would not need to exceed 4×0.79, or 3.16 sq in.

Referring to Table 1–1, we find

Bars	Perimeters	Areas
1-#8	3.142	0.79
4-#7	11.000	2.41
Totals	14.142 in.	3.20 sq in.

Accept, therefore, the combination of 1-#8 and 4-#7 bars.

Problem 5–6–A. The total uniformly distributed load on a continuous beam is 70,000 lb. The width of the beam is 10 in. and the effective depth is 24 in. The longitudinal steel reinforcement for the top bars consists of 4-#7 bars. Assuming that the concrete is $f'_c = 3000$ psi, compute the unit bond stress. Is it excessive?

5–7. Anchorage. The greatest tensile stress in longitudinal reinforcement occurs at the point of maximum bending moment. In order to prevent slipping of the bars in the concrete, there must be a sufficient length of the bars on each side of this point to provide an adequate anchorage.

Tensile negative reinforcement in any span of a continuous, restrained, or cantilever beam must be anchored adequately by bond or hooks in or through the supporting member. Within any such span every reinforcing bar shall be extended at least 12 diameters beyond the point at which it is no longer needed to resist stress.

Not less than one fourth of the area of the positive reinforcement in continuous beams shall extend into the support a distance of 6 in.

In simple beams, or at the outer ends of freely supported end spans of continuous beams, at least one third of the positive reinforcement shall extend into the support a distance of 6 in.

By the term *standard hook* is meant a complete semicircular turn with a radius of bend on the axis of the bar of not less than 3 and not more than 6 bar diameters, plus an extension of at least 4 bar diameters at the free end of the bar, or a 90° bend having a radius of not less than 4 bar diameters plus an extension of 12 bar diameters. See Fig. 5–9(b) and (c). Hooks are used principally when

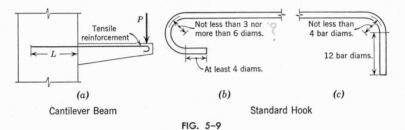

(a)   (b)   (c)

Cantilever Beam   Standard Hook

FIG. 5–9

there is insufficient room to permit an adequate length of straight reinforcement. Plain bars in footing slabs should be anchored with hooks; the outer faces of the hooks should not be less than 3 in. nor more than 6 in. from the face of the footing.

As already noted, the greatest stress in tensile longitudinal reinforcement occurs at the section of the beam at which the bending moment is maximum. In a cantilever beam the maximum bending moment is at the face of the support. See Fig. 3–4(e) and (f). Reference to Fig. 5–9(a) shows that the reinforcement must be embedded in the concrete a sufficient length (marked L in the figure) so that the bond resistance will equal the tensile stress in the reinforcement. To derive a formula giving this relation, let

L = the length the bars are embedded in the concrete support, in inches,

D = the diameter of a round reinforcing bar,

f_s = the tensile unit stress in the longitudinal reinforcement, in pounds per square inch,

u = the bond stress per unit of surface area of the bar, in pounds per square inch. For 3000-psi concrete, u, in top bars, is limited to 90 psi for plain bars and 210 psi for deformed bars. See Table 4–2.

The area of a round bar is $\pi D^2/4$, and therefore the total tension in the bar is $f_s \times \dfrac{\pi D^2}{4}$. The perimeter of a circle is πD, hence the surface area of the embedded bar is $\pi D \times L$, and $\pi D \times L \times u$ is the bond stress of the reinforcement having an embedment of L in. As the bond stress must equal tensile stress,

$$f_s \times \frac{\pi D^2}{4} = \pi D \times L \times u$$

or

$$L = \frac{f_s D}{4u} \tag{14}$$

Example. Four #10 bars constitute the tensile longitudinal reinforcement in the cantilever beam, as indicated in Fig. 5–9(a). Assuming that they are stressed to 18,000 psi and that the allowable bond stress is 210 psi, determine L, the length of the embedment.

SOLUTION. The diameter, D, of a #10 bar is 1.27 in., $f_s = 18,000$ psi, and $u = 210$ psi. Then, by use of equation

$$L = \frac{f_s D}{4u} \tag{14}$$

$$L = \frac{18,000 \times 1.27}{4 \times 210} = 27.2 \text{ in.}$$

the length of the embedment of each of the four bars.

Problem 5–7–A. A cantilever beam, as indicated in Fig. 5–9(a), has tensile reinforcement consisting of 3-#7 bars. If the tensile unit stress is 20,000 psi and the bond unit stress is 175 psi, determine the required length of embedment.

CHAPTER 6

DESIGN OF RECTANGULAR BEAMS

6–1. Design of Beams. The design of a beam consists in determining its cross-sectional dimensions and reinforcement in accordance with given data. These data are the loads and span, the allowable unit stresses of the concrete and steel, and the type of concrete, expressed by n, the ratio of the modulus of elasticity of steel to the modulus of elasticity of the concrete. We must also know the end conditions of the beam, whether it is a fully continuous, semi-continuous, or a simple beam. This information determines the bending moment coefficient to be used. The superimposed load may be determined by the live load and floor area, walls, columns, or smaller beams to be supported. The live load is dependent on the type of occupancy.

Bear in mind that a beam or slab cannot be designed without making due allowance for its own weight. The procedure is to assume the probable size of the beam and to compute its weight in accordance with these dimensions. Reinforced stone-concrete is generally assumed to weigh 150 lb per cu ft. When the dimensions of the beam have been computed, as a result of the live and assumed dead load, they are checked against the assumed size to see that a sufficient allowance was made for its weight.

To determine the cross-sectional dimensions, it is customary first to assume the width of the beam and to compute the depth accordingly. Obviously, a great number of combinations are possible, but for reasons of economy the width of rectangular beams should be from one half to three quarters the effective depth. The clear distance between lateral supports of a beam should never exceed 32 times the least width of the compression flange.

Note that d, computed by use of formula (6), Art. 4–5, is the *effective depth* and that additional concrete is placed below the reinforcement for fireproofing or for protection against the weather. For beams, $1\frac{1}{2}$ is a usual allowance for fireproofing; girders may require 2 in., and slabs generally have 1 in. or even as little as $\frac{3}{4}$ in. if the reinforcement is placed carefully.

Assume that d, computed by equation (6), Art. 4–5, is 17.7 in. Allowing 0.5 in. for one half the thickness of the reinforcement and 1.5 in. for fireproofing, the *total* depth of the beam would be 17.7 + 0.5 + 1.5 = 19.7 in. It is desirable to use whole numbers for beam dimensions, and therefore 20 in. would be accepted as the *total* depth. Making the actual depth slightly greater than the required theoretical depth is a common procedure. When this happens, it is desirable to take advantage of the increased depth. In this instance d, the *effective* depth, becomes 20 − (0.5 + 1.5) = 18 in., and this figure is used in the formula $A_s = \dfrac{M}{f_s j d}$ for computing the area of the longitudinal steel reinforcement.

In computing the bending moments, the *length of span* must be considered. For freely supported beams and slabs the span length should be considered to be the clear span plus the depth of the beam or slab but should not exceed the distance between centers of supports. When slabs and beams are built integrally with their supports, the span length may be taken as the clear span between faces of supports. Many designers prefer to consider center to center of supports as the span length for continuous beams in determining the bending moments.

6–2. Spacing of Bars in Beams. In designing a beam, the usual procedure is to assume b, the width, and to compute the effective depth d in accordance with this assumption. If bent-up bars are used, it is desirable to use an *even* number of bars for the main tensile reinforcement. If, for instance, four bars are used for a continuous beam, there will be four bars in the bottom of the beam at the center of the span where the bending moment is positive. Two of these bars are straight and extend to the center lines of the supports or a minimum of 6 in. beyond the face of the supports. The other two bars are bent at the $\frac{1}{5}$ points of the span and continue over the supports at the upper part of the beam. The two bent bars from the adjacent spans likewise continue over the supports, thus providing four bars to resist the negative bending moments. See Fig. 6–1 where the reinforcement consists of two bars.

Therefore, it is important to have in mind the probable number of bars in assuming the width of the beam. The minimum clear distance between bars should not be less than the nominal diameter of the bars, not less than 1 in. nor less than $1\frac{1}{3}$ times the maximum size of the coarse aggregate. All reinforcing bars should be placed accurately and properly secured in position by concrete or metal chairs, spacers, or bolsters.

Table 6–1 is presented as a guide in selecting beams of adequate width for the probable number of reinforcing bars. It has been

TABLE 6–1. NUMBER OF BARS IN BEAMS

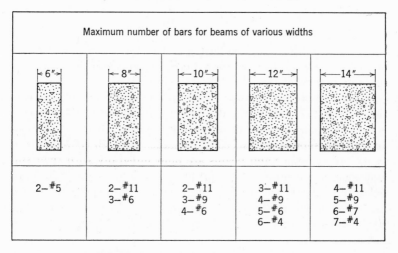

Maximum number of bars for beams of various widths				
⟵ 6″ ⟶	⟵ 8″ ⟶	⟵ 10″ ⟶	⟵ 12″ ⟶	⟵ 14″ ⟶
2–#5	2–#11 3–#6	2–#11 3–#9 4–#6	3–#11 4–#9 5–#6 6–#4	4–#11 5–#9 6–#7 7–#4

compiled in accordance with the requirements noted in the preceding paragraph. An allowance of $1\frac{1}{2}$ in. for fireproofing is made outside the reinforcement on each side of the beam, and there is also an allowance for #3 U-stirrups. The widths required for webs of *joists* are 2 in. less than the widths required for beams. It should be noted that this table gives the *maximum* size of bars for certain beam widths. For instance, we find in the table that 4-#9 bars may be used in a beam 12 in. in width. Obviously, four smaller bars may be used in a beam of the same width as, for example, 4-#7 bars.

Where reinforcement in beams or girders is placed in two or more layers, the clear distance between layers shall not be less than 1 in.

and the bars in the upper layer shall be placed directly above those in the bottom layer.

Table 1–1 gives the sizes of standard reinforcing bars. No other sizes should be used. It is advisable to use bars of one size in a beam when possible. Two sizes in the same beam may be used, but they should be adjacent sizes. It is preferable to use the largest suitable size of bar. Bar sizes smaller than #6 cost more per pound and require more setting labor per pound of reinforcement.

6–3. Design Steps for Rectangular Beams. The following sequence of steps may be followed in the design of a rectangular reinforced concrete beam.

Step 1. Loads. Determine the load or loads the beam will be required to support. In computing the approximate weight of the beam, b, the width, is assumed and the total depth is approximated by allowing 1 in. of depth for each clear foot of span. Stone-concrete is estimated to weigh 150 lb per cu ft.

Step 2. Maximum shear. Compute the magnitude of the reactions, R_1 and R_2 and V, the maximum vertical shear. If the beam is symmetrically loaded, as is usually the case, the two reactions are equal in magnitude and each is equal to one half the sum of the loads. If a simple beam is unsymmetrically loaded, R_1 and R_2, the reactions, are computed by the principle of moments,* and the magnitude of the greater reaction is equal to V, the value of the maximum vertical shear. For review, read the discussion on Vertical Shear in Art. 3–3.

Step 3. Maximum bending moment. Compute M, the maximum bending moment, in inch-pounds. In general, the maximum bending moments are $M = \dfrac{Wl}{12}$ for interior spans of continuous beams, sometimes called fully continuous beams, $M = \dfrac{Wl}{10}$ for end spans of continuous beams or semicontinuous beams, and $M = \dfrac{Wl}{8}$ for simple beams. Review Arts. 3–7 and 3–8 for a discussion of bending moments. It is advisable in this step to determine the value of the bending moment in units of *inch-pounds*, not *foot-*

* See Art. 42, *Simplified Mechanics and Strength of Materials*, by Harry Parker, John Wiley and Sons, New York, 1951.

pounds. This is an error frequently made, for, if foot-pounds instead of inch-pounds are used in the succeeding step, the depth of the beam will be in error.

Step 4. Depth of beam. Compute d, the effective depth of the beam, in inches, by use of the equation

$$d = \sqrt{\frac{M}{Kb}} \qquad \text{Formula (6), Art. 4–5}$$

in which d = the effective depth of the beam, in inches,

   M = the maximum bending moment, in inch-pounds,

   K = a formula coefficient corresponding to the allowable unit stresses and n, as given in Table 4–1,

   b = the width of beam in inches, the dimension assumed in Step 1.

Step 5. Area of tensile reinforcement. Compute the area of the main tensile reinforcement by the equation

$$A_s = \frac{M}{f_s jd} \qquad \text{Formula (7), Art. 4–5}$$

or

$$A_s = pbd \qquad \text{Formula (8), Art. 4–5}$$

in which A_s = the cross-sectional area of the main tensile reinforcement, in square inches,

   f_s = the allowable tensile unit stress in the longitudinal reinforcing bars, in pounds per square inch,

j and p = formula coefficients corresponding to the allowable unit stresses and n, as given in Table 4–1,

   M, b, and d are as noted under Step 4.

If d, found in Step 4, is to be used as the effective depth, equation (7) or (8) may be used; either will give the same result. If d is increased to provide for a beam in whole inches, equation (7) should be used to take advantage of the increased effective depth. For review, see Art. 4–11.

Step 6. Shearing unit stress. Compute v, in the equation

$$v = \frac{V}{jbd} \qquad \text{Formula (10), Art. 5–2}$$

in which v = unit shearing stress, in pounds per square inch,

V = the maximum vertical shear computed in Step 2, in pounds,

j = 0.875 or $\frac{7}{8}$, the formula coefficient used in computations for shear,

b and d are as noted in Step 4.

If the value of v is greater than v_c, the allowable unit stress given in Table 4–2, web reinforcement, must be used. For 3000 psi concrete, v_c is limited to 90 psi. Review Art. 5–2.

Step 7. Space required for stirrups. If web reinforcement is necessary, as determined in Step 6, determine the distance from the supports in which the stirrups are required. If the load on the beam is uniformly distributed and the reactions are equal, compute a in the equation

$$a = \frac{L}{2}\left(\frac{v'}{v}\right) \qquad \text{Formula (11), Art. 5–3}$$

in which a = the distance from the supports in which web reinforcement (stirrups) is required, in feet,

L = the span of the beam, in feet,

$v' = v - v_c$, where v = the unit shearing stress found in Step 6 and v_c = the allowable shearing unit stress of concrete given in Table 4–2, 90 psi for 3000 psi concrete,

v' = the excess shear to be resisted by the stirrups, in pounds per square inch.

See Art. 5–3 for other requirements.

Step 8. Stirrup spacing. If web reinforcement is required, as determined in Step 6, compute s in the equation

$$s = \frac{A_v f_v}{v'b} \qquad \text{Formula (12), Art. 5–4}$$

in which s = the spacing of the stirrups, in inches.

A_v = the total sectional area of the legs of one stirrup in square inches. A #3 bar has an area of 0.11 sq in., therefore a #3 U-stirrup, having two legs, has a total sectional area of $2 \times 0.11 = 0.22$ sq in. Similarly, A_v for a #4 U-stirrup = $2 \times 0.2 = 0.4$ sq in.

f_v = the allowable tensile unit stress in the web reinforcement, in pounds per square inch. This value is
18,000 psi or 20,000 psi, depending on the building
code specifications.

v' = $v - v_c$, as noted under Step 7, in pounds per square
inch.

b = the width of the beam, in inches.

The first stirrup is usually placed at a distance $s/2$ from the support. Regardless of s determined by formula (12), the maximum
spacing of stirrups is $\dfrac{d - m}{2}$. For symmetrically loaded beams,
the stirrup spacing is the same at both ends of the beam. Review
Art. 5–4.

Step 9. Bond stress. Determine the bond stress by the equation

$$u = \frac{V}{\Sigma_0 jd} \qquad \text{Formula (13), Art. 5–6}$$

in which u = the unit bond stress, in pounds per square inch,

V = the maximum vertical shear, in pounds,

Σ_0 = the sum of the perimeters of all the longitudinal tensile reinforcing bars at the section considered, in
inches,

j = 0.875 or $\tfrac{7}{8}$, the formula coefficient used in computations for bond,

d = the effective depth of the beam, in inches.

For 3000 psi concrete, the allowable bond stress is 210 psi for top
bars and 300 psi for others. See Table 4–2. If u, as found by
formula (13), exceeds the allowable unit stress, the depth of the
beam may be increased or a greater number of smaller bars may
be used, thereby increasing the value of Σ_0. See Art. 5–6.

Step 10. Bends, laps, and hooks. If bent-up bars are used,
designate the position of the bends of the main tensile reinforcement, length of laps, hooks, web reinforcement, cut-offs, etc. It
is advisable to make a diagram giving this information. This
drawing should contain *all* the information a builder would require
to construct the beam exactly as it has been designed.

6–4. Design of a Fully Continuous Rectangular Beam. The following example illustrates the application of the steps given in Art. 6–3 for the design of a rectangular beam.

Example. An interior span of a fully continuous beam having a clear span of 22 ft 0 in. has a superimposed uniformly distributed load of 1200 lb per linear ft. Let it be required to design the beam in accordance with the following data:

3000-psi concrete will be used,

$n = 10$,

$f_s = 20,000$ psi,

$f_c = 1350$ psi,

$v_c = $ limited to 90 psi,

$v = $ limited to 240 psi,

$u = $ limited to 210 psi for top bars and 300 psi for others,

end conditions = fully continuous.

SOLUTION. *Step 1.* To compute the approximate weight of the beam, estimate 1 in. of depth for each foot of span. Then $1 \times 22 = 22$ in., the estimated total depth of the beam. Deducting 2.5 in. for fireproofing, stirrups, and one half the thickness of longitudinal reinforcement, $22 - 2.5 = 19.5$ in., the estimated effective depth. Therefore, assume that b is 10 in.

The number of square feet in the cross section of the beam is $\dfrac{10 \times 22}{144}$. As the beam is 22 ft 0 in. in length and weighs 150 lb per cu ft, the total estimated weight of the beam is

$$\frac{10 \times 22}{144} \times 22 \times 150 = 5042 \text{ lb}$$

The total estimated uniformly distributed load $W = (22 \times 1,200) + 5042 = 31,442$, say 31,400 lb.

Step 2. The reactions, and consequently the maximum vertical shear, are each equal to one half the total load. Therefore,

$$V = R_1 = R_2 = \tfrac{1}{2} \times 31,400 = 15,700 \text{ lb}$$

Step 3. This is an interior span of a continuous beam. Reference to Fig. 3–3 shows that both the positive moment at the center of the span and the negative moment over the supports are $wl^2/12$, which, of course, is the same as $Wl/12$. See Art. 3–7. Then, substituting in the formula $M = \dfrac{Wl}{12}$, the value of the maximum bending moment $M = \dfrac{31,400 \times 22 \times 12}{12} = 690,800$ in-lb. In this equation 12 in the numerator converts the bending moment to inch-pounds. We might have computed M in foot-pounds and afterward multiplied by 12 to accomplish the same thing, but having all the mathematics in one operation simplifies the computations.

Step 4. Referring to Table 4–1, we find, in accordance with allotted unit stresses, $K = 236$. Then, substituting the known quantities,

$$d = \sqrt{\frac{M}{Kb}} = \sqrt{\frac{690,800}{236 \times 10}} = \sqrt{293} = 17.1 \text{ in.}$$

the effective depth. If we allow 0.5 in. for one half the thickness of the reinforcing bars and 2 in. for stirrups and fireproofing, the total depth of the beam $= 17.1 + 0.5 + 2 = 19.6$ in. Since it is desirable to use whole inches for the dimensions of the beam, we shall accept a total depth of 20 in. If we take advantage of this increase in depth,

$$d = 20 - (0.5 + 2) = 17.5 \text{ in.}$$

the effective depth of the beam. Note that the 22-in. total depth used in Step 1 for approximating the weight of the beam is in excess of 20 in. and therefore the allowance of 5042 lb is ample.

Step 5. By formula,

$$A_s = \frac{M}{f_s j d} \qquad \text{or} \qquad A_s = \frac{690,800}{20,000 \times 0.866 \times 17.5} = 2.28 \text{ sq in.}$$

the total required area of the main tensile reinforcement at the center of the span and over the supports.

By referring to Table 1–1, we find that 2-#10 bars have a cross-sectional area of 2.54 sq in. and therefore are accepted. Table 6–1 indicates that 2-#10 bars may be placed in a beam 10 in. in width.

Step 6. By formula,

$$v = \frac{V}{jbd} \quad \text{or} \quad v = \frac{15,700}{0.875 \times 10 \times 17.5} = 103 \text{ psi}$$

the shearing unit stress. We note that this figure is within 240 psi, the limiting value, and that, since it exceeds 90 psi, the limiting value for v_c, it will be necessary to use stirrups.

Step 7. The excess shear to be carried by the stirrups is v'. Its value is $v' = v - v_c$ or $v' = 103 - 90 = 13$ psi. Then $a = \frac{L}{2}\left(\frac{v'}{v}\right)$ or $a = \frac{22}{2}\left(\frac{13}{103}\right) = 1.39$ ft, the distance from the supports in which stirrups are theoretically required. However, for a continuous or restrained beam that does not have a slab cast to provide T-beam action, the specification requirement given in Art. 5–3, relating to dimension a, must be considered.

The inflection points for continuous beams having equal spans and equal uniformly distributed loads are assumed to be at points one fifth of the span from the faces of the supports. See Art. 3–5. Then, applying the specification requirement,

$$a = \frac{L}{5} + \frac{L}{16} = \frac{22}{5} + \frac{22}{16} = 4.4 + 1.38 = 5.78 \text{ ft} \quad \text{or} \quad 5 \text{ ft } 10 \text{ in.}$$

or

$$a = \frac{L}{5} + \text{depth} = \frac{22}{5} + \frac{20}{12} = 4.4 + 1.67 = 6.07 \text{ ft} \quad \text{or} \quad 6 \text{ ft } 1 \text{ in.}$$

The second value, being the greater, will be used. This is the distance from the face of the supports in which stirrups are required.

Step 8. We assume that the stirrups are made of #3 bars, U-shaped. The area of one bar being 0.11 sq in., the cross-sectional area of the two legs of one stirrup will be $2 \times 0.11 = 0.22$ sq in., the value of A_v.

The specification requirement, given in Art. 5–3, requires that the web reinforcement carry at least two thirds of the total shear at a section in which there is a negative bending moment. Therefore, v' becomes $\frac{2}{3} \times 103$ or $v' = 69$ psi. Now, assuming f_v to be 20,000 psi and substituting in the formula,

$$s = \frac{A_v f_v}{v'b} = \frac{0.22 \times 20,000}{69 \times 10} = 6.4 \text{ in.}, \qquad \text{say 6 in.}$$

the stirrup spacing.

In accordance with the maximum stirrup-spacing requirement explained in Art. 5–4, the maximum spacing permitted is $\frac{d - m}{2} = \frac{17.5 - 2.5}{2} = 7.5$ in.; hence we shall accept $s = 6$ in.

The first stirrup is placed 3 in. from the face of the support, and the remaining stirrups have 6 in. spacing until the distance of 6 ft 1 in. is reached. Consequently, a total of thirteen stirrups is required *at each end of the beam*.

Step 9. The perimeter of a #10 bar is 3.99 in., Table 1–1, and since there are two main tensile reinforcing bars the sum of the perimeters is 2×3.99. Substituting the known quantities in the formula,

$$u = \frac{V}{\Sigma_0 jd} \qquad \text{or} \qquad u = \frac{15,700}{2 \times 3.99 \times 0.875 \times 17.5} = 128 \text{ psi}$$

the unit bond stress. Since 128 psi is less than 210 psi, the allowable, the selected reinforcement is acceptable.

Step 10. One of the two main tensile reinforcing bars will be turned up at a 45° angle at a distance of one fifth of the span from the supports, or 4 ft 5 in., as shown in Fig. 6–1. The bent bars will continue over the supports to the fourth points of the adjacent spans. The straight bars are extended to the center lines of the supports. Note that there are 2-#10 bars at the bottom of the beam at the center of the span and also at the top of the beam over the supports, thus providing for both the positive and negative bending moments.

Alternate design. In order to satisfy the trend toward simplification in designing, detailing, fabrication, and placing of reinforcement, many designers use separate straight bars in both the bottoms and tops of the beams in place of bent bars. The slight cost in excess weight in this arrangement over the combination of

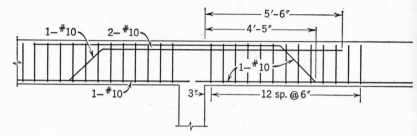

Bend bars at fifth points of span
Bent bars to extend to fourth points of adjacent spans
Straight bars to end at center of supports
Stirrups to be #3 U-shaped
Fireproofing to be 1½″ clear to stirrups

FIG. 6–1

straight and bent bars is probably balanced by the ease of preparing design and shop drawings, bills of materials, and fabrication and placing of reinforcement. Bars not fabricated according to drawings, or those lost or mislaid, are more easily replaced if no bending is involved.

By the use of an arrangement of straight bars only, the reinforcement would be placed as shown in Fig. 6–2. Note that #3 ties are substituted for the U-shaped stirrups to aid in placing and holding the top bars in position. The spacing of the ties is the same as that required for the stirrups.

Problem 6–4–A. An interior span of a fully continuous beam 19 ft 0 in. between faces of supports has a uniformly distributed load, exclusive of the weight of the beam, of 22,000 lb. Design the beam in accordance with the following data:

$$f'_c = 2500 \text{ psi}$$

$$f_s = 18,000 \text{ psi}$$

$$f_c = 1125 \text{ psi}$$

$$n = 12$$

$$v_c = \text{limited to 75 psi}$$

$$v = \text{limited to 200 psi}$$

$$u = \text{limited to 175 psi for top bars}$$
$$\text{and 250 psi for all others}$$

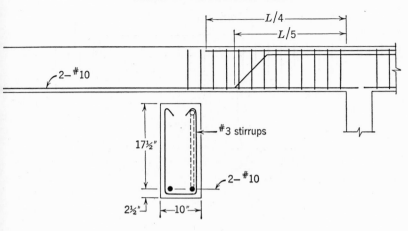

6–5. Design of a Semicontinuous Beam. Figure 3–2(g) shows the shear and moment diagrams for a continuous beam having a uniformly distributed load with the extreme ends of the beam *supported without restraint.* We use the term *free ends.* The values given for shear and moments in this diagram are theoretical and are not the values commonly used in design. Notice particularly that there is no moment at the free ends and that the values of the shear at the end and first interior support are not equal. Some designers ignore this difference in magnitude and consider the two reactions, and therefore the shear, to be the same at both supports. This is incorrect. The proper method is to consider the free end support to be $0.4 \times W$, W being the distributed load on the end span and $0.6 \times W$ the magnitude of the first interior support, as indicated in Fig. 3–2. The true reactions depend upon the degree of restraint, that is, upon the physical bond between the beam and its support. The following problem will be solved on the assumption that $R_1 = 0.4W$ and $R_2 = 0.6W$, W being the load on the end span, and that the positive bending moment between the supports is equal to $Wl/10$. These values are commonly used.

Example. Let it be required to design the end span of a continuous beam having the extreme end of the beam simply supported. The total uniformly distributed superimposed load is 16,500 lb and the clear span is 18 ft 0 in. Specification data:

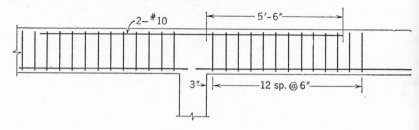

Bottom bars to end at center of supports
Top bars to extend to fourth points of span
Ties to be of #3 bars
Fireproofing to be 1½" clear to ties

FIG. 6–2

f'_c = 3000 psi

f_s = 20,000 psi

f_c = 1350 psi

v_c = limited to 90 psi

v = limited to 240 psi

u = limited to 210 psi for top bars and 300 psi for others

n = 10

SOLUTION.   The design steps given in Art. 6–3 will be followed as in the preceding example.

Step 1.   Allowing 1 in. of depth for each foot of span,

1.0 × 18 = 18 in., the estimated total depth.

Allowing 2.5 in. for fireproofing, ties, or stirrups, and one half the diameter of the longitudinal reinforcement, 18 − 2.5 = 15.5 in., the estimated effective depth.   Therefore, assume that b is 10 in.
Then

$$\frac{10 \times 18}{144} \times 18 \times 150 = 3375 \text{ lb}, \qquad \text{say } 3400 \text{ lb}$$

the estimated weight of the beam.

W = 16,500 + 3400 = 19,900 lb, the total uniformly distributed load.

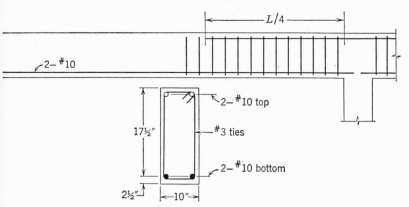

Step 2. Since the reactions for the end span, as previously explained, are not equal,

$$R_1 = 19,900 \times 0.4 = 7960 \text{ lb}$$

$$R_2 = 19,900 \times 0.6 = 11,940 \text{ lb}$$

Therefore the maximum shear at the end support $V = 7960$ lb, and at the first interior support $V = 11,940$ lb.

Step 3. The maximum bending moment between the supports is

$$M = \frac{Wl}{10} \qquad \text{(See Fig. 3–3.)}$$

or

$$M = \frac{19,900 \times 18 \times 12}{10} = 430,000 \text{ in-lb}$$

Step 4. Referring to Table 4–1, $K = 236$. Then,

$$d = \sqrt{\frac{M}{Kb}} = \sqrt{\frac{430,000}{236 \times 10}} = \sqrt{182} = 13.5 \text{ in.}$$

the effective depth.

If we allow 0.5 in. for one half the thickness of the reinforcing bars and 2 in. for fireproofing and ties or stirrups, $13.5 + 2.5 = 16$ in., the total depth of the beam. The estimated depth of 18 in. in Step 1, to determine the approximate weight, is acceptable.

Step 5. The total depth of the beam, as determined in Step 4, is in full inches, and d, the effective depth, will be exactly the same as determined by formula (6). Therefore formula (8), $A_s = pbd$, is applicable. We find in Table 4–1, $p = 0.0136$.

Then $A_s = pbd = 0.0136 \times 10 \times 13.5 = 1.84$ sq in., the total cross-sectional area of the main tensile reinforcement.

As has been stated, formula (7) might have been used. Notice

$$A_s = \frac{M}{f_s jd} = \frac{430,000}{20,000 \times 0.866 \times 13.5} = 1.84 \text{ sq in.}$$

the same result.

Referring to Table 1–1, we find

the area of 2-#7 bars = 1.20 sq in.
the area of 1-#8 bar = 0.79 sq in.
_____

total area of bars = 1.99 sq in.

Therefore we will use 2-#7 and 1-#8 bars for the longitudinal reinforcing bars.

At the left support, R_1.
Step 6.

$$v = \frac{V}{jbd} = \frac{7960}{0.875 \times 10 \times 13.5} = 68 \text{ psi}$$

the shearing unit stress. This quantity being less than the limiting value of v_c, 90 psi, no stirrups will be required at the left support.

Step 7. Not required.
Step 8. Not required.
At the right support, R_2.
Step 6.

$$v = \frac{V}{jbd} = \frac{11,940}{0.875 \times 10 \times 13.5} = 101 \text{ psi}$$

the shearing unit stress. Stirrups will be required since this value exceeds 90 psi.

Step 7. $v' = v - v_c$, or $v' = 101 - 90 = 11$ psi, the excess shear to be carried by the stirrups.

Since the two reactions are unequal in magnitude, the shear

diagram is similar to that shown in Fig. 5–2(*b*). The point of zero shear is $0.6 \times L$, or $0.6 \times 18 = 10.8$ ft from the fixed support. See Art. 5–3. Then,

$$a = \frac{L}{2}\left(\frac{v'}{v}\right)$$

and, substituting 10.8 ft for $\dfrac{L}{2}$,

$$a = 10.8\left(\frac{11}{101}\right) = 1.17 \text{ ft}, \qquad \text{say 1 ft 2 in.}$$

Since, however, this shear stress occurs at a section requiring reinforcement for a negative bending moment, the distance a must also comply with the specification requirements explained in Art. 5–3. Then,

$$a = \frac{L}{5} + \frac{L}{16} = \frac{18}{5} + \frac{18}{16} = 3.6 + 1.13 = 4.73 \text{ ft}, \qquad \text{say 4 ft 9 in.}$$

or

$$a = \frac{L}{5} + \text{depth} = \frac{18}{5} + \frac{16}{12} = 3.6 + 1.33 = 4.93 \text{ ft}, \quad \text{say 4 ft 11 in.}$$

Since 4 ft 11 in. is the greater value, it will be accepted.

Step 8. As explained in Art. 5–3, the web reinforcement must carry two thirds of the total shear at the section; hence v' becomes $\frac{2}{3} \times 101$, or 68 psi. Using #3 U-shaped stirrups $A_v = 2 \times 0.11 = 0.22$ sq in. Assuming $f_v = 20{,}000$ psi,

$$s = \frac{A_v f_v}{v' b} = \frac{0.22 \times 20{,}000}{68 \times 10} = 6.5 \text{ in.}, \qquad \text{say 6 in.}$$

Referring to Art. 5–4, the maximum allowable stirrup (or tie) spacing is

$$s = \frac{d - m}{2} = \frac{13.5 - 2.5}{2} = 5.5 \text{ in.}, \qquad \text{say 5 in.}$$

Since this maximum spacing is less than that computed above, a spacing of 5 in. must be accepted.   Thirteen #3 ties will be used, as shown in Fig. 6–3.

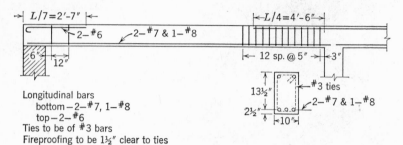

Longitudinal bars
    bottom – 2 – #7, 1 – #8
    top – 2 – #6
Ties to be of #3 bars
Fireproofing to be 1½" clear to ties

FIG. 6–3

Step 9.   The perimeters of #7 and #8 bars are 2.749 in. and 3.142 in., respectively.   See Table 1–1.   Then,

$$u = \frac{V}{\Sigma_0 jd} = \frac{11,940}{[(2 \times 2.749) + 3.142] \times 0.875 \times 13.5} = 117 \text{ psi}$$

Since this is less than 300 psi, the limiting value for the bond stress for bottom bars, the selections are accepted.

Step 10.   The three longitudinal tensile bars are used for the positive bending moment and are placed at the bottom of the beam. Although, theoretically, there is no bending moment over the left support, at R_1, it is good practice to provide some reinforcement at the top of the beam.   Referring to Art. 4–12, we see that the minimum amount of reinforcement for a beam is $A_s = 0.005bd$ or $A_s = 0.005 \times 10 \times 13.5 = 0.68$ sq in.   Two #6 bars ($A_s = 0.88$ sq in.) are used at the top of the beam, carried to the $\frac{1}{7}$ point of clear span ($\frac{1}{7} \times 18 = 2.57$ ft) and hooked at the exterior end to provide for bond stresses.   To hold these top bars in place ties are added as shown in Fig. 6–3.

The reinforcement over R_2, the first interior support, is found as explained in Art. 6–4.   It is not shown in Fig. 6–3; it would be determined by the design of the interior span.

Problem 6–5–A.   The end span of a continuous beam is 20 ft 0 in. between faces of supports.   The extreme end of the beam is simply supported.   If the superimposed uniformly distributed load is 14,000 lb, design the beam in accordance with the following data:

$$f'_c = 2500 \text{ psi}$$

$$f_s = 20,000 \text{ psi}$$

$$f_c = 1125 \text{ psi}$$

$$v_c = \text{limited to 75 psi}$$

$$v = \text{limited to 200 psi}$$

$$u = \text{limited to 175 psi for top bars}$$
$$\text{and 250 psi for others}$$

$$n = 12$$

6–6. Design of a Fully Continuous Girder. A girder with concentrated loads in addition to its own weight presents a problem requiring special attention. To illustrate the design of such a beam consider the following example.

Example. A girder having a span of 18 ft 0 in. between centers of supports has concentrated loads of 20,500 lb, each placed at the third points of the span. This is the interior span of a continuous beam and therefore the ends are considered to be fully continuous. Design data are as follows:

$$f'_c = 3000 \text{ psi}$$

$$f_s = 20,000 \text{ psi}$$

$$f_c = 1350 \text{ psi}$$

$$v_c = \text{limited to 90 psi}$$

$$v = \text{limited to 240 psi}$$

$$u = \text{limited to 210 psi for top bars and 300 psi for others}$$

$$n = 10$$

SOLUTION. *Step 1.* To design a girder of this type, it is important to remember that its depth should be greater than that of the beams framing into it. Most designers make the girders at least 1 in. deeper than the beams. In practice, it is customary to design the floor construction in this sequence: slabs, beams, and girders. Consequently, the beam depths are always established before designing the girder.

The approximate allowance of 1 in. of depth for each foot of span applies only to beams with uniformly distributed loads. For this girder we allow $1\frac{1}{4}$ in. for each foot of span. Then

$$1\tfrac{1}{4} \times 18 = 22.5 \text{ in.,} \qquad \text{say 23 in.}$$

We assume that the width of the girder is 12 in. Then the estimated weight of the girder is $\dfrac{12 \times 23}{144} \times 18 \times 150 = 5175$ lb, say 5200 lb.

Step 2. The total load on the beam is

$$20{,}500 + 20{,}500 + 5200 = 46{,}200 \text{ lb}$$

The beam being symmetrically loaded, the reactions are equal and

$$V = R_1 = R_2 = \frac{46{,}200}{2} = 23{,}100 \text{ lb}$$

Step 3. Concentrated loads at the third points is a common type of loading. Referring to Fig. 3–4(c), we find that the maximum bending moment for a *simple beam* is $PL/3$. Then

$$M = \frac{PL}{3} = \frac{20{,}500 \times 18 \times 12}{3} = 1{,}476{,}000 \text{ in-lb}$$

However, the end conditions for this beam are *fully continuous;* hence the moment for the concentrated loads, found by the assumption that the beam is a simple beam, may be reduced by multiplying by $\frac{8}{12}$, as explained in Art. 3–8. Therefore $M = 1{,}476{,}000 \times \frac{8}{12} = 984{,}000$ in-lb. The maximum moment for the weight of the beam, 5200 lb, is

$$M = \frac{WL}{12} = \frac{5200 \times 18 \times 12}{12} = 93{,}600 \text{ in-lb}$$

Note that this is the bending moment for a *fully continuous beam*
Adding the two bending moments,

$$984{,}000 + 93{,}600 = 1{,}077{,}600 \text{ in-lb}$$

the maximum bending moment at the center of the span as well as over the supports.

Step 4. The value of K, found in Table 4–1, is 236. Then

$$d = \sqrt{\frac{M}{Kb}} \qquad \text{or} \qquad d = \sqrt{\frac{1,077,600}{236 \times 12}} = 19.5 \text{ in.}$$

the effective depth. Total depth of the beam $= 19.5 + 0.5 + 2 = 22$ in. In this equation 0.5 in. is one half the thickness of the reinforcing bars and 2 in. is the allowance for fireproofing and stirrups. In Step 1 the estimated depth of 23 in. for approximating the weight of the beam is ample.

Step 5. By Table 4–1, $p = 0.0136$. Then

$$A_s = pbd \qquad \text{or} \qquad A_s = 0.0136 \times 12 \times 19.5 = 3.18 \text{ sq in.}$$

Four #8 bars have a cross-sectional area of 3.16 sq in. See Table 1–1. Although this area is 0.02 sq in. less than that which is theoretically required, the error is less than 1% and may be accepted without risking the safety of the structure. Table 6–1 shows that 4-#8 bars may be accommodated in a beam 12 in. wide.

Step 6.

$$v = \frac{V}{jbd} \qquad \text{or} \qquad v = \frac{23,100}{0.875 \times 12 \times 19.5} = 113 \text{ psi}$$

the shearing unit stress at the supports. Since this value exceeds v_c, 90 psi, stirrups are required.

Step 7. Formula (11) applies to beams having only a uniformly distributed load and therefore is not applicable to this beam. Figure 3–4(c) shows that the value of V, the shear, has the same magnitude between the support and the first concentrated load. Therefore, stirrups will be required in this distance. See the second example in Art. 5–3 in reference to Fig. 5–3. By computations, it is found that the value of v immediately to the right of the first concentrated load is less than 5 psi, showing that web reinforcement is unnecessary between the concentrated loads.

The maximum shear for this girder occurs at a section requiring reinforcement for a negative bending moment; hence the length of beam requiring web reinforcement must also comply with the specification requirements explained in Art. 5–3.

For a fully continuous beam with equal concentrated loads at the third points, the inflection points occur at a distance approximately $\frac{2}{9}$ of the span length from the supports. Therefore

$$a = \frac{2}{9}L + \frac{L}{16} = \left(\frac{2}{9} \times 18\right) + \frac{18}{16} = 4.0 + 1.13$$
$$= 5.13 \text{ ft}, \qquad \text{say 5 ft 2 in.}$$

or

$$a = \frac{2}{9}L + \text{depth} = \left(\frac{2}{9} \times 18\right) + \frac{22}{12} = 4.0 + 1.83$$
$$= 5.83 \text{ ft}, \qquad \text{say 5 ft 10 in.}$$

Since neither of these distances is in excess of 6 ft, the distance from the supports to the concentrated loads, stirrups between the supports and the concentrated loads will be used.

Step 8. The web reinforcement must be sufficient to carry at least two thirds of the total shear; therefore, $v' = v - v_c = 113 - 90 = 23$ psi, and $\frac{2}{3} \times 113 = 75$ psi, the shearing stress to be used in determining the stirrup spacing.

We shall use #4 U-shaped stirrups; hence $2 \times 0.2 = 0.4$ sq in., the value of A_v. Assuming $f_v = 20,000$ psi,

$$s = \frac{A_v f_v}{v'b} = \frac{0.4 \times 20,000}{75 \times 12} = 8.9 \text{ in.}$$

the stirrup spacing.

But the maximum spacing permitted is

$$s = \frac{d - m}{2} = \frac{19.5 - 2.5}{2} = 8.5 \text{ in.}$$

Therefore, we accept #4 stirrups with 8-in. spacing, as shown in Fig. 6–4. Although the stresses do not require it, some designers

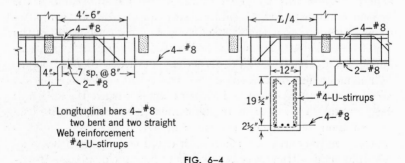

Longitudinal bars 4–#8
   two bent and two straight
Web reinforcement
   #4-U-stirrups

FIG. 6–4

prefer to use stirrups in that portion of the beam between the two concentrated loads. The spacing often used is the width of the beam, in this instance, 12 in.

Step 9. By referring to Table 1–1, we find that the perimeter of a #8 bar is 3.14 in. Then

$$u = \frac{V}{\Sigma_0 jd} = \frac{23{,}100}{(4 \times 3.14) \times 0.875 \times 19.5} = 108 \text{ psi}$$

the unit bond stress. As 210 psi is the limiting value for top bars, the reinforcement is acceptable.

Step 10. Two of the 4-#8 bars are bent up at the $\frac{2}{3}$th points of the span and extended over the supports to the fourth points of the adjacent spans. The remaining two bars are run straight, at the bottom of the beam, to the center lines of the columns.

Problem 6–6–A. An interior span of a fully continuous girder is 22 ft 0 in. between faces of supports. There is one concentrated load of 18,000 lb at the center of the span. Design the girder according to the following data:

$$f'_c = 2500 \text{ psi}$$

$$f_s = 18{,}000 \text{ psi}$$

$$f_c = 1125 \text{ psi}$$

$$v_c = \text{limited to 75 psi}$$

$$v = \text{limited to 200 psi}$$

$$u = \text{limited to 175 psi for top bars} \\ \text{and 250 psi for others}$$

$$n = 12$$

6–7. Typical Beams. In the design of reinforced concrete beams certain identical problems occur many times. Figure 6–5 shows three types of beam spans, a single span with no restraint at the ends, an end span, and an interior span. The load on each beam is W, the uniformly distributed load on one span. For each beam important design data are given.

As explained in Art. 6–4, the longitudinal tensile reinforcement may consist of a system of bent (trussed) and straight bars or an arrangement of straight bars, some at the top and others at the bottom of the beam. Figure 6–5 shows the system of bent and straight bars. Theoretically, the bent bars are turned up at the

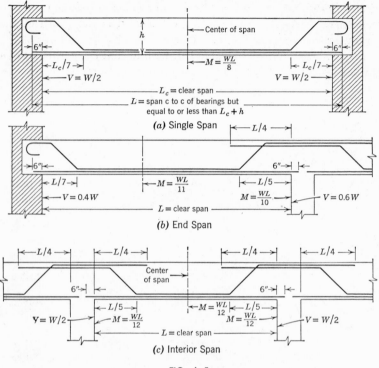

(a) Single Span

(b) End Span

(c) Interior Span

FIG. 6–5

inflection points, and these points are indicated as fractions of L, the span. In order to provide adequate bond, the lengths of the bars are shown. If straight bars are used for the negative moments over the supports, the lengths of embedment are identical with the lengths shown for the bent bars. Where the length $L/4$ is shown, it might have said "$L/4$ or 17 bar diameters, whichever is the greater."

For each beam the maximum vertical shear and maximum bending moment are shown. These are the magnitudes usually employed, but some designers prefer other values. For instance, Fig. 6–5(c) shows the maximum bending moment for an interior span to be $WL/12$, whereas certain codes require the use of $WL/11$ for the negative moment at the face of the support and $WL/16$ for the positive moment at the center of the span. The value of V

at the first interior support for an end span is shown as $0.6W$, although some codes use $1.15W/2$ or $0.575W$. Bending moments are generally computed by taking L as the clear span between faces of supports. For single spans, L is properly taken as the distance center to center of supports but a distance not greater than the clear span plus the depth of the beam.

CHAPTER 7

DESIGN OF T-BEAMS

7–1. T-Beams. When a beam and slab are poured at one time, resulting in a monolithic construction, a portion of the slab on each side of the beam may be considered as the flange of a T-beam. The portion of the beam below the slab serves as the web, sometimes called the stem, and the T-section, when computed as such, produces an economic form of construction. See Fig. 7–1(a). As in

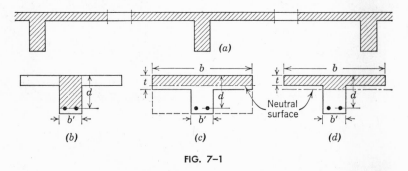

FIG. 7–1

the case of rectangular beams, the concrete above the neutral surface, in simple beams, resists the compressive stresses and the main tensile reinforcing bars resist all the tensile stresses. It is important to bear in mind that only the area formed by the width of the web, b', and the effective depth, d, are to be considered in computing resistance to shear or diagonal tension and to bending over the supports. The overhanging portions, or flanges, are not to be included in computations for these stresses.

When the principal reinforcement in a slab, which is considered as the flange of a T-beam, is parallel to the beam, transverse reinforcement must be provided in the slab. For this reinforcement, the spacing of the bars shall not exceed five times the thickness of the slab or in any case 18 in. This requirement does not apply to a rib in ribbed-floor construction.

7–2. Width of Flange. In computing the area of the concrete resisting compressive stresses, there are several limitations to the width of flange to be considered. The effective flange width to be used in designing T-beams shall not exceed one fourth the span length of the beam. Its overhanging width on either side of the web shall not exceed eight times the thickness of the slab or one half the clear distance to the next beam.

For beams having a flange on one side only, the effective overhanging flange width shall not exceed one twelfth of the span length of the beam, or six times the thickness of the slab, or one half the clear distance to the next beam.

7–3. Ratio of Width to Depth of Web. In determining the width of the web, we must have in mind the probable number of reinforcing bars that will be used. For T-beams, two layers of bars are frequently used. When this is the case, remember that d, the effective depth, is taken from the uppermost fiber of the concrete to the *centroid* of the reinforcement.

In proportioning the width to the depth of the web, the clear story height of the room must be given consideration. To provide maximum head room and a minimum of light obstruction, wider and shallower beams are desirable. It is customary, unless practical conditions prevent, to have b', the width of the web, from one half to one third of d, the effective depth.

7–4. Depth of a T-Beam. In simple and continuous T-beams the flanges resist compressive stresses at the mid-span. In T-beams that are continuous over supports the flanges are in the tension zone. The concrete flanges are unable to resist tension, and only the rectangular hatched area, $b'd$, shown in Fig. 7–1(b), can be considered as resisting bending stresses. To determine the depth of a continuous T-beam, the negative bending moment at the support is first computed, and the effective depth of this rectangular area is found by the use of formula (6), $d = \sqrt{\dfrac{M}{Kb}}$. After the depth, based on the negative bending moment, has been established, it is checked to see that the area $b'd$ is adequate to resist the shearing stresses.

Because of the relatively large flange areas, the compressive stresses in simple T-beams are invariably well within the allowable stresses. Thus, for simple T-beams, the effective depth is determined by the shearing stresses in the area $b'd$, Fig. 7–1(b).

The shearing unit stress for both simple and continuous T-beams is found by the use of formula (15).

Since by formula (10), Art. 5–2, $v = \dfrac{V}{jbd}$, for T-beams we may write

$$b'd = \frac{V}{vj} \tag{15}$$

in which b' = the width of the web of the T-beam, in inches,

d = the effective depth of the beam, in inches,

V = the maximum vertical shear, in pounds,

v = the allowable shearing unit stress, as given in Table 4–2, in pounds per square inch,

j = $\frac{7}{8}$ or 0.875, the value used in computations for shear.

Thus, if we know the values of V, v, and j, the area of the T-beam resisting shear, $b'd$, is readily determined. As has been implied, numerous combinations are possible, but a ratio of b' to d of one half to one third is the commonest. The foregoing equation is used to establish the depth of the T-beam if the depth is determined by the resistance of the concrete to shear.

Example. The total load on a simple T-beam, symmetrically loaded, including its own weight, is 68,000 lb. Assuming that v is limited to 240 psi, compute the effective depth of the beam as determined by resistance to shear.

SOLUTION. As the beam is symmetrically loaded, each reaction R_1 and R_2 and therefore $V = 68,000 \times \frac{1}{2} = 34,000$ lb.

$$b'd = \frac{V}{vj} \tag{15}$$

or

$$b'd = \frac{34,000}{240 \times 0.875} = 162 \text{ sq in.}$$

the cross-sectional area of the beam resisting shear.

The width of the web should be kept in full inches, avoiding fractions, and the combination of $b' = 8$ in. and $d = 21$ in. provides acceptable dimensions. Note that 21 in. is the effective depth and that the total depth will be greater, depending on the reinforcement and necessary fireproofing. Another acceptable combination is $b' = 9$ in. and $d = 18$ in., but the smaller effective depth will require a greater area of tensile reinforcement.

Example. A fully continuous T-beam has a clear span between faces of supports of 19 ft 0 in. and a uniformly distributed load, including its own weight, of 50,000 lb. Determine the effective depth and width of web in accordance with the following data:

$$f'_c = 2500 \text{ psi}$$

$$f_c = 1125 \text{ psi}$$

$$f_s = 20,000 \text{ psi}$$

$$v = \text{limited to 200 psi}$$

$$n = 12$$

SOLUTION. The negative bending moment at the supports is $M = \dfrac{Wl}{12}$. (See Art. 3–7.)   Then,

$$M = \frac{50,000 \times 19 \times 12}{12} = 950,000 \text{ in-lb}$$

Referring to Table 4–1, $K = 196$, and assuming b to be 10 in.,

$$d = \sqrt{\frac{M}{Kb}} \quad \text{or} \quad d = \sqrt{\frac{950,000}{196 \times 10}} = \sqrt{484} = 22 \text{ in.}$$

Thus, with respect to bending stresses, a T-beam with an effective depth of 22 in. and a 10-in. width of web is satisfactory. The next step is to test a web of these dimensions for shear.

The maximum vertical shear is $\frac{1}{2} \times 50,000 = 25,000$ lb. Then, substituting the known quantities in formula (15),

$$v = \frac{V}{b'jd} \quad \text{or} \quad v = \frac{25,000}{10 \times 0.875 \times 22} = 130 \text{ psi}$$

the shearing unit stress. Since this stress does not exceed 200 psi, the allowable, the web dimensions are acceptable.

Problem 7–4–A. A simple T-beam has a total uniformly distributed load of 70,000 lb. If v is limited to 200 psi, determine the required width of web and effective depth of the beam.

Problem 7–4–B. Determine the effective depth and width of web of a fully continuous T-beam having a clear span between faces of supports of 16 ft 0 in. and a distributed load, including its own weight, of 30,000 lb. Specification data:

$$f'_c = 3000 \text{ psi}$$

$$f_c = 1350 \text{ psi}$$

$$f_s = 20,000 \text{ psi}$$

$$v = \text{limited to 240 psi}$$

$$n = 10$$

7–5. Area of Tensile Reinforcement in T-Beams.

The exact formulas to be used in determining the area of the main tensile reinforcement in T-beams depend upon the location of the neutral surface. Depending on b and t, the width and thickness of the flange, and d, the effective depth, the neutral surface may lie in either the flange or the web. These two conditions are illustrated in Fig. 7–1(c) and (d).

Referring to Fig. 7–1(c), we note that the neutral surface of the T-beam lies in the flange. The hatched area indicates the portion of the beam under compression. Suppose that concrete occupied the rectangular spaces below the slab indicated by the dotted lines. As only the concrete above the neutral surface resists compressive stresses, the bending strength of the beam would not be increased by the additional concrete. Therefore, with respect to bending, a T-beam in which the neutral surface lies in the flange may be considered as a rectangular beam and the formulas for a rectangular beam are applicable, b being the width of the beam and d the effective depth. These formulas would apply also to a T-beam in which the neutral surface coincided with the lower surface of the slab.

When the condition which is illustrated in Fig. 7–1(d) occurs, the neutral surface being in the web, a small portion of the web is under compression and therefore the formulas for rectangular beams do not apply. The exact formulas for this condition are somewhat complicated and tedious to use; consequently simplified formulas, approximately correct and erring on the side of safety, are generally employed.

If a diagram were constructed to show the distribution of the compression stresses, the center of pressure would lie above the center of the slab. The lever arm of the resisting couple would never be less than $d - \frac{1}{2}t$. Therefore, the following two formulas, approximately correct, may be used in safety.

$$A_s = \frac{M}{f_s[d - (t/2)]} \tag{16}$$

and

$$f_c = \frac{2M}{bt[d - (t/2)]} \tag{17}$$

in which A_s = the area of the main tensile reinforcement, in square inches,

M = the maximum bending moment, in inch-pounds,

f_s = the allowable tensile unit stress in the steel, in pounds per square inch,

f_c = the compressive unit stress on the extreme fibers of the concrete, in pounds per square inch,

b = the effective width of the flange, in inches,

d = the effective depth of the beam, in inches,

t = the thickness of the flange, in inches.

Formula (16) is used to determine the area of the tensile reinforcement. Formula (17) is used to check the compressive unit stress in the concrete of *simply supported beams;* it should not exceed the allowable stress permitted by the specifications. For continuous T-beams it must be remembered that over the supports the flange is on the tension side. When it is necessary to check the compressive stresses over the supports, the beam is rectangular in section and the methods used for the design of beams with double reinforcement may be employed. See Art. 8-2.

7-6. Design Steps for T-Beams. Although many of the steps in the design of T-beams are similar to those for rectangular beams given in Art. 6-3, it should be noted that the depth of a T-beam is determined by the rectangular cross section resisting the negative bending moment and shear. In formulas (16) and (17) t, the thickness of the flange, is one of the factors. In the design of a beam-and-slab floor construction the slab is designed first, and therefore its thickness is determined before the design of the T-beam. The following sequence of steps may be used.

Step 1. Loads. Determine the live and dead loads the beam will be required to support. The weight of the slab is determined by its thickness, but the weight of the web projecting below the slab must be approximated. Its weight is generally 10 to 15% of the total load to be supported. Stone-concrete is assumed to weigh 150 lb per cu ft.

Step 2. Maximum vertical shear. Compute R_1 and R_2, the reactions, and V, the maximum vertical shear. If the beam is symmetrically loaded, the reactions, and therefore the maximum vertical shear, are each equal to one half the total load.

Step 3. Maximum bending moment. Compute the maximum bending moment as explained in Arts. 3–7 and 3–8.

Step 4. Depth of beam. The effective depth of a continuous beam is first determined by the resistance of the area $b'd$ in Fig. 7–1(b) to the negative bending moment. Assume the width of web and use formula (6), $d = \sqrt{\dfrac{M}{Kb}}$, Art. 4–5, to determine d, the effective depth. In using this formula, the term b is b', the width of the web. The cross-sectional area $b'd$ having been established, its dimensions are now checked by formula (15) to see that v, the allowable shearing unit stress, is not exceeded.

$$b'd = \frac{V}{vj} \qquad \text{Formula (15), Art. 7–4}$$

in which b' = the width of the web, in inches,

d = the effective depth of the beam, in inches,

V = the maximum vertical shear, in pounds,

v = the allowable shearing unit stress, in pounds per square inch,

$j = \frac{7}{8}$, or 0.875, the value used in computations for shear.

For using formula (15), the value of v is given in Table 4–2. For 3000-psi concrete, $v = 240$ psi.

For simple T-beams the area $b'd$ is found by use of formula (15),

$b'd = \dfrac{V}{vj}.$ The width of web, b', is usually taken to be one half to one third of d, the effective depth.

Step 5. Area of tensile reinforcement. Compute the area of the main tensile reinforcement by use of the equation

$$A_s = \frac{M}{f_s[d - (t/2)]} \qquad \text{Formula (16), Art. 7–5}$$

in which A_s = the total area of the main tensile reinforcement, in square inches,

$\quad M$ = the maximum bending moment, in inch-pounds,

$\quad f_s$ = the allowable tensile unit stress in the steel, in pounds per square inch,

$\quad d$ = the effective depth of the beam, in inches,

$\quad t$ = the thickness of the flange, in inches.

Because of the relatively large width of flange, the compressive stresses in the concrete are generally well within the allowable. For simply supported beams f_c may be checked by use of formula (17), Art. 7–5.

Step 6. Length of beam requiring stirrups. If the load on the beam is uniformly distributed and the reactions equal in magnitude, determine the distance from the supports in which web reinforcement (stirrups) is required by use of the formula

$$a = \frac{L}{2}\left(\frac{v'}{v}\right) \qquad \text{Formula (11), Art. 5–3}$$

in which a = the distance from the support in which stirrups are required, in feet,

$\quad L$ = the span of the beam, in feet,

$\quad v' = v - v_c$, and v_c = the allowable unit shearing stresses as given in Table 4–2.

Step 7. Stirrup spacing. Determine the spacing of the stirrups by use of the formula

$$s = \frac{A_v f_v}{v' b'}$$

similar to formula (12), Art. 5–4, in which s = the spacing of the stirrups in inches and b' = the width of the web in inches. The remaining terms are similar to those given in Step 8, Art. 6–3, for rectangular beams.

Step 8. Bond stress. Determine the bond stress by use of the formula

$$u = \frac{V}{\Sigma_0 jd} \qquad \text{Formula (13), Art. 5–6}$$

where u = the unit bond stress in pounds per square inch. The remaining terms in this equation are similar to those given in Step 9, Art. 6–3, for rectangular beams.

Step 9. Bends, laps, and hooks. Specify the position of the bends of the bent bars, if any, length of laps, hooks, if required, and web reinforcement.

7–7. Design of a T-Beam.

Example. Design a fully continuous T-beam having a span of 22 ft 0 in. between faces of supports. The slab is 6 in. in thickness on which there is a live load of 120 psf. The distance, center to center of adjacent beams, is 12 ft 0 in. Specification data:

$$f'_c = 3000 \text{ psi}$$

$$f_s = 20{,}000 \text{ psi}$$

$$f_c = 1350 \text{ psi}$$

$$v_c = 90 \text{ psi}$$

$$v = \text{limited to } 240 \text{ psi}$$

$$u = 210 \text{ psi for top bars and } 300 \text{ psi for others}$$

$$n = 10$$

SOLUTION. *Step 1.*

$$\text{Weight of the slab} = \frac{6}{12} \times 150 = \quad 75 \text{ psf}$$

$$\text{Live load} \qquad\qquad = 120 \text{ psf}$$

$$\text{Total load on slab} \qquad = 195 \text{ psf}$$

As the beams are 12 ft 0 in. on centers, $12 \times 195 = 2340$ lb, the live and dead loads on the beam *per linear foot* not including the weight of the web.

The weight of the web must be estimated. It is usually 10 to 15% of the load. In this instance let us assume it to be 300 lb per linear ft.

Then $2340 + 300 = 2640$ lb per linear ft. Thus the total live and dead loads on the beam will be $2640 \times 22 = 58,080$ lb, say 58,000 lb.

Step 2. $V = R_1 = R_2 = 58,000 \times \frac{1}{2} = 29,000$ lb, the maximum vertical shear.

Step 3. Since this beam is fully continuous by data,

$$M = \frac{Wl}{12} \qquad \text{(See Art. 3-7.)}$$

Then

$$M = \frac{Wl}{12} = \frac{58,000 \times 22 \times 12}{12} = 1,276,000 \text{ in-lb}$$

Step 4. Assume that b' is 12 in. Referring to Table 4–1, we find that $K = 236$ and $j = 0.866$. Then,

$$d = \sqrt{\frac{M}{Kb}} \qquad \text{or} \qquad d = \sqrt{\frac{1,276,000}{236 \times 12}} = 21.2 \text{ in.}$$

Allowing 2.5 in. for one half the longitudinal tensile reinforcement, stirrup, and fireproofing, $21.2 + 2.5 = 23.7$ in., say 24 in., the total depth of the T-beam. Thus $24 - 2.5 = 21.5$ in., the effective depth. Since $b' = 12$ in. and $d = 21.5$ in. are suitable dimensions with respect to bending stress, they are now checked to see that the allowable shearing unit stress, 240 psi, is not exceeded. Thus

$$v = \frac{V}{jb'd} \qquad \text{Formula (15), Art. 7-4}$$

and

$$v = \frac{29,000}{0.875 \times 12 \times 21.5} = 129 \text{ psi}$$

As 129 psi does not exceed 240 psi, the web dimensions are acceptable for both bending and shear.

The weight of the web can now be computed. As the slab is 6 in. thick, $24 - 6 = 18$ in., the depth of web projecting below the slab. Then,

$$\frac{18 \times 12}{144} \times 150 = 225 \text{ lb}$$

the weight of the web per linear foot of length. This is less than 300 lb, the estimated weight given in Step 1.

Step 5. The reinforcement for the positive bending between supports is

$$A_s = \frac{M}{f_s[d - (t/2)]}$$ Formula (16), Art. 7–5

Then

$$A_s = \frac{1,276,000}{20,000[21.5 - (6/2)]} = 3.44 \text{ sq in.}$$

The reinforcement in the top of the beam over the supports is

$$A_s = \frac{M}{f_s jd} = \frac{1,276,000}{20,000 \times 0.866 \times 21.5} = 3.42 \text{ sq in.}$$

Select 1-#9 and 2-#10 bars for both top and bottom reinforcement. $A_s = 1.0 + 2.54 = 3.54$ sq in. See Fig. 7–2.

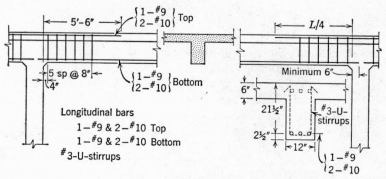

Longitudinal bars
1–#9 & 2–#10 Top
1–#9 & 2–#10 Bottom
#3-U-stirrups

FIG. 7–2

Step 6.

$$v' = v - v_c \quad \text{or} \quad v' = 129 - 90 = 39 \text{ psi}$$

$$a = \frac{L}{2}\left(\frac{v'}{v}\right) = \frac{22}{2} \times \left(\frac{39}{129}\right) = 3.33 \text{ ft}$$

the distance from the supports in which stirrups are required.

Step 7. Assuming the stirrups to be #3 U-stirrups, the area of a #3 bar is 0.11 sq in., Table 1–1, and therefore $A_v = 2 \times 0.11 = 0.22$ sq in. Accepting $f_v = 18,000$ psi and substituting in the formula

$$s = \frac{A_v f_v}{v'b'} \qquad\qquad \text{Formula (12), Art. 5-4}$$

$$s = \frac{0.22 \times 18,000}{39 \times 12} = 8.5 \text{ in.,} \qquad \text{say 8 in.}$$

the spacing of the stirrups.

$$\frac{d - m}{2} = \frac{21.5 - 2.5}{2} = 9.5 \text{ in.}$$

the maximum spacing permitted. The first stirrup will be placed at 4 in. from the face of the support and the remainder, in the 3-ft 4-in. distance, at 8 in. spacing.

Step 8. The perimeters of #9 and #10 bars are 3.54 in. and 3.99 in., respectively. Then

$$u = \frac{V}{\Sigma_0 jd} = \frac{29,000}{[(1 \times 3.54) + (2 \times 3.99)] \times 0.875 \times 21.5} = 134 \text{ psi}$$

the bond unit stress. Since 134 psi is less than 210 psi, the bars are acceptable for both top and bottom reinforcing bars.

Step 9. The bottom bars are extended at least 6 in. into the supports. The top bars are extended to the quarter points of the clear spans on each side of the supports. See Fig. 7-2. There will be six #3 U-shaped stirrups at each end of the beam.

Problem 7-7-A. A fully continuous T-beam has a clear span of 20 ft 0 in. between faces of supports. The thickness of the slab is 5 in., and the live load is 100 psf. If the adjacent T-beams are 12 ft 0 in. on centers, let it be required to design the T-beams according to the following data:

$$f'_c = 2500 \text{ psi}$$

$$f_s = 18,000 \text{ psi}$$

$$f_c = 1125 \text{ psi}$$

$$v_c = 75 \text{ psi}$$

$$v = 200 \text{ psi}$$

$$u = \text{limited to 175 psi for top bars and 250 psi for others}$$

$$n = 12$$

CHAPTER 8

BEAMS REINFORCED
FOR COMPRESSION

8–1. Compression Reinforcement in Beams. When the cross-sectional dimensions of a beam are limited by architectural or structural conditions, it may be that there is an insufficient concrete area to provide for the compressive stresses. When this condition exists, steel reinforcement is placed in that part of the beam in which the stresses are compressive to supplement the concrete in resisting compressive stresses. Beams containing reinforcement for both tension and compression are frequently known as *double reinforced beams*. In order to hold the compression reinforcement in position, it should be anchored by ties or stirrups not less than $\frac{1}{4}$ in. in diameter and spaced not farther apart than 16 bar diameters or 48 tie diameters. Stirrups or ties shall be used over the distance where the compression steel is required. In addition to providing lateral support, these ties serve to resist diagonal tension.

8–2. Design Formulas for Double Reinforcement. The design of a double reinforced beam is begun by first computing M, the total maximum bending moment to be resisted. Next we compute M_1, the moment the beam would resist with balanced reinforcement on the tension side only. A_{s1} is the area of the steel required to resist the moment M_1. Then $M - M_1 = M_2$, the excess moment for which additional reinforcement must be added for both compression and tension. Referring to Fig. 8–1, we note that d is the depth of the beam from the uppermost fiber to the center of the tensile reinforcement and that d' is the distance from the center of the compression steel to the extreme concrete fiber in compression. Then the lever arm of the couple for M_2 is $d - d'$.

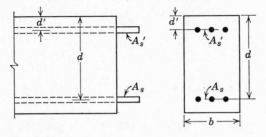

Double Reinforcement

FIG. 8–1

In the subsequent formulas for use in the design of double reinforced beams the notation is as follows:

b = the width of the beam, in inches.

d = the distance from the compression face of the
beam to the center of the tensile reinforcement,
in inches.

d' = the distance from the compression face of the
beam to the center of the compression reinforcement, in inches.

f_s = the allowable tensile unit stress in the steel, in
pounds per square inch.

$K, k,$ and j = coefficients found in Table 4–1 corresponding to
the stresses used.

M = the total bending moment to be developed, or
$M = M_1 + M_2$, in inch-pounds.

M_1 = the moment the beam can develop without compression reinforcement, in inch-pounds.

M_2 = the moment requiring additional tension and
compression reinforcement, in inch-pounds.

A_s = the total tensile reinforcement, or $A_s = A_{s1} +
A_{s2}$, in square inches.

A_{s1} = the area of tensile steel required by the moment
M_1, in square inches.

A_{s2} = the area of additional tensile steel to develop
M_2, in square inches.

A'_s = the area of the compression steel, in square
inches.

Having determined the total live and dead loads the beam will be required to support, M, the maximum bending moment, is computed as explained in Arts. 3–7 and 3–8.

In this type of problem the area of the cross section of the beam is limited. Assuming that the width is b and the effective depth d, M_1 is computed by the equation

$$M_1 = Kbd^2 \quad \text{or} \quad d = \sqrt{\frac{M_1}{Kb}} \quad \text{Formula (6), Art. 4–5}$$

Then

$$M_2 = M - M_1 \quad \text{(By definition; see notation.)}$$

The area of the tensile reinforcement, in accordance with M_1, is found by the equation

$$A_{s1} = \frac{M_1}{f_s j d}$$

This equation is, of course, merely a modified form of equation (7), Art. 4–5.

Next,

$$A_{s2} = \frac{M_2}{f_s(d - d')}$$

another form of equation (7), Art. 4–5, in which the lever arm of the couple is $d - d'$ instead of jd.

By definition given in the notation,

$$A_s = A_{s1} + A_{s2}$$

Finally, the area of the compression reinforcement is computed by the equation

$$A'_s = A_{s2} \times \frac{1 - k}{k - (d'/d)} \times \frac{n}{n - 1} \quad (18)$$

This equation does not give an exact area, but it is approximately correct and errs on the side of safety.

The *web reinforcement* for a beam with compression reinforcement is designed in the same manner as for beams with only tensile reinforcement. Stirrups or $\frac{1}{4}$-in. ties spaced 12 in. apart must be used to provide lateral support for the compression steel where such steel is required. These ties are similar to the ties used in tied reinforced concrete columns.

8-3. Design of a Beam with Compression Reinforcement.

Example. A fully continuous beam having a clear span of 20 ft 0 in. has a limited cross section of 12 x 18 in. The uniformly distributed load, not including the weight of the beam, is 44,500 lb. Design the beam in accordance with the following data:

$f_s = 20,000$ psi

$f_c = 1350$ psi

$v_c = 90$ psi

$v = 240$ psi

$u =$ limited to 210 psi for top bars and 300 psi for others

$n = 10$

SOLUTION. Referring to Table 4–1, we find that $K = 236$, $k = 0.403$, and $j = 0.866$. The weight of the beam is

$$\frac{12 \times 18}{144} \times 20 \times 150 = 4500 \text{ lb}$$

Then the total load on the beam, W, $= 44,500 + 4500 = 49,000$ lb. The maximum bending moment, $M = Wl/12$ (see Art. 3–7), or

$$M = \frac{49,000 \times 20 \times 12}{12} = 980,000 \text{ in-lb}$$

Assuming that the centers of the longitudinal upper and lower reinforcing bars are $2\frac{1}{2}$ in. from the upper and lower surfaces of the beam,

$$d = 18 - 2.5 = 15.5 \text{ in.} \quad \text{and} \quad d' = 2.5 \text{ in.}$$

(See Figs. 8–1 and 8–2.) Then

$$M_1 = Kbd^2 = 236 \times 12 \times 15.5^2 = 680,000 \text{ in-lb}$$

$$M_2 = M - M_1 = 980,000 - 680,000 = 300,000 \text{ in-lb}$$

$$A_{s1} = \frac{M_1}{f_s jd} = \frac{680,000}{20,000 \times 0.866 \times 15.5} = 2.53 \text{ sq in.}$$

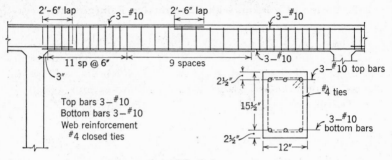

FIG. 8–2

$$A_{s2} = \frac{M_2}{f_s(d - d')} = \frac{300,000}{20,000(15.5 - 2.5)} = 1.15 \text{ sq in.}$$

$$A_s = A_{s1} + A_{s2} = 2.53 + 1.15 = 3.68 \text{ sq in.}$$

the area of the tensile reinforcement.

$$A'_s = A_{s2} \times \frac{1 - k}{k - (d'/d)} \times \frac{n}{n - 1} \qquad \text{Formula (18), Art. 8–2}$$

$$A'_s = 1.15 \times \frac{1 - 0.403}{0.403 - (2.5/15.5)} \times \frac{10}{10 - 1} = 3.16 \text{ sq in.}$$

the area of the compression reinforcement.

The area of the tensile reinforcement, A_s, is 3.68 sq in. Three #10 bars have an area of 3.81 sq in. and are acceptable.

The required compression reinforcement is A'_s, 3.16 sq in. Table 1–1 shows that 4-#8 bars have this area, but for simplicity 3-#10 are used for both top and bottom reinforcement.

Since the tensile reinforcement for the positive moment at the center of the span must serve as compression reinforcement for the negative moment at the support, it must be extended into the support to develop the compressive stress. To avoid the use of bars of great length or a great number of closely spaced bars (those of the column, beam, and girder) over the support, the bottom bars are lapped with those from the adjacent span, the lap starting at the face of the column. The length of the lap should be 24 bar diameters.

Note also that the tensile reinforcement for the negative moment at the support becomes the compression reinforcement for the positive moment at the center of the span. Hence the upper bars are lapped at the center of the span, the length of lap also conforming with the building code requirements. See Fig. 8-2.

The next step is to investigate the shearing stresses. Since the total load on the beam is 49,000 lb, $V = 49,000 \times \frac{1}{2}$, or 24,500 lb. Then

$$v = \frac{V}{jbd}$$ Formula (10), Art. 5-2

$$v = \frac{24,500}{0.875 \times 12 \times 15.5} = 150 \text{ psi}$$

As this stress exceeds 90 psi, web reinforcement is required.

$$v' = v - v_c \quad \text{or} \quad v' = 150 - 90 = 60 \text{ psi}$$

$$a = \frac{L}{2}\left(\frac{v'}{v}\right)$$ Formula (11), Art. 5-3

or $a = \dfrac{20}{2} \times \dfrac{60}{150} = 4$ ft 0 in., the theoretical distance from the supports in which web reinforcement is required. However, as explained in Art. 5-3, there are two other requirements that determine this distance. Thus

$$a = \frac{L}{5} + \frac{L}{16} = \frac{20}{5} + \frac{20}{16} = 4 + 1.25 = 5.25 \text{ ft}$$
or
$$a = \frac{L}{5} + \text{depth} = \frac{20}{5} + \frac{18}{12} = 4 + 1.5 = 5.5 \text{ ft}$$

Of the three distances, 4 ft, 5.25 ft, and 5.5 ft, the last 5.5 ft, is the greatest; hence the web reinforcement is used in this distance from each support.

In Art. 5-3 we find, also, that for this condition the web reinforcement must carry at least two thirds of the total shear. Thus $\frac{2}{3} \times 150 = 100$ psi.

Assume that #4 ties will be used for web reinforcement and that $f_v = 20,000$ psi. Then

$$A_v = 2 \times 0.2 = 0.4 \text{ sq in.}$$

$$s = \frac{A_v f_v}{v'b}$$ Formula (12), Art. 5-4

or

$$s = \frac{0.4 \times 20,000}{100 \times 12} = 6.7 \text{ in.}$$

the theoretical spacing of the ties. The maximum spacing, given in Art. 5–4, is $\frac{d - m}{2}$ or

$$s = \frac{15.5 - 2.5}{2} = 6.5 \text{ in.}$$

Therefore we accept #4 ties with 6-in. spacing for a distance of 5 ft 6 in. from the supports.

At the central part of the beam we will use #4 ties, with approximately 12-in. spacing, to hold the longitudinal bars in their proper positions.

The last step is to test the bond stress.

$$u = \frac{V}{\Sigma_0 jd} \qquad \text{Formula (13), Art. 5–6}$$

The perimeter of a #10 bar is 3.99 in., Table 1–1. Then

$$u = \frac{24,500}{(3 \times 3.99) \times 0.875 \times 15.5} = 151 \text{ psi}$$

the bond stress. This stress is less than 210 psi, the allowable for top bars; consequently the 3-#10 bars are acceptable. See Fig. 8–2.

Problem 8–3–A. The clear span of a fully continuous beam, 10 x 20 in. in cross section, is 17 ft 0 in. The uniformly distributed load, exclusive of the wieght of the beam, is 55,000 lb. Design the beam in accordance with the following data:

$$f_s = 20,000 \text{ psi}$$

$$f_c = 1350 \text{ psi}$$

$$v_c = 90 \text{ psi}$$

$$v = 240 \text{ psi}$$

$$u = 210 \text{ psi for top bars and} \\ 300 \text{ psi for others}$$

$$n = 10$$

CHAPTER 9

REINFORCED CONCRETE
FLOOR SYSTEMS

9–1. Floor Systems. In general, there are four types of reinforced concrete floor systems:

1. One-way solid slab and beam
2. Two-way solid slab and beam
3. Ribbed floors
4. Flat-slab or girderless floors, solid or ribbed

Each particular system has its distinct advantages, depending upon the spacing of the columns, the magnitude of the loads to be supported, length of spans, and the cost of construction. The floor area of a building and the purpose for which the building is to be used largely determine the position of the columns. In order to simplify the framing, the columns should be placed on the same center lines whenever possible. It is desirable also to repeat bays of the same dimensions, thus providing uniformity of floor construction. Although the arrangement of the plan of a building frequently determines the column spacing, approximately square bays are generally desirable. Column spacing of 20 ft, more or less, has proved to be most economical, but this depends, of course, on the type of floor construction to be used. When warranted by the size of the building operation, a number of trial designs may be made, and the most satisfactory arrangement with respect to economic considerations is thus selected.

9–2. Live Loads. In designing a floor, both the *live* and *dead* loads must be considered. The live loads are governed by the type of occupancy of the building. Minimum live loads for floors and roofs are given in the building regulations of the various cities, and

TABLE 9–1. MINIMUM LIVE LOADS

Occupation or Use	Live Load, Pounds per Square Foot
Apartments	
Private suites	40
Corridors	100
Rooms for assembly	100
Buildings for public assembly	
Corridors	100
Rooms with fixed seats	60
Rooms with movable seats	100
Dwellings	40
Factories	125
Garages	100
Hotels	
Private rooms	40
Public rooms	100
Office buildings	
Offices	80
Public spaces	100
Restaurants	100
Schools	
Assembly rooms	100
Classrooms with fixed seats	40
Classrooms with movable seats	80
Corridors	100
Stairways and firetowers	100
Stores	
First floors	125
Upper floors	75
Theatres	
Corridors, aisles, and lobbies	100
Fixed seats areas	60
Stage	150

the designer is required to make his computations in accordance with the loads specified. In general, live loads are due to human occupancy, furniture, equipment, stored materials, and, occasionally, movable partitions. For roofs, live loads consist of snow and wind loads.

Building codes differ in the magnitude of live loads to be used in the design of buildings. The architect or engineer must consult the code having jurisdiction and use the loads that are prescribed. Table 9–1 is a compilation of live loads assembled from various municipal building codes. It is presented here as a source of reference. Consult your own building code and note the minimum live loads you are required to use in your designs.

It should be noted that the loads given in the table are *minimum* values. Frequently a code requires that the floors for manufacturing buildings be designed to support possible loads of 3000 or 4000 lb covering an area of 3 or 4 sq ft at any position. Again, a building may be used for storage of some particularly heavy material. In such a case, the designer must ascertain the probable height to which the material will be stored, thus determining the live floor load to be used in the design. The probable maximum loads should always be estimated as accurately as possible.

Very often partitions in office buildings are moved from one position to another in accordance with the wishes of the occupant. Actually, partitions constitute dead loads, but, since their positions may be altered, it is customary to provide for such *movable partitions* by adding 15 to 20 psf to the live loads.

9–3. Dead Loads. In designing a floor slab, the actual weight of the materials of construction must be added to the live load to obtain what is sometimes called the *design load*. The weight of items, such as the floor covering or a suspended ceiling, are readily determined by referring to Table 9–2. The actual thickness of the structural slab, however, must be estimated to establish the allowance to make for its weight. The procedure is first to assume a slab thickness. Add together the weights of all the materials of the floor construction, including the allowance for the assumed slab, and the live load. This gives the design load, and the slab is then designed in accordance with this load. When the required depth of slab has been computed, it is compared with the depth originally assumed. If the depth made in determining the design load is smaller than the computed depth, a greater thickness is assumed and the process is repeated. It is not difficult to make rather accurate approximations of slab thicknesses after the designer has had experience. Safe load tables, such as Table 9–5, are convenient references for determining the allowance to be made for the weight of the slab.

TABLE 9–2.   WEIGHTS OF BUILDING MATERIALS

FLOORS

Materials	Pounds per Square Foot
Board flooring, per inch of thickness	3
Granolithic flooring, per inch of thickness	12
Floor tile, per inch of thickness	10
Asphalt mastic, per inch of thickness	12
Wood block, per inch of thickness	4
Cinder-concrete fill, per inch of thickness	6
Stone-concrete slab, per inch of thickness	12
Slag-concrete slab, per inch of thickness	10
Ceiling, suspended, metal lath and plaster	10
Ceiling, pressed steel	2

ROOFS

Materials	Pounds per Square Foot
Three-ply roofing felt and gravel	$5\frac{1}{2}$
Five-ply roofing felt and gravel	$6\frac{1}{2}$
Roofing tile, cement	15 to 20
Roofing tile, clay, shingle type	12 to 14
Roofing tile, Spanish	8 to 10
Slate, $\frac{1}{4}$ in. thick	$9\frac{1}{2}$
Slate, $\frac{3}{8}$ in. thick	$14\frac{1}{2}$
2 in. Book tile	12
Sheathing, wood, 1 in. thick	3
Skylight, $\frac{3}{8}$ in. glass in galvanized iron frame	$7\frac{1}{2}$

TABLE 9–2.   WEIGHTS OF BUILDING MATERIALS (*Continued*)

WALLS AND PARTITIONS

Materials	Pounds per Square Foot
8 in. Brick wall	80
12 in. Brick wall	120
17 in. Brick wall	160
4 in. Brick, 8 in. tile backing	75
9 in. Brick, 4 in. tile backing	100
8 in. Wall tile	35
12 in. Wall tile	45
3 in. Clay-tile partition	18
4 in. Clay-tile partition	19
6 in. Clay-tile partition	25
4 in. Glass-block	18
3 in. Gypsum-block partition	11
4 in. Gypsum-block partition	13
2 in. Solid plaster partition	20
4 in. Stud partition, plastered both sides	22
Steel sash, glazed	10

MASONRY

Materials	Pounds per Cubic Foot
Ashlar masonry, granite	165
Ashlar masonry, limestone	160
Ashlar masonry, sandstone	140
Brick masonry, common	120
Brick masonry, pressed	140
Concrete, plain stone	145
Concrete, reinforced stone	150
Concrete, cinder	110
Rubble masonry, limestone	150
Rubble masonry, sandstone	130

The actual weight of concrete depends principally upon the kind of aggregate that is used. Usually 150 lb per cu ft is taken as the weight of stone concrete. For estimating the weight of slabs, it is convenient to assume the weight to be 144 lb per cu ft. In this case, a layer of concrete 1 ft square and 1 in. thick weighs 12 lb. Then, if we assume the slab to be 4 in. thick, the weight allowance is 4 × 12, or 48 psf. Similarly a 5-in. slab weighs 60 psf, etc. These weights, however, are only approximate, and the computed thickness must always be compared with the assumed thickness to see that an ample weight is provided for.

9–4. One-Way Slabs. Probably the most commonly used type of reinforced concrete floor construction consists of a solid slab supported by two parallel beams, the beams framing into girders, and the girders in turn framing into columns. The reinforcement in the slab runs in *one direction only*, from beam to beam, hence the slab is known as a *one-way slab* or *one-way solid slab*. The slab is of uniform thickness, and there is no filler material. The number of beams in a panel depends upon the column spacing and the live load to be supported. The beams are spaced uniformly and generally frame into the girders at the center, third, or quarter points. This type of framing is called the *beam-and-girder floor*. It is readily constructed and the formwork is simple. The one-way solid slab is economical for medium and heavy live loads for comparatively short spans, 6 to 12 ft long. For light live loads, 40 to 60 psf, the spans may be increased, but long spans for one-way slabs result in comparatively large dead loads.

A beam-and-girder floor with the beams framing into the girder at the third points is illustrated in Fig. 9–1. To design the slab, a strip 12 in. wide is considered as indicated by the hatched area. The design of the slab is simply the design of a rectangular beam 12 in. wide and having a uniformly distributed load. The effective depth and the tensile steel reinforcement are computed for the 12-in. strip of slab, and the same spacing of bars is continued for the entire length of the slab. In addition to the tensile reinforcement in the slab, #3 bars are run parallel to the beams. These are known as *temperature bars*, their size and spacing depending on the slab thickness. They serve to provide against the effect of shrinkage and changes in temperature and also to distribute possible load concentrations over larger areas.

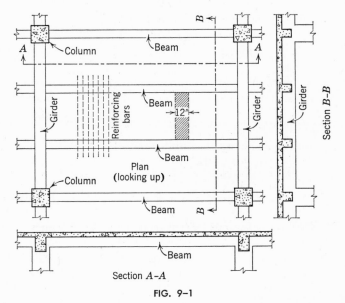

Section *A-A*

FIG. 9-1

Web reinforcement is not practicable in slabs, and v, the shearing unit stress, must be kept within v_c, as given in Table 4-2. For slabs of short spans with large loads, the shearing stresses may be greater than the allowable values. For such a condition, the depth of the slab must be increased, thereby reducing the value of v. For slabs having average loads and span lengths, it will be found that the shearing unit stress is invariably well within the allowable values.

A stipulation contained in many building codes requires that the minimum thickness of solid slabs be $\frac{1}{32}$ of the clear distance between supports. Sometimes the codes require a minimum thickness $\frac{1}{30}$ of the span for floor slabs and $\frac{1}{32}$ of the span for roof slabs.

9-5. Shrinkage and Temperature Reinforcement. Floor and roof slabs having one-way reinforcement must be reinforced for shrinkage and temperature stresses by reinforcing bars placed at right angles to the main tensile reinforcement. The minimum ratios of shrinkage and temperature reinforcement to the concrete area are given in Table 9-3. In no case shall these reinforcing bars be placed farther apart than five times the slab thickness nor more than 18 in.

Example. Determine the temperature reinforcement required for a 4-in. floor slab when deformed bars are used.

SOLUTION. Consider the concrete floor area to be a strip 12 in. wide; its cross-sectional area then is 4 x 12, or 48 sq in. In accordance with Table 9–3, the area of temperature reinforcement for this 12-in. strip is 0.002 × 48 or 0.096 sq in. For a strip 1 in. wide, the required area is (0.096 ÷ 12) sq in. Let us assume that #3 bars are to be used. By Table 1–1 we find that the area of a #3 bar is 0.11 sq in. Then the number of inches of width required to give 0.11 sq in. is $0.11 \times \dfrac{12}{0.096}$ or 13.7, say 13.5 in. The temperature reinforcement, therefore, will be spaced 13.5 in. on centers.

TABLE 9–3.   SHRINKAGE AND TEMPERATURE REINFORCEMENT *

Minimum Ratios of Reinforcement Area to Concrete Area

Slabs where plain bars are used	0.0025
Slabs where deformed bars are used	0.0020
Slabs where wire fabric is used, having welded intersections not farther apart in the direction of stress than 12 in.	0.0018

* Taken by permission from *Building Code Requirements for Reinforced Concrete*, published by the American Concrete Institute.

Problem 9–5–A. What temperature reinforcement should be used for a 5-in. floor slab when plain bars are used?

Problem 9–5–B. #4 deformed bars are to be used for temperature reinforcement for a $9\frac{1}{2}$-in. solid floor slab. Determine their spacing.

9–6. Area of Tensile Reinforcement in Slabs. In floor and roof slabs the maximum spacing of the main tensile reinforcement is three times the slab thickness. In designing the slab, A_s, the area of the tensile reinforcement, is computed for a strip of slab 12 in. wide. Table 9–4 gives the spacings of bars of various sizes *for slabs 12 in. wide.* This table is of great convenience in selecting the proper reinforcement after A_s has been computed.

Example. Let us assume that A_s, the area of the tensile reinforcement for a strip of slab 12 in. wide, has been computed and

TABLE 9-4. AREAS OF BARS IN REINFORCED CONCRETE SLABS
PER FOOT OF WIDTH

Areas of Bars in Square Inches

Spacing, Inches	#2	#3	#4	#5	#6	#7	#8	#9	#10	#11
3	0.20	0.44	0.79	1.23	1.77	2.41	3.14	4.00		
$3\frac{1}{2}$	0.17	0.38	0.67	1.05	1.51	2.06	2.69	3.43	4.36	
4	0.15	0.33	0.59	0.92	1.33	1.80	2.36	3.00	3.81	4.68
$4\frac{1}{2}$	0.13	0.29	0.52	0.82	1.18	1.60	2.09	2.67	3.39	4.16
5	0.12	0.26	0.47	0.74	1.06	1.44	1.88	2.40	3.05	3.74
$5\frac{1}{2}$	0.11	0.24	0.43	0.67	0.96	1.31	1.71	2.18	2.77	3.40
6	0.10	0.22	0.39	0.61	0.88	1.20	1.57	2.00	2.54	3.12
$6\frac{1}{2}$	0.09	0.20	0.36	0.57	0.82	1.11	1.45	1.85	2.35	2.88
7	0.08	0.19	0.34	0.53	0.76	1.03	1.35	1.71	2.18	2.67
$7\frac{1}{2}$	0.08	0.18	0.31	0.49	0.71	0.96	1.26	1.60	2.03	2.50
8	0.07	0.17	0.29	0.46	0.66	0.90	1.18	1.50	1.91	2.34
$8\frac{1}{2}$	0.07	0.16	0.28	0.43	0.62	0.85	1.11	1.41	1.79	2.20
9	0.07	0.15	0.26	0.41	0.59	0.80	1.05	1.33	1.69	2.08
$9\frac{1}{2}$	0.06	0.14	0.25	0.39	0.56	0.76	0.99	1.26	1.60	1.97
10	0.06	0.13	0.24	0.37	0.53	0.72	0.94	1.20	1.52	1.87
11	0.05	0.12	0.21	0.33	0.48	0.66	0.86	1.09	1.39	1.70
12	0.05	0.11	0.19	0.31	0.44	0.60	0.78	1.00	1.27	1.56

found to be 0.43 sq in. Assuming that we wish to use #4 bars,
what distance should they be placed on centers?

SOLUTION. By referring to Table 1–1, it is found that a #4 bar
has an area of 0.2 sq in. If the area of reinforcement required for
a 12-in. width is 0.43 sq in., the required area of a strip 1 in. wide is
0.43 ÷ 12. The number of inches necessary to give 0.2 sq in., the
area of one #4 bar, is

$$0.2 \times \frac{12}{0.43} = 5.5$$

Therefore $5\frac{1}{2}$ in. is the required spacing of the #4 bars.

Without computations, we might have referred to Table 9–4 and obtained the same result. Suppose, for instance, we had decided to use #5 bars. Instantly the table gives us a spacing of $8\frac{1}{2}$ in. How convenient it is!

Problem 9–6–A. The area of tensile reinforcement required for a 12-in. wide strip of slab is 0.22 sq in. If #3 bars are used, compute their distance on centers and check the result with Table 9–4.

9–7. Design Steps for a One-Way Solid Slab.

A solid slab with one-way reinforcement is designed by the consideration of an imaginary strip of slab 12 in. wide, as indicated in Fig. 9–1. The problem then is merely the design of a rectangular beam having a width of 12 in. Therefore, the design steps for a rectangular beam, given in Art. 6–3, may be used for the design of a slab with one-way reinforcement. Web reinforcement, however, is never used in one-way slabs.

As previously explained, before proceeding with the computations it is necessary to assume a depth of slab in order to determine the dead load. In general, the depth is dependent on the length of span and the magnitude of the superimposed load. A rough rule, however, for approximating the depth is to allow 0.4 to 0.5 in. of depth for each foot of span. To the assumed weight of slab is added any other dead loads such as floor finish or suspended ceiling and the live load, thus determining the design load in pounds per square foot of floor area.

Where slabs of uniform thickness are *built integrally* with their supports, the span length may be taken as the *clear distance between faces of supports*, the width of support being neglected. Since the beams and slabs are poured at one time for the usual beam-and-girder type of floor, this condition generally exists for one-way slabs. Very often, however, it is convenient to consider the span length of slabs to be the distance from center to center of beams. This results in a conservative design and errs on the side of safety.

If a monolithic finish, 1 in. or more thick, is added to the slab, it must not be included as part of the effective depth.

When solid slabs are used with beam-and-girder construction, the minimum thickness of floor slabs is 3.5 in., and 3 in. is the limiting thickness of roof slabs. These are the usual limitations, but the local building regulations should always be consulted.

9–8. Design of a One-Way Solid Slab. The following illustrative problem is typical of those that occur constantly in practice. The "steps" enumerated are given in Art. 6–3, the design procedure for rectangular beams.

Example. The floor construction of a building is the beam-and-girder system with a one-way solid slab, as illustrated in Fig. 9–1. Let it be required to design the slab for an interior clear span of 12 ft 0 in. in accordance with the following data: live load, 100 psf; floor finish, 25 psf; suspended plaster ceiling and movable partitions. The minimum slab thickness is $\frac{1}{30}$ × span. Design specifications:

$$f'_c = 3000 \text{ psi}$$
$$f_s = 20,000 \text{ psi}$$
$$f_c = 1350 \text{ psi}$$
$$v_c = \text{limited to 90 psi}$$
$$u = \text{limited to 300 psi}$$
$$n = 10$$

SOLUTION. Referring to Table 4–1, we find the following formula coefficients: $K = 236$, $k = 0.403$, $j = 0.866$, and $p = 0.0136$.

Step 1. Determining the design load:

live load	= 100	
floor finish	= 25	
suspended ceiling	= 10	(Table 9–2)
movable partitions	= 15	(Art. 9–2)

total superimposed load = 150 psf

The minimum slab thickness for a clear span of 12 ft is, by data, (12 × 12) ÷ 30 = 4.8 in., say 5 in. Assuming the thickness to be 0.4 in. for each foot of span, 0.4 × 12 = 4.8 in. Consequently, to estimate the weight of the slab, assume the depth to be 5 in. Then, at 12 lb per inch of thickness, 12 × 5 = 60 lb, the estimated weight per square foot of floor area.

Thus, the design load is 150 + 60, or 210 psf. Since the imaginary strip of slab is 12 in. in width and 12 ft in length, the total uniformly distributed load, $W = 210 \times 12 = 2520$ lb.

Step 2. Maximum shear. The maximum vertical shear,

$$V = \tfrac{1}{2} \times 2520 = 1260 \text{ lb}$$

Step 3. Maximum bending moment. This being an interior span, the slab is fully continuous and the maximum positive and negative bending moments are each $M = \dfrac{Wl}{12}$ (Art. 3–7). Then

$$M = \frac{2520 \times 12 \times 12}{12} = 30{,}240 \text{ in-lb}$$

Step 4. Depth of slab. The effective depth of the slab is found by formula (6), Art. 4–5.

$$d = \sqrt{\frac{M}{Kb}} = \sqrt{\frac{30{,}240}{236 \times 12}} = 3.3 \text{ in.}$$

If we assume that one half the thickness of the tensile reinforcement is 0.25 in. and that there is 0.75 in. of fireproofing below the bars, the total depth of the slab will be $3.3 + 0.25 + 0.75 = 4.3$ in., say 5 in. Note that this is the thickness assumed in estimating the weight of the slab in Step 1. Since the total depth is 5 in., the effective depth will be $5 - (0.25 + 0.75)$, or $d = 4$ in.

Step 5. Area of tensile reinforcement. By formula (7), Art. 4–5,

$$A_s = \frac{M}{f_s jd} = \frac{30{,}240}{20{,}000 \times 0.866 \times 4.0} = 0.44 \text{ sq in.}$$

the area of the tensile reinforcement in a 12-in. wide strip of slab. Referring to Table 9–4, select #4 bars spaced $5\tfrac{1}{2}$ in. on centers. This selection is provisional; Step 9 will determine whether or not these bars are acceptable. The alternate bars will be bent, as indicated in Fig. 9–2. Another system would be to place straight bars at the bottom of the slab for the positive moment with other straight bars at the top of the slab over the supports for the negative moment. To avoid confusion, the reinforcement for the adjacent spans is not shown in Fig. 9–2. If bent bars are used, bent bars from the adjoining spans are extended over the supports, thus providing the same steel area for both positive and negative bending moments.

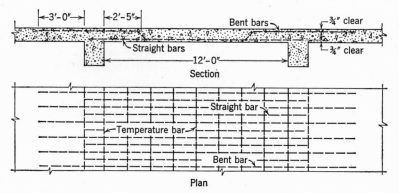

Section

Plan

FIG. 9–2

Step 6. Shearing unit stress. By formula (10), Art. 5–2,

$$v = \frac{V}{jbd} = \frac{1260}{0.875 \times 12 \times 4} = 30 \text{ psi}$$

This shearing unit stress is within the 90 psi permitted, hence web reinforcement is not required. As stirrups are not practical in slabs, it would be necessary to increase the depth of the slab if the shearing unit stress had exceeded the allowable. This is seldom necessary.

Steps 7 and 8. These steps do not apply to slabs.

Step 9. Bond stress. The perimeter of a #4 bar is found in Table 1–1 to be 1.57 in. Since the spacing of the bars is $5\frac{1}{2}$ in., the number of bars in each 12-in. wide strip of slab is 12/5.5, or 2.18. Determining the bond stress by formula (13), Art. 5–6,

$$u = \frac{V}{\Sigma_0 jd} = \frac{1260}{(2.18 \times 1.57) \times 0.875 \times 4} = 105 \text{ psi}$$

This unit bond stress does not exceed 300 psi, the limiting value, and thus the #4 bars, spaced $5\frac{1}{2}$ in. on centers, are accepted.

Step 10. Bends and laps. The slab is fully continuous and if straight bars are not employed, as noted in Step 5, alternate bars are bent up at the fifth points of span and extended over the supports to the fourth points of the adjacent spans. The remaining bars are straight, placed in the bottom of the slab, and extended 6 in. into the supports or made continuous. In this example $\frac{3}{4}$ in.

of concrete has been used for fireproofing. This is the minimum thickness, and some codes require a full inch. In any case, the fireproofing is taken as the full distance from the face of the bar. Temperature bars are run at right angles to the main tensile reinforcement. As required in accordance with Table 9–3, $12 \times 5 \times 0.002 = 0.12$ sq in. Therefore, referring to Table 9–4, we shall use #3 bars, 11 in. on centers for the temperature reinforcement.

Problem 9–8–A. Design a one-way solid slab for an interior clear span of 11 ft 0 in. The live load is 60 psf, the floor finish is 30 psf, and there is a suspended plaster ceiling. Specification data:

$$f'_c = 2500 \text{ psi}$$
$$f_s = 20,000 \text{ psi}$$
$$f_c = 1125 \text{ psi}$$
$$v_c = \text{limited to 75 psi}$$
$$u = \text{limited to 250 psi}$$
$$n = 12$$

9–9. Distribution of Bars in One-Way Slabs. For fully continuous slabs, the bending moments at the center of the span and at the support are equal; hence there should be the same amount of tensile reinforcement at each point. This may be accomplished by bending up alternate bars at the fifth points of the span and extending them over the supports to the quarter points of the adjacent spans. The remaining bars are straight, placed in the bottom of the slab, and continued for several spans if desired. At their terminations they should extend at least 6 in. into the supports.

The illustrative problem in Art. 9–8 discussed an interior span, a fully continuous slab. For end spans, the slabs are semicontinuous, the bending moment being greater, $Wl/10$. Although not theoretically exact, many designers accept the same depth of slab that is used for the interior spans but add 20% reinforcement. To be exact, the end spans should have their depths determined in accordance with the bending moment. The reinforcing bars at the top termination of end spans should be hooked.

9–10. Safe Load Table for One-Way Slabs. A convenient method of determining the depth of slabs and the required reinforcement is by use of Table 9–5. This table has been computed for the following unit stresses, $f_s = 20,000$ psi, $f_c = 1350$ psi, $n = 10$, and the fireproofing is $\frac{3}{4}$ in. thick. Note that the thickness of the slab, given in the first column, is the *total* thickness, including the fireproofing. Attention is also called to the fact that the loads given are the safe *superimposed* loads and do not include the weight of the slab.

Example. By use of Table 9–5, determine the depth of a one-way slab and the longitudinal tensile reinforcement for an end span of 9 ft 6 in., the superimposed load being 180 psf. Design data: $f_s = 20,000$ psi, $f_c = 1350$ psi, and $n = 10$.

SOLUTION. Referring to Table 9–5, we see that a slab having a total thickness of 4 in., with #4 bars spaced 5 in. on centers, will support a superimposed load of 181 psf for an end span of 9 ft 6 in. and is accepted.

Now let us verify this design.

Assuming the total depth of the slab to be 4 in.,

$$
\begin{aligned}
\text{superimposed load} &= 180 \\
\text{weight of slab} = \tfrac{4}{12} \times 150 &= 50 \\
\hline
\text{design load} &= 230 \text{ psf}
\end{aligned}
$$

Total load on a 12-in. wide strip of slab $= 230 \times 9.5 = 2158$ lb $= W$.

$$
M = \frac{Wl}{10} = \frac{2158 \times 9.5 \times 12}{10} = 24,900 \text{ in-lb}
$$

the maximum bending moment.

For the stresses given as specification data, $K = 236$ and $j = 0.866$, Table 4–1. Then,

$$
d = \sqrt{\frac{M}{Kb}} = \sqrt{\frac{24,900}{236 \times 12}} = \sqrt{8.75} = 2.96 \text{ in.}
$$

the effective depth. Assuming one half a bar diameter to be 0.25 in. and that there will be 0.75 in. clear fireproofing, $2.96 + 0.25 + 0.75 = 3.96$ in., say 4 in. the total thickness of the slab. Hence $4 - (0.25 + 0.75) = 3$ in., the effective depth.

$$
A_s = \frac{M}{f_s j d} = \frac{24,900}{20,000 \times 0.866 \times 3} = 0.48 \text{ sq in.}
$$

TABLE 9-5. SAFE LOADS FOR CONCRETE SLABS—ONE-WAY REINFORCEMENT

($f_s = 20,000$ psi, $f_c = 1350$ psi, $n = 10$, $\frac{3}{4}''$ clear protection, approximate balanced reinforcing)

Safe Superimposed Load in Pounds per Square Foot — Span in Feet and Inches

Total Slab Thickness (in.)	Size (#)	Spacing (in.)	Area (in.²)	Weight of Slab (psf)	Condition of Continuity of Span	4-0	4-6	5-0	5-6	6-0	6-6	7-0	7-6	8-0	8-6	9-0	9-6	10-0	10-6	11-0	11-6	12-0	12-6	13-0	13-6	14-0
3	4	7	0.34	38	Simple	433	334	264	211	181	140	116	96	80	66	55										
					End			339	273	233	184	154	129	109	92	78										
					Interior				336	276	229	193	163	139	118	101										
3½	4	6	0.40	44	Simple				336	276	228	191	160	136	115	98	84	71	60							
					End						296	250	211	181	155	133	116	100	86							
					Interior							308	262	226	195	169	148	129	112							
4	4	5	0.48	50	Simple							290	246	210	180	156	135	116	101	88	76	65				
					End								320	275	237	208	181	158	139	122	107	94				
					Interior									340	294	259	228	199	176	157	139	123				
4½	5	6½	0.57	56	Simple									292	253	220	192	167	146	129	113	99	87	76	66	
					End										330	288	254	222	196	175	155	148	123	109	97	
					Interior												316	278	247	222	198	176	158	142	127	

Note: Slabs for loads to left of heavy line do not exceed $L/30$ and should be used for floor slabs.

Slabs for loads to right of heavy line do not exceed $L/36$ and may be used for roof slabs.

Config →	A	B	C	D	E	F
	63	69	75	81	88	94
	0.62	0.74	0.83	0.88	0.96	1.06
	6	5	4½	6	5½	5
	5	5	5	6	6	6
	5	5½	6	6½	7	7½
Simple / End / Interior	81 / 117 / 153	121 / 170 / 216	160 / 219 / 277	197 / 267 / 336	243 / 326	297
Simple / End / Interior	92 / 131 / 169	135 / 186 / 237	177 / 240 / 299	219 / 294	268	
Simple / End / Interior	104 / 146 / 197	151 / 206 / 261	197 / 265 / 333	247 / 321		
Simple / End / Interior	118 / 163 / 219	169 / 216 / 288	219 / 292	268		
Simple / End / Interior	133 / 182 / 231	189 / 253 / 318	245 / 325			
Simple / End / Interior	151 / 205 / 258	212 / 282 / 352	273			
Simple / End / Interior	171 / 229 / 288	238 / 315	305			
Simple / End / Interior	193 / 257 / 321	269				
Simple / End / Interior	219 / 289	303				
Simple / End / Interior	249 / 327					
Simple / End / Interior	285					

the area of reinforcement for a 12-in. wide strip of slab. Referring to Table 9–4, accept #4 bars with 5 in. spacing. This is the same design found by use of the table.

Table 9–5 is based on an approximate balanced reinforcement, which means that both the concrete and steel are stressed to their allowable stresses. In the first example under Art. 9–8 the depth of slab was arbitrarily increased to 5 in. in compliance with the specification requirement. Table 9–5 shows that a $4\frac{1}{2}$-in. slab with #5 bars at $6\frac{1}{2}$-in. spacing will support a superimposed load of 176 lb; the superimposed load in the example is only 150 lb but the $4\frac{1}{2}$-in. slab is less than $L/30$. Note the heavy line in Table 9–5. Slabs for loads to the left of this line do not exceed $\frac{1}{30}$ of the span and should be used for floor slabs. Slabs for loads to the right of this line may be used for roofs. This table is of particular convenience in making preliminary panel layouts or in approximating the depths of slabs to estimate their weight.

9–11. Two-Way Slabs. Slabs Supported on Four Sides.

When a floor panel is square, or nearly so, having beams or walls on four sides, it is generally economical to use two sets of reinforcing bars placed at right angles to each other. These bars in two directions transfer the loads to the four supporting beams or walls. Slabs thus reinforced are known as *two-way slabs* or *slabs supported on four sides*.

Although economical with respect to saving material, the design of such slabs presents certain complications. Consider the rectangular slab, shown in Fig. 9–3(a), supported on four beams at the sides. Imagine that there are two 12-in. wide strips, X and Y, parallel to the long and short sides and that there is a uniformly distributed load of w psf on the entire slab area. We know that the deflection of the area A, at the intersection of the two strips, must be the same for each strip. The deflection curves for the two strips are shown adjacent to the sides of the slab. The two deflections, Δ_X and Δ_Y for the area A must be equal. Since the strips have unequal lengths, the loads on the two strips cannot be equal, and this leads to a complicated distribution of loads which varies from point to point. In the case of a rectangular panel with one side longer than the other a greater load must be carried in the shorter span, S, than in the longer span, L. The magnitude of

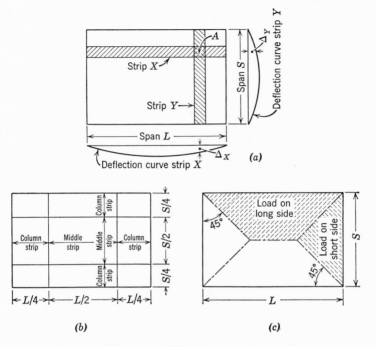

FIG. 9–3

load transmitted in each direction depends not only on the relative lengths of the sides of the slab but also on the conditions of continuity that occur at the four sides.

The load distribution is further complicated by the fact that no strip can act independently from adjacent strips, as would be assumed in computing deflections. Tests have shown that this interaction of adjacent strips reduces the bending moments obtained by considering each individual pair of intersecting strips. Because of these complications, most codes refrain from giving rules for the apportioning of loads to the long and short spans but give, instead, moment coefficients which are to be used with the total load. See Table 9–6.

When the longer span, L, becomes more than twice as large as the shorter span, S, almost no load is carried in the longer direction; hence the slab becomes a one-way slab of span S.

TABLE 9–6.   MOMENT COEFFICIENTS FOR TWO-WAY SLABS *

Moments	Short Span						Long Span, All Values of m
	Values of m						
	1.0	0.9	0.8	0.7	0.6	0.5 and Less	
Case 1—Interior panels							
Negative moment at—							
Continuous edge	0.033	0.040	0.048	0.055	0.063	0.083	0.033
Discontinuous edge	—	—	—	—	—	—	—
Positive moment at midspan	0.025	0.030	0.036	0.041	0.047	0.062	0.025
Case 2—One edge discontinuous							
Negative moment at—							
Continuous edge	0.041	0.048	0.055	0.062	0.069	0.085	0.041
Discontinuous edge	0.021	0.024	0.027	0.031	0.035	0.042	0.021
Positive moment at midspan	0.031	0.036	0.041	0.047	0.052	0.064	0.031
Case 3—Two edges discontinuous							
Negative moment at—							
Continuous edge	0.049	0.057	0.064	0.071	0.078	0.090	0.049
Discontinuous edge	0.025	0.028	0.032	0.036	0.039	0.045	0.025
Positive moment at midspan	0.037	0.043	0.048	0.054	0.059	0.068	0.037
Case 4—Three edges discontinuous							
Negative moment at—							
Continuous edge	0.058	0.066	0.074	0.082	0.090	0.098	0.058
Discontinuous edge	0.029	0.033	0.037	0.041	0.045	0.049	0.029
Positive moment at midspan	0.044	0.050	0.056	0.062	0.068	0.074	0.044
Case 5—Four edges discontinuous							
Negative moment at—							
Continuous edge	—	—	—	—	—	—	—
Discontinuous edge	0.033	0.038	0.043	0.047	0.053	0.055	0.033
Positive moment at midspan	0.050	0.057	0.064	0.072	0.080	0.083	0.050

* Reproduced by permission of the American Concrete Institute from *Building Code Requirements for Reinforced Concrete* (A.C.I. 318-56).

The American Concrete Institute, in their *Building Code Requirements for Reinforced Concrete*, gives two methods that may be used in the design of two-way slabs. "Method 2" is employed in the illustrative example that follows. The terms used in following the procedure are

C = the moment coefficient for two-way slabs, as given in Table 9–6.

m = the ratio of short span to long spans, S/L.

S = the length of short span.

w = the total uniform load in pounds per square foot.

In the design of a two-way slab two strips of floor are considered. One is the *middle strip*, one half the panel in width, symmetrical about the panel center line, and extending through the panel in the direction in which the moments are considered. The other is the *column strip*, one half the panel in width and occupying the two quarter-panel areas outside the middle strip. These strips are shown in Fig. 9–3(*b*).

The coefficients for the bending moments for the middle strips of the slab are given in Table 9–6. The moments are computed by the formula

$$M = CwS^2$$

In computing the moments in the column strips, the code permits a reduction of two thirds of the corresponding moments in the middle strip. The five "cases" in the table relate to conditions of continuity at the edges of the panel. Note that in Case 5, a panel in which all four edges are discontinuous, a negative bending moment over the supports must be considered.

The loads on the supporting beams may be computed on the assumption that the load is distributed as shown in Fig. 9–3(*c*). The bending moments on the beams may be determined, approximately, by using an equivalent load per linear foot of beam as follows:

$$\text{for the short span} = \frac{wS}{3}$$

$$\text{for the long span} = \frac{wS}{3} \times \frac{3 - m^2}{2}$$

The shearing stresses in the slab may be computed on the assumption that the load on the panel is distributed to the supports in the same manner.

The code further specifies that the slab thickness be not less than 4 in. nor less than the perimeter of the slab divided by 180. The spacing of the reinforcement shall be not more than three times the slab thickness and the ratio of reinforcement shall be at least 0.0025.

When two sets of reinforcing bars are used, one set is placed directly on the other. It is advantageous to place the bars in the short direction, carrying the greater load, under the longer bars.

9-12. Design of a Two-Way Slab. In designing a two-way slab, strips of slab 12 in. wide are considered, one running in the long and one in the short direction. As the strips are actually rectangular beams, the design steps outlined in Art. 6-3 will be followed.

Example. An interior floor panel having dimensions of $L = 20$ ft and $S = 16$ ft is subjected to a live load of 60 psf. The floor finish weighs 25 psf. The end conditions are fully continuous in both directions. Design the slab for two-way reinforcement in accordance with the following specifications:

$$f_s = 20,000 \text{ psi}$$

$$f_c = 1350 \text{ psi}$$

$$v = \text{limited to 90 psi}$$

$$u = \text{limited to 300 psi}$$

$$n = 10$$

SOLUTION. *Step 1. Loads.* Referring to Table 4-1, $K = 236$, $j = 0.866$, and $p = 0.0136$. The minimum slab thickness is 4 in., or the panel perimeter divided by 180. The perimeter is $2(16 + 20) = 72$ ft, or 864 in. Thus $\frac{864}{180} = 4.8$ in., say 5 in. Then the loads are

live load	=	60
floor finish	=	25
weight of slab, $\frac{5}{12} \times 150 =$		63
		---
total		148 psf, the value of w

Step 2. Maximum shear. In this problem, $m = S/L$ or $m = \frac{16}{20} = 0.80$. The approximate uniformly distributed loads on the supporting beams are the following:

For the short span, slab shear in the long direction, $=$

$$\frac{wS}{3} = \frac{148 \times 16}{3} = 791 \text{ lb per linear ft}$$

For the long span, slab shear in the short direction, =

$$\frac{wS}{3} \times \frac{3 - m^2}{2} = \frac{148 \times 16}{3} \times \frac{3 - 0.8^2}{2} = 932 \text{ lb per linear ft}$$

Step 3. Maximum bending moments. Since the slab is fully continuous at all edges, an interior panel, the bending moment coefficients are given in Case 1 of Table 9–6. As found in Step 2, $m = 0.80$. Then $M = CwS^2$.

Short span,

negative moment $M = 0.048 \times 148 \times 16^2 = 1820$ ft-lb
$= 21,800$ in-lb

positive moment $M = 0.036 \times 148 \times 16^2 = 1365$ ft-lb
$= 16,400$ in-lb

Long span,

negative moment $M = 0.033 \times 148 \times 16^2 = 1250$ ft-lb
$= 15,000$ in-lb

positive moment $M = 0.025 \times 148 \times 16^2 = 948$ ft-lb
$= 11,300$ in-lb

Step 4. Depth of slab. For the short span, the negative moment is the greater, 21,800 in-lb, $d = \sqrt{\dfrac{M}{Kb}}$. Formula (6), Art. 4–5,

$$d = \sqrt{\frac{21,800}{236 \times 12}} = 2.78 \text{ in.}$$

the required effective depth. For the long span

$$d = \sqrt{\frac{15,000}{236 \times 12}} = 2.32 \text{ in.}$$

the required effective depth.

Assuming the bars for the short direction to be #4 placed in the upper layer over the supports and that the fireproofing is $\frac{3}{4}$ in., the effective depth, if the total thickness of the slab is 5 in., is $5 - [0.75 + (\frac{1}{2} \times 0.5)] = 4$ in. Note that this distance is greater than the 2.78 in. required. For the long direction, the reinforcing bars will be in the lower layer over the supports where they cross the bars for the short direction. Again assuming the bars to be #4, $5 - [0.75 + 0.5 + (\frac{1}{2} \times 0.5)] = 3.5$ in., the effective depth in the long direction. This depth also is greater than the 2.32 in. required. Thus we see that the 5-in. total slab thickness assumed in Step 1 is acceptable.

Step 5. Area of tensile steel. The required area of tensile reinforcement, for each 12-in. wide middle strip of slab is found by

$$A_s = \frac{M}{f_s jd} \qquad \text{Formula (7), Art. 4–5}$$

For the short direction,

$$\text{negative } A_s = \frac{21,800}{20,000 \times 0.866 \times 4} = 0.314 \text{ sq in.}$$

Accept #4 bars spaced $7\frac{1}{2}$ in. on centers (Table 9–4).

$$\text{positive } A_s = \frac{16,400}{20,000 \times 0.866 \times 4} = 0.236 \text{ sq in.}$$

Accept #4 bars spaced 10 in. on centers (Table 9–4).
For the long direction,

$$\text{negative } A_s = \frac{15,000}{20,000 \times 0.866 \times 3.5} = 0.248 \text{ sq in.}$$

Accept #4 bars spaced $9\frac{1}{2}$ in. on centers (Table 9–4).

$$\text{positive } A_s = \frac{11,300}{20,000 \times 0.866 \times 3.5} = 0.186 \text{ sq in.}$$

Accept #4 bars spaced 13 in. on centers (Table 9–4).

Step 6. Shearing unit stress. The approximate uniformly distributed loads on the supporting beams were found in Step 2. These loads are the loads per linear foot of beam, the reactions of the 12-in. wide strips of slab, and, consequently, are the maximum vertical shears in the slab.

$$v = \frac{V}{jbd} \qquad \text{Formula (10), Art. 5–2}$$

Then, for the short direction,

$$v = \frac{932}{0.875 \times 12 \times 4} = 23 \text{ psi}$$

the maximum shearing unit stress.

For the long direction,

$$v = \frac{791}{0.875 \times 12 \times 3.5} = 22 \text{ psi}$$

the shearing unit stress. Since for both the long and short directions the shearing stresses are less than 90 psi, the allowable, the slab is acceptable with respect to shear.

Steps 7 and 8. These steps do not apply to slabs.

Step 9. Bond stress. The maximum vertical shear is the shear resulting from the slab load in the short direction, 932 lb per linear ft of slab. Since there will be #4 bars at 10-in. spacing, $\frac{12}{10} = 1.2$ bars, the number of bars for each 12-in. wide strip of slab. The perimeter of a #4 bar is 1.57 in. (Table 1–1). Then,

$$u = \frac{V}{\Sigma_0 jd} \qquad \text{Formula (13), Art. 5–6}$$

or

$$u = \frac{932}{1.2 \times 1.57 \times 0.866 \times 4} = 143 \text{ psi}$$

the unit bond stress.

For the long direction, the #4 bars have 13-in. spacing. $\frac{12}{13} = 0.924$, the number of bars in each 12-in. wide strip. $V = 791$ lb. Then,

$$u = \frac{791}{0.924 \times 1.57 \times 0.866 \times 3.5} = 180 \text{ psi}, \quad \text{the unit bond stress}$$

For both the long and short directions, the bond stress is less than 300 psi, the allowable; therefore, the proposed reinforcement is acceptable with respect to bond stresses.

Step 10. Bends, laps, etc. In this example there are no bent bars; straight bars are used for both the top and bottom reinforcement. The top bars are extended to the $\frac{1}{4}$ points of the adjacent panels and the bottom bars extend at least 6 in. into the supporting beams. If the panel has any discontinuous edges, the top bars at these points will be hooked.

As previously stated, the code permits a reduction of moments in the column strips of two thirds of the corresponding moments in the middle strip. Hence, the steel areas required in the column strips may be two thirds of the A_s values computed in Step 5 or the spacing may be increased, $\frac{3}{2}$ times the spacing used for the middle strips. The latter procedure will be followed.

Thus the spacings in the column strips are as follows:

For the short direction,

negative moment spacing = $7.5 \times 1.5 = 11.3$ in., accept 11 in.
positive moment spacing = $10 \times 1.5 = 15$ in., accept 15 in.

For the long direction,

negative moment spacing = $9.5 \times 1.5 = 14.3$ in., accept 14 in.
positive moment spacing = $13 \times 1.5 = 19.5$ in.

Since the maximum spacing permitted is 3×5, or 15 in., accept a spacing of 15 in.

The reinforcing bars for the two-way slab are shown in Fig. 9–4. Top bars are shown on two sides only; they occur, of course, on all four sides.

9–13. Beams Supporting Two-Way Slabs. For beams supporting two-way slabs, an exact analysis of load distribution is extremely complicated. The code, however, states that the loads on the supporting beams may be assumed to be the loads within the tributary areas shown in Fig. 9–3(c). Bending moments for the beams may be determined, approximately, by using an equivalent load per linear foot of beam as follows:

$$\text{for the short span} = \frac{wS}{3}$$

$$\text{for the long span} = \frac{wS}{3} \times \frac{3 - m^2}{2}$$

Hence, for the beams supporting the two-way slab in the example in Art. 9–12, these are the equivalent uniformly distributed loads.

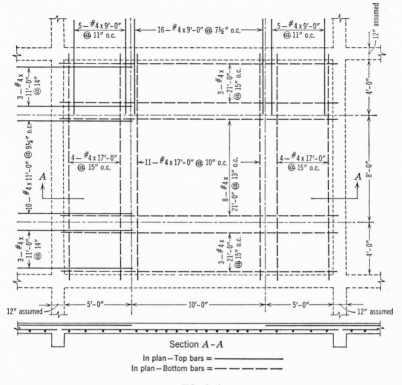

Section A-A

In plan — Top bars = ——————
In plan — Bottom bars = — — — — —

FIG. 9–4

For the short support, load in the long direction $= \dfrac{148 \times 16}{3} =$ 791 lb per linear ft.

For the long support, load in the short direction $= \dfrac{148 \times 16}{3} \times \dfrac{3 - 0.8^2}{2} = 932$ lb per linear ft.

9–14. Ribbed Slabs. For medium span lengths with light or medium live loads, ribbed slabs have proved to be an economical type of floor construction. They are not so well suited to heavy concentrated loads as the solid one- or two-way slabs. A ribbed slab consists of a number of relatively small adjacent T-beams, the open spaces between the webs or ribs being formed usually by clay tile, gypsum tile, or steel forms.

A typical ribbed slab with *clay-tile fillers* is indicated in Fig. 9–5(*a*). The tiles used are generally 12 x 12 in. in plan with depths

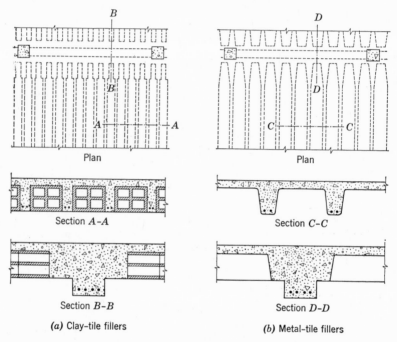

(a) Clay-tile fillers   *(b)* Metal-tile fillers

FIG. 9–5

of 4, 6, 8, 10, 12, and 15 in. The usual practice is to place the tiles 16 in. on centers, thus making the web 4 in. wide. The layer of concrete placed on top of the tile is generally 2 or $2\frac{1}{2}$ in. thick. Reinforcement for this type of construction may consist of two bars placed in the lower part of the web, one bent and one straight, or of straight bars placed in the top and bottom parts of the web. Temperature reinforcement consists of wire mesh or #2 bars run at right angles to the web. As the bottom surface of the tile and web are in the same plane, the ribbed slab with tile fillers permits a flat plastered ceiling. Sometimes 4-in. wide flat tile are placed at the bottom of the web to afford an entire tile surface for plastering.

The purpose of these "facers" is to prevent possible plaster discolorations under the web.

Metal-tile fillers are frequently used for ribbed floors. This is commonly known as "tin-pan" construction. The metal forms are usually 36 in. long, with 6-, 8-, 10-, 12-, and 14-in. depths. They are placed on centers in such a manner as to make the web 4 to 7 in. wide at the lowest point. Form widths are generally 20 or 30 in.; a common condition is a form 20 in. wide, placed 25 in. on centers, to make a web 5 in. in width at the bottom, as shown in Fig. 9–6(a).

The metal forms may be removed or left in place after the supporting formwork has been taken down. To provide a greater web area near the supports, where the shearing stresses may exceed the allowable, special metal cores with the sides tapered in plan are used; see Fig. 9–6(b). The degree of tapering generally is such that the web is increased 4 in. in width. As in the case of clay-tile fillers, a 2-, $2\frac{1}{2}$-, or 3-in. slab is placed over the metal-tile forms, the slab and web forming a T-section.

Gypsum-tile fillers have the advantage of providing a relatively lightweight ribbed floor with a flush ceiling. Although they are made in various sizes, a common width is 19 in. When placed 24 in. on centers, these blocks form a web 5 in. wide. When blocks 12 in. wide are used, they are placed 16 in. on centers, thus forming 4-in. wide webs.

Table 9–7 gives the approximate weights of various ribbed floors in pounds per square foot of floor area. The dimensions, and therefore the weights, of the different fillers vary with different manufacturers. This table of weights has been prepared for ribbed floors with *one-way reinforcement*. Certain ribbed floors are designed for two-way reinforcement, in which case special types of fillers are used. For metal tile, for instance, the forms are enclosed on four sides and are known as *domes*.

The maximum span of a ribbed slab should not exceed 24 times the total depth of slab and web combined.

9–15. Design of a Ribbed Slab with Metal-Tile Fillers. As the slab placed over the filler tile is cast integrally with the web or ribs, they form a T-section. Hence the computations for this type of construction are similar to those used for T-beams, and the design steps given in Art. 7–6 are followed in the next example.

TABLE 9–7. WEIGHTS OF RIBBED FLOORS IN POUNDS PER SQUARE FOOT

Terra-Cotta-Tile Filler, Webs 4" Wide and 16" on Centers

Depth of Tile in Inches	Thickness of Slab in Inches		
	2	$2\frac{1}{2}$	3
4	50	58	65
6	63	70	75
8	75	80	87
10	85	93	98
12	97	103	110

Metal-Tile Filler, Webs 5" Wide and 25" on Centers

Depth of Tile in Inches	Thickness of Slab in Inches		
	2	$2\frac{1}{2}$	3
6	42	48	55
8	48	54	61
10	54	60	67
12	61	67	74
14	68	75	81

Gypsum-Block Filler, Webs 5" Wide and 24" on Centers

Depth of Blocks in Inches	Thickness of Slab in Inches		
	2	$2\frac{1}{2}$	3
6	54	60	66
8	60	66	72
10	68	74	80
12	76	82	88

Example. A typical interior panel of a floor is to be designed for a ribbed slab using metal-tile fillers. The clear span of the T-beam construction thus formed is 20 ft and the end conditions are fully continuous. The live load is 60 psf, the finished floor is 23 psf, and a suspended ceiling of plaster on metal lath will be constructed. Let it be required to design the floor in accordance with the following data:

$$f_s = 20,000 \text{ psi}$$

$$f_c = 1350 \text{ psi}$$

$$v_c = \text{limited to 90 psi}$$

$$u = \text{limited to 300 psi}$$

$$n = 10$$

Referring to Table 4–1, we find the following formula coefficients: $K = 236$, $j = 0.866$, and $p = 0.0136$.

SOLUTION: *Step 1. Loads.* Let us assume that the metal forms are 10 in. in depth and that the slab thickness is 2 in. Referring to Table 9–7, we note that this type of ribbed floor weighs 54 psf. Then,

live load	= 60	
floor finish	= 23	
suspended ceiling	= 10	(Table 9–2)
ribbed slab	= 54	(Table 9–7)
total load	= 147 psf	

The ribs will be 5 in. wide at their lowest point. As they will be placed 25 in. on centers, $25 \div 12 = 2.08$, the number of square feet of floor area on each linear foot of rib.

$147 \times 2.08 = 306$ lb, the load per linear foot of rib.

$W = 306 \times 20 = 6120$ lb, the total uniformly distributed load on each rib.

Step 2. Maximum shear. The maximum shear will occur at the supports and will be equal to one half the total load.

$$V = \frac{W}{2} = \frac{6120}{2} = 3060 \text{ lb}$$

Step 3. Maximum bending moment. As the T-beams are fully
continuous, $M = \dfrac{Wl}{12}$ (Art. 3–7). Then,

$$M = \frac{Wl}{12} = \frac{6120 \times 20 \times 12}{12} = 122{,}400 \text{ in-lb}$$

This is the maximum bending moment at the center of the span
and also over the supports.

Step 4. Depth of beam. As explained in Art. 7–4, the rectangular
web area $b'd$ is first investigated to see that it is ample to resist the
bending stresses over the supports. In this problem the total
depth of the beam is $10 + 2$, or 12 in. If we assume that one half
the thickness of the reinforcing bars is 0.25 in. and that there is
0.75 in. of fireproofing, $12 - (0.25 + 0.75) = 11$ in. See Fig.
9–6(a). This is d, the effective depth at both the supports and at
the center of the span. The width of the rectangular web area $b'd$
at the supports is 5 in. This is b', the width of the web.

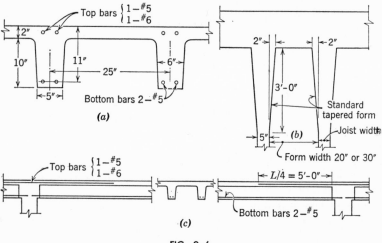

FIG. 9–6

We know that $M = Kbd^2$, M being the bending moment, and
Kbd^2, the resisting moment. See Art. 4–10. Thus

$$Kbd^2 = 236 \times 5 \times 11 \times 11 = 142{,}800 \text{ in-lb}$$

the resisting moment for this rectangular area. But we have seen in Step 3 that for this beam M is only 122,400 in-lb. Since 142,800 in-lb is greater than the required 122,400 in-lb, the 5 x 11 in. web area is adequate for bending stresses over the supports.

Next we investigate this area for shear, using formula (15), Art. 7–4:

$$b'd = \frac{V}{vj} \quad \text{or} \quad v = \frac{V}{b'jd}$$

Since the width of the web is 5 in. at the base and is tapered, the average width is assumed to be 6 in.; then $b' = 6$ in. Thus

$$v = \frac{3060}{6 \times 0.875 \times 11} = 53 \text{ psi}$$

the shearing unit stress. This stress is less than 90 psi, the allowable, and, therefore, web reinforcement is not required. The web area is adequate for both bending and shearing stresses.

If the shearing unit stress had exceeded the allowable, tapered metal forms would have been used at the ends of the ribs to have avoided the use of stirrups. This would have increased the width of the web 4 in. at the supports, making the area $b'd$ greater and thus reducing the value of v. The taper is 36 in. in length, and it would also be necessary to investigate v at the section in which the taper begins. See Fig. 9–6(b).

Step 5. Area of tensile reinforcement. For this T-beam, the depth of the flange is the depth of the covering slab, or $t = 2$ in. Then by equation (16), Art. 7–5,

$$A_s = \frac{M}{f_s[d - (t/2)]} = \frac{122,400}{20,000[11 - (2/2)]} = 0.61 \text{ sq in.}$$

Accept, temporarily, 2-#5 bars for the bottom reinforcement, $A_s = 2 \times 0.31 = 0.62$ sq in. (Table 1–1).

The negative moment at the supports is resisted by a rectangular area, not a T-section, and the tensile reinforcement at the top of the beam over the supports is found by formula (7), Art. 4–5.

$$A_s = \frac{M}{f_s jd} = \frac{122,400}{20.000 \times 0.866 \times 11} = 0.64 \text{ sq in.}$$

Accept 1-#6 and 1-#5 bars (0.44 + 0.31 = 0.75 sq in.) for these top bars.

Steps 6 and 7. These steps do not apply to this problem.

Step 8. Bond stress. There will be two reinforcing bars in each rib, and the perimeter of each #5 bar is 1.96 in. (Table 1–1). Then by equation (13), Art. 5–6,

$$u = \frac{V}{\Sigma_0 jd} = \frac{3060}{(2 \times 1.96) \times 0.875 \times 11} = 81 \text{ psi}$$

This bond stress is less than 300 psi, the allowable, and the 2-#5 bars at the bottom of the beam are acceptable. It is unnecessary to check the bond stress for the top bars because V is the same for both top and bottom bars and the sum of the perimeters of the top bars is greater than those at the bottom.

Step 9. Bends, laps, and hooks. We shall use straight bars for both top and bottom reinforcement. There are no bent bars. The bottom bars will be extended 6 in. into the supports. The top bars will extend from the $\frac{1}{4}$ point of span, across the supports to the $\frac{1}{4}$ point of the adjacent span. See Fig. 9–6(*c*). The top bars at the noncontinuous ends of semicontinuous beams are hooked.

Example. A fully continuous ribbed slab using metal-tile fillers has a clear span between faces of supports of 22 ft and a uniformly distributed load, including its own weight, of 580 lb per linear ft. The bottom of the rib has a width of 5 in., and the effective depth of the steel reinforcement is 13 in. Investigate the shearing unit stress, assuming that v_c is limited to 90 psi.

SOLUTION: The load on the beam is 580 lb per linear ft. Then, since the length of the beam is 22 ft, $580 \times 22 = 12{,}760$ lb, the total uniformly distributed load.

Each reaction = $12{,}760 \times \frac{1}{2} = 6380$ lb, and this is V, the magnitude of the maximum vertical shear at the face of the supports.

The web is 5 in. wide at the bottom. It tapers outward so that its average width is 6 in. The area resisting shear is $b'd$, 6 x 13 in. Then,

$$v = \frac{V}{jbd} = \frac{6380}{0.875 \times 6 \times 13} = 94 \text{ psi}$$

the maximum shearing unit stress. This exceeds the allowable.

It is not practical to use stirrups or ties in ribbed-slab construction; consequently we will increase the width of the web 4 in. at the face of supports by the use of tapered forms. See Fig. 9–6(b). The area resisting shear at the support now is 10 x 13 in. Then,

$$v = \frac{V}{jbd} \quad \text{and} \quad v = \frac{6380}{0.875 \times 10 \times 13} = 56 \text{ psi}$$

This stress is within 90 psi, the allowable, and is satisfactory.

The tapered forms are 36 in. in length, and at this distance from the face of the support the area resisting shear is only 6 x 13 in. See Fig. 9–6(b). Now let us compute the magnitude of V, the total vertical shear, at 3 ft from the support.* Then, at 3 ft from the face of the support,

$$V = 6380 - (3 \times 580) = 4640 \text{ lb}$$

and

$$v = \frac{4640}{0.875 \times 6 \times 13} = 68 \text{ psi}$$

the shearing unit stress at the point at which the taper begins. This stress is well within the 90-psi limit. Hence we see that the use of tapered forms reduces the shearing unit stresses and avoids deeper webs, wider webs, or the use of web reinforcement. It should be noted that this example considered only shearing stresses. To design a ribbed slab, bending stresses should also be investigated. This was illustrated in the first example under this article.

Problem 9–15–A. Let it be required to design an interior panel of a ribbed floor, using 12-in. deep metal-tile fillers with a $2\frac{1}{2}$-in. thickness of slab. The clear span between faces of supports is 22 ft 0 in. The live load is 65 psf and the floor finish is 22 psf. Specification data:

$$f_s = 20,000 \text{ psi}$$

$$f_c = 1125 \text{ psi}$$

$$v_c = \text{limited to 75 psi}$$

$$u = \text{limited to 250 psi}$$

$$n = 12$$

* See Art. 66, *Simplified Mechanics and Strength of Materials*, by Harry Parker, John Wiley and Sons, New York.

9–16. Design of a Ribbed Slab with Clay-Tile Fillers. A ribbed slab with clay-tile fillers again presents a floor consisting of a number of small T-sections side by side. The tile used as fillers is generally 12 x 12 in. in plan, with depths ranging from 4 to 12 in. in increments of 2 in. To design a floor of this type, the first step is to assume a depth of tile and covering slab. If it is found that the shearing stresses are excessive, they may be reduced by using tiles of greater depth, or tiles 8 in. wide, instead of 12 in., may be used at the ends of the T-sections. The use of a narrower tile results in a wider web or rib, and the increased area of concrete reduces the shearing stress. The design procedure is similar to that outlined for T-beams in Art. 7–6, the same steps being followed in the next example.

Example. Let it be required to design a ribbed-slab floor with clay-tile fillers for the span of 18 ft 6 in. center to center of supporting end beams, as shown in Fig. 9–7(b). The live load is 80 psf, the floor finish is 10 psf, and plaster is to be added to the underside of the flush ceiling. The end conditions are fully continuous. Specification data:

$$f_s = 18,000 \text{ psi}$$
$$f_c = 900 \text{ psi}$$
$$v_c = \text{limited to } 60 \text{ psi}$$
$$u = \text{limited to } 200 \text{ psi}$$
$$n = 15$$

SOLUTION: *Step 1.* *Loads.* The formula coefficients for the unit stresses given as data are $K = 165$, $k = 0.429$, $j = 0.857$, and $p = 0.0107$.

We shall assume that the filler tile is 8 in. deep, that the covering slab is 2 in. thick, and that the ribs are 4 in. wide. See Fig. 9–5(a).

Tabulating the loads:

live load	=	80	
floor finish	=	10	
plastered ceiling	=	10	(Table 9–2)
ribbed slab	=	75	(Table 9–7)
total load	=	175 psf	

The use of 12-in. wide tile with 4-in. ribs gives a rib spacing of 16 in. on centers. Therefore each rib supports a floor area of $\frac{16}{12}$, or 1.3 ft in width. At 175 psf, the load per linear foot on one rib is 1.3 x 175, or 228 lb. The end beams supporting this type of ribbed slab frequently have the section shown in Fig. 9–7(*b*); hence

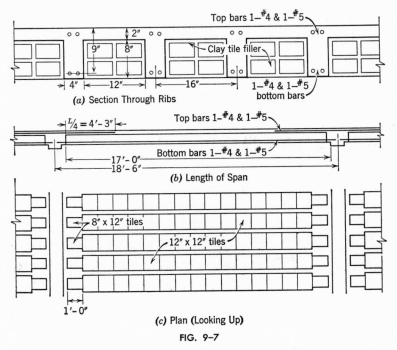

(*a*) Section Through Ribs

(*b*) Length of Span

(*c*) Plan (Looking Up)

FIG. 9–7

we may consider 17 ft as the span length of the T-sections of the ribbed floor. Then $W = 228 \times 17 = 3876$ lb, the total uniformly distributed load on one T-beam.

Step 2. Maximum shear. The maximum vertical shear occurs at the ends of the beams and is equal to one half the total load, or $V = \frac{1}{2} \times 3876 = 1938$ lb.

Step 3. Maximum bending moment. As the end conditions are fully continuous, $M = \dfrac{Wl}{12}$, Art. 3–7. Then,

$$M = \frac{3876 \times 17 \times 12}{12} = 65,892, \qquad \text{say } 65,900 \text{ in-lb}$$

the maximum values over the supports as well as at the center of
the span, the negative and positive bending moments.

Step 4. Depth of beam. In Step 1 the depth of the beam was assumed to be 8 in. of tile, with 2 in. of concrete slab covering, making
a total thickness of 10 in. Assuming 0.25 in. for one half the thickness of the tensile reinforcement and 0.75 in. for the fireproofing
below the bars, $d = 10 - (0.25 + 0.75) = 9$ in., the effective
depth of the T-beam. See Fig. 9–7(a). Let us investigate this
section to determine whether or not it is adequate to resist bending
and shearing stresses.

The negative moment over the supports is resisted by a rectangular web area of which $b' = 4$ in. and $d = 9$ in. Hence the resisting moment is found by quantity Kbd^2, Art. 4–10. Then,

$$165 \times 4 \times 9 \times 9 = 53,500 \text{ in-lb}$$

However, we know that the bending moment is 65,900 in-lb,
and, since the area provides a resisting moment of only 53,500 in-lb,
the rectangular area, 4 x 9 in., is too small.

The simplest method of increasing the resisting moment is to
increase the width of the web *at the support* by using tile 8 in. wide
instead of 12 in. See Fig. 9–7(c). This increases the width of the
web 4 in., making it 8 in. wide, and the resisting moment becomes

$$Kbd^2 = 165 \times 8 \times 9 \times 9 = 107,000 \text{ in-lb}$$

Since this resisting moment is greater than 65,900 in-lb, the bending moment, the web area is adequate for resisting bending stresses
at the face of the support.

The next step is to determine how many of these 8-in. wide tiles
(12 in. in length) must be used before we start the 12-in. wide tiles.
That is, at what distance from the face of the support is the bending moment equal to or smaller than the resisting moment afforded
by the 4-in. wide web? An exact answer could be found by plotting
a bending-moment diagram. This requires considerable time and
a quicker and sufficiently accurate method is as follows:

Consider the bending moment diagram for an interior span of the
continuous beam shown in Fig. 3–2(g). We see that the negative
bending moment decreases, almost in a straight line, from a maximum value at the support to a zero value at the inflection point.

The inflection point is considered to be at a point one fifth the span length from the support, in our example $\frac{17}{5}$, or a distance of 3.4 ft.

Suppose we use only one tile 8 in. wide and 12 in. long. Then the rib 4 in. wide would begin at 1 ft from the support. Since the 1-ft length is approximately $\frac{1}{3}$ of 3.4 ft, the negative bending moment has decreased about $\frac{1}{3}$ of its maximum value of 65,900 in-lb. Then,

$$65,900 - \frac{65,900}{3} = 43,930 \text{ in-lb}$$

the approximate value of the bending moment at 1 ft from the support. However, this bending moment is less than the resisting moment of the 4 x 9 in. web area which we found to be 53,500 in-lb. Therefore only one 8-in. wide tile (12 in. in length) at the support will be required insofar as bending is concerned.

Now let us investigate the 8-in. wide web, at the face of the support, for shear. By formula (15), Art. 7–4,

$$v = \frac{V}{jb'd} \qquad \text{or} \qquad v = \frac{1938}{0.875 \times 8 \times 9} = 31 \text{ psi}$$

which is acceptable, since it is less than 60 psi, the allowable.

At 1 ft from the face of the support, $V = 1938 - (1 \times 228) = 1710$ lb.*

At this section, the web has a width of 4 in. Then,

$$v = \frac{1710}{0.875 \times 4 \times 9} = 54 \text{ psi}$$

This is less than 60 psi, the allowable; hence the 4-in. wide web at this section is acceptable. If the stress had been greater than the allowable, one or more 8-in. wide tiles would have been required.

Step 5. Area of tensile reinforcement. The thickness of the covering slab is 2 in., actually the thickness of the flange of the T-beam section. Then $t = 2$ and, by formula (16), Art. 7–5,

$$A_s = \frac{M}{f_s[d - (t/2)]} = \frac{65,900}{18,000(9 - 2/2)} \qquad \text{or} \qquad A_s = 0.46 \text{ sq in.}$$

the area of the tensile reinforcement for the positive bending moment. Therefore for the bottom bars we will use one #4 and one

---

* See Art. 66, *Simplified Mechanics and Strength of Materials.*

#5 bars. $(0.2 + 0.31 = 0.51$ sq in.) For the negative reinforcement at the top of the beam over the supports,

$$A_s = \frac{M}{f_s jd} \qquad \text{Formula (7), Art. 4–5}$$

or

$$A_s = \frac{65,900}{18,000 \times 0.857 \times 9} = 0.47 \text{ sq in.}$$

Accept one #4 and one #5 bars over the supports.

Steps 6 and 7. Web reinforcement is not used in ribbed slabs, and the shearing stresses are kept within the allowable. Thus these two steps do not apply.

Step 8. Bond stress. The perimeters of #4 and #5 bars are 1.57 in. and 1.96 in., respectively. Then, by formula (13), Art. 5–6,

$$u = \frac{V}{\Sigma_0 jd} = \frac{1938}{(1.57 + 1.96) \times 0.875 \times 9} = 70 \text{ psi}$$

the unit bond stress. This stress being well within the allowable, 200 psi, the proposed bars are accepted.

Step 9. Bends, laps, and hooks. In this example there are no bent bars. In each rib there are 1-#4 and 1-#5 straight bars for both positive and negative reinforcement. The top bars extend from the $\frac{1}{4}$ point of one span, across the support, to the $\frac{1}{4}$ point of the adjacent span. The bottom bars extend a distance of 6 in. into the supports. Top bars at the noncontinuous ends of semi-continuous beams should terminate with hooks.

Problem 9–16–A. A ribbed-slab floor constructed of clay-tile fillers, 10 in. in depth with a 2-in. covering slab, has a span of 21 ft 6 in. between centers of supports similar to the beam in Fig. 9–7(*b*). The ends are fully continuous. Design the floor for a total live and dead load of 5800 lb on each rib. Specification data:

$$f_s = 20,000 \text{ psi}$$

$$f_c = 1350 \text{ psi}$$

$$v_c = \text{limited to 90 psi}$$

$$u = \text{limited to 210 psi for top bars} \\ \text{and 300 psi for others}$$

$$n = 10$$

9–17. Flat-Slab Floors. A flat-slab floor consists of a relatively large rectangular slab supported directly by columns without beams or girders. The slab is commonly reinforced with bars running in two directions. The slab may be of uniform thickness, or an approximately square symmetrical area directly above the column may be made thicker than the remaining slab, as indicated in Fig. 9–8(a). This area of increased thickness is called a *drop panel*

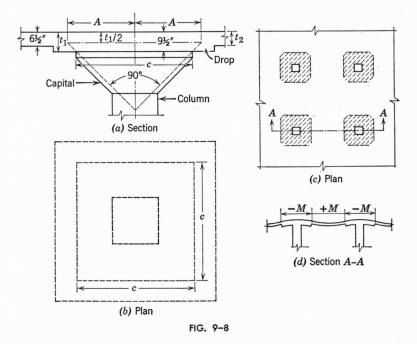

(a) Section

(b) Plan

(c) Plan

(d) Section A–A

FIG. 9–8

or *drop*. For flat-slab floors, it is customary to employ flared heads or capitals on the columns. The columns are generally square in cross section, but rectangular or circular cross sections are also used.

Columns without capitals are sometimes used to provide a slab with a flat underside throughout. This type of floor is called *flat-plate construction*.

Flat-slab floors are economical in use of material and provide a rigid type of construction. These floors are particularly suitable for industrial buildings having large live loads and for buildings in which the column capitals are not objectionable. Among the advantages claimed for the flat-slab floor are the simplified formwork, better lighting due to the absence of beams and girders, a saving in height for given clear story heights, a uniform surface for suspending sprinkler systems, piping, and shafting, and, because of the absence of sharp corners, better resistance to fire.

The commonest method of reinforcing flat slabs is the two-way system. The two-way system consists of two sets of bars placed parallel to the center lines of the columns.

9–18. Distribution of Stresses in Flat Slabs. It is extremely difficult to determine exactly the distribution and magnitude of the stresses in a flat slab. These floors are designed by empirical rules, as laid down in the various building codes. The designer is obliged to consult the code having jurisdiction in his locality and to design his structure accordingly. These empirical rules may be used only when certain limitations are complied with; otherwise a more exact analysis is necessary. These limitations are

1. The construction shall consist of at least three continuous panels in each direction.

2. The ratio of length to width of panels shall not exceed 1.33.

3. The grid pattern shall consist of approximately rectangular panels. The successive span lengths in each direction shall differ by not more than 20% of the longer span.

In addition to the notation used in the design of beams, there are certain other terms that apply particularly to flat slabs:

A = distance of critical section for bending moments over columns from center line of column, in feet, as indicated in Fig. 9–8(a).

c = effective support size, the diameter of the largest circular cone with a 90° vertex angle that can be included in the outlines of the column capital, measured at the bottom of the slab or drop panel, in feet. When a column is without a concrete capital, the dimension c shall be taken as that of the column in the direction considered. See Fig. 9–8(a).

L = span length of a flat slab panel, center to center of supports, in feet. In rectangular panels L is the longer span.

M_0 = numerical sum of assumed positive and average negative moments at the critical design sections.

t_1 = thickness in inches of slabs without drop panels or through drop panel, if any. See Fig. 9–8(a).

t_2 = thickness in inches of slabs with drop panels at points beyond the drop panel. See Fig. 9–8(a).

w' = uniformly distributed unit dead and live loads, in pounds per square foot.

W = total dead and live loads on the panel, in pounds.

The thickness of t_1 and t_2 shall not be less than the following:

$$t_1 = L/36, \quad \text{or 5 in.,} \quad \text{or } 0.028L \left(1 - \frac{2c}{3L} \right) \sqrt{\frac{w'}{f'_c/2000}} + 1\tfrac{1}{2} \text{ in.}$$

whichever is the largest.

$$t_2 = L/40, \quad \text{or 4 in.,} \quad \text{or } 0.024L \left(1 - \frac{2c}{3L} \right) \sqrt{\frac{w'}{f'_c/2000}} + 1 \text{ in.}$$

whichever is the largest.

The side or diameter of the drop panel, if any, shall be at least 0.33 times the span in the parallel direction.

The maximum total thickness at the drop panel used in computing reinforcement over the column shall be $1.5 \times t_2$.

The dimension c of the column capital is generally taken between $0.20L$ and $0.25L$.

A portion of a flat-slab floor area is indicated in Fig. 9–8(c), the solid squares representing the supporting columns. If we consider the floor load to be uniformly distributed, it is obvious that a certain area over each column, indicated by hatching, is subjected to tensile stresses in the upper part of the slab, a negative bending moment. It is evident also that between the columns, outside the hatched areas, the slab tends to bend concave upward, the tensile stresses are in the bottom of the slab, and the bending moment is positive. See Fig. 9–8(d). The dash lines indicate the approximate position of the inflection points. Although an exact analysis of the moments and stresses in the slab is quite complicated, arbitrary methods based on both theory and experiment are laid down in building codes. By use of these empirical rules a satisfactory design is accomplished.

9–19. Bending Moments in Flat Slabs. A flat-slab panel is considered as consisting of *middle* and *column strips* having the dimensions shown in Fig. 9–9. When considering moments in the opposite direction, the panel is divided into similar strips running at right angles to those shown.

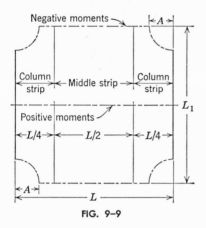

FIG. 9–9

The *numerical sum of the positive and negative bending moments* in the direction of either side of a rectangular panel shall be assumed as not less than

$$M_0 = 0.09WLF\left(1 - \frac{2c}{3L}\right)^2$$

in which $F = 1.15 - c/L$, but not less than 1.

The sections for negative moments are taken along the edges of the panel on lines joining the column centers, except that they follow a circle of radius A about the column center, instead of passing through it, as shown in Fig. 9–9. In computing compressive stresses due to bending, three fourths of the width of the column strip is used as the width of the section, except that on a section through a drop panel three fourths of the width of the drop panel shall be used. The sections for positive moments are taken on the center lines of the panel. See Fig. 9–9. Note that the preceding equation gives the *sum* of positive and negative moments; the distribution of the moments is given in Table 9–8.

9–20. Shearing Stresses in Flat Slabs. The shearing unit stresses in flat slabs are investigated at two sections:

1. In flat slabs the shearing unit stress on vertical sections which follow a periphery b, at distance d, beyond the edges of the column or column capital and parallel or concentric with it, shall not exceed the following values for the concrete when computed by the formula

$$v = \frac{V}{jbd}$$

TABLE 9–8. MOMENTS TO BE USED IN DESIGN OF AN INTERIOR PANEL OF FLAT SLAB

Two-Way System with Drop Panel

Column strip, negative moment	$0.50M_o$
Column strip, positive moment	$0.20M_o$
Middle strip, negative moment	$0.15M_o$
Middle strip, positive moment	$0.15M_o$

Two-Way System without Drop Panel

Column strip, negative moment	$0.46M_o$
Column strip, positive moment	$0.22M_o$
Middle strip, negative moment	$0.16M_o$
Middle strip, positive moment	$0.16M_o$

(a) $0.03f'_c$, but not more than 100 psi when at least 50% of the total negative reinforcement required for bending in the column strip passes through the periphery.

(b) $0.025f'_c$, but not more than 85 psi when 25%, which is the least value permitted, of the total negative reinforcement required for bending in the column strip passes through the periphery.

2. In flat slabs with drop panels the shearing unit stress on vertical sections which lie at a distance d, beyond the edges of the drop panel, and parallel with them, shall not exceed $0.03f'_c$ nor 100 psi. At least 50% of the total negative reinforcement required for bending in the column strip shall be within the width of strip directly above the drop panel.

9–21. Design of a Flat-Slab Floor. The design of a flat-slab floor is accomplished by strict adherence to formulas and rules given in building codes. These codes are far from being uniform and are frequently modified. The foregoing discussion is a very brief outline of the requirements set forth in the American Concrete Institute's *Building Code Requirements for Reinforced Concrete.* Many important items have been purposely omitted, as, for instance, length of bars, points of bend, etc. It is recommended that the reader of this text refer to the building code governing construction in his locality and note the requirements. The following example illustrates the general procedure to be used in design.

Example. Design an interior panel of a flat-slab floor having a column spacing of 20 ft on centers in both directions. The floor slab will be a two-way system with drop panels. The live load is 200 psf. Specification data:

$$f'_c = 3000 \text{ psi}$$

$$f_c = 1350 \text{ psi}$$

$$f_s = 20{,}000 \text{ psi}$$

$$v_c = \text{limited to } 90 \text{ psi}$$

$$n = 10$$

SOLUTION: In accordance with the foregoing unit stresses, the formula coefficients found in Table 4–1 are $K = 236$, $k = 0.403$, $j = 0.866$, and $p = 0.0136$.

Step 1. Determine the slab and drop dimensions. It is first necessary that certain assumptions be made. Since the panel is square, $L = L_1 = 20$ ft 0 in. The length of the capital is assumed to be $0.25L$, or $0.25 \times 20 = 5$ ft; therefore the capital will be 5 ft square. The minimum length of the drop panel is $0.33L$, or $0.33 \times 20 = 6$ ft 8 in., say 7 ft square.

The minimum thickness of the slab is $t_2 = L/40 = (20 \times 12)/40 = 6$ in. Note that it is greater than 4 in., the minimum permitted. Accept, temporarily, $t_2 = 6$ in.

It is advantageous to use the maximum thickness of the drop panel, thereby reducing the concrete stresses and steel areas over the supports. Then $t_1 = 1.5 \times t_2 = 1.5 \times 6 = 9$ in. Accept, temporarily, $t_1 = 9$ in.

The next step is to compute w' in accordance with the assumed thicknesses of t_1 and t_2:

$$
\begin{array}{lr}
\text{live load} & = 200 \\
\text{6-in. slab} & = 75 \\
\hline
\text{total} & = 275 \text{ psf}
\end{array}
$$

To this must be added the weight of the drop which is distributed over the entire panel area of 20 x 20, or 400 sq ft.

$$\text{weight of drop} = \frac{9-6}{12} \times 7^2 \times 150 \times \frac{1}{400} = 4.6, \quad \text{say 5 psf}$$

Then $w' = 275 + 5 = 280$ psf. Now we can check t_2, the minimum thickness being

$$t_2 = 0.024L \left(1 - \frac{2c}{3L}\right) \times \sqrt{\frac{w'}{f'_c/2000}} + 1.0$$

or

$$t_2 = 0.024 \times 20 \left(1 - \frac{2 \times 5}{3 \times 20}\right) \times \sqrt{\frac{280}{3000/2000}} + 1.0 = 6.45 \text{ in.}$$

But this depth is greater than the assumed 6 in., and we must repeat the computations using $t_2 = 6.5$ in. For t_1, $t_1 = 1.5 \times 6.5 = 9.75$ in. Try $t_1 = 9.5$ in.

Again computing w',

$$
\begin{aligned}
&\text{live load} &&= 200 \\
&\text{6.5-in. slab, } \frac{6.5}{12} \times 150 &&= 81 \\
&\text{drop, } \frac{9.5 - 6.5}{12} \times 7^2 \times 150 \times \frac{1}{400} = &&\ 5 \\
&\quad w' &&= 286 \text{ psi}
\end{aligned}
$$

$$\text{minimum } t_2 = 0.024 \times 20 \left(1 - \frac{2 \times 5}{3 \times 20}\right) \times \sqrt{\frac{286}{3000/2000}} + 1$$

$$= 6.5 \text{ in., } \quad \text{accept } t_2 = 6.5 \text{ in.}$$

$$\text{minimum } t_1 = 0.028 \times 20 \left(1 - \frac{2 \times 5}{3 \times 20}\right) \times \sqrt{\frac{286}{3000/2000}} + 1\tfrac{1}{2}$$

$$= 7.95 \text{ in., } \quad \text{accept } t_1 = 9.5 \text{ in.}$$

Step 2. Compute shear stresses. In flat slabs the shearing unit stresses are checked at two sections, one in the slab and the other in the drop. Since the thicknesses of the slab and drop are represented by the letters t_2 and t_1, it is convenient to represent their effective depths as d_2 and d_1 and their respective shearing stresses as V_2 and v_2 and V_1 and v_1. Thus the shear must be checked in the drop at a distance of d_1 from the edge of the capital and in the slab at d_2 distance from the edge of the drop. See Fig. 9–10.

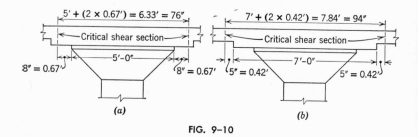

FIG. 9–10

Bear in mind that there will be two layers of bars crossing each other at right angles over the columns. Allowing 0.75 in. for fireproofing and two #6 bars crossing each other, the average distance of the bars from the tension face of the concrete becomes $0.75 + 0.75 = 1.5$ in. The effective depths in the drop, therefore, may be assumed to be $d_1 = 9.5 - 1.5 = 8$ in. and in the slab, $d_2 = 6.5 - 1.5 = 5$ in.

The critical shear V_1 at a distance of d_1 from the edge of the capital [see Fig. 9–10(a)] is $V_1 = 286 \times (20^2 - 6.34^2) = 103,000$ lb. Then

$$v_1 = \frac{V_1}{jb_1d_1} = \frac{103,000}{0.875 \times (4 \times 76) \times 8} = 48 \text{ psi}$$

This stress is less than 90 psi, and the 9.5 in. drop thickness is acceptable.

Again, the critical shear V_2 at d_2 distance from the edge of the drop panel [see Fig. 9–10(b)] is $V_2 = 286(20^2 - 7.84^2) = 97,000$ lb and $v_2 = \dfrac{97,000}{0.875 \times (4 \times 94) \times 5} = 59$ psi. The allowable shearing unit stress is 90 psi; hence the slab thickness, 6.5 in., is accept-able. Accept

$$t_1 = 9.5 \text{ in.} \quad \text{and} \quad t_2 = 6.5 \text{ in.}$$

Step 3. Compute M_0, the bending moment. Referring to Art. 9–19, $M_0 = 0.09WLF \left(1 - \dfrac{2c}{3L}\right)^2$; in this formula $F = 1.15 - \dfrac{c}{L}$, but not less than 1. Thus

$$F = 1.15 - (5/20) = 0.90, \quad \text{use } F = 1$$

and

$$W = 286 \times 20 \times 20 = 114{,}400 \text{ lb}$$

Then

$$M_0 = 0.09 \times 114{,}400 \times 20 \times 1 \times \left(1 - \frac{2 \times 5}{3 \times 20}\right)^2$$

$$= 143{,}000 \text{ ft-lb} \quad \text{or} \quad 1{,}716{,}000 \text{ in-lb}$$

Note that this quantity, M_0, is the numerical sum of both the positive and negative bending moments in the direction of either side of the rectangular panel.

Step 4. Compute the critical bending moments. Referring to Table 9–8, we find the bending moments to be used in a flat slab two-way system with a drop panel. Thus,

column strip, negative moment $= 0.50 \times M_0 = 0.50 \times 1{,}716{,}000$
$$= 858{,}000 \text{ in-lb}$$

column strip, positive moment $= 0.20 \times M_0 = 0.20 \times 1{,}716{,}000$
$$= 343{,}200 \text{ in-lb}$$

middle strip, negative moment $= 0.15 \times M_0 = 0.15 \times 1{,}716{,}000$
$$= 257{,}400 \text{ in-lb}$$

middle strip, positive moment $= 0.15 \times M_0 = 0.15 \times 1{,}716{,}000$
$$= 257{,}400 \text{ in-lb}$$

Step 5. Compute Areas of Steel Reinforcement. To determine the areas of steel reinforcement required at various sections of the slab, we will use formula (7), Art. 4–5, $A_s = \dfrac{M}{f_s jd}$.   This requires that we first determine the effective depths at the various positions.

Assume that #6 bars will be used for the negative moment in the column strip and that #5 bars will be used for all other reinforcement.   Since there are two layers of rods at right angles, one above the other, to resist the negative bending moment over the column with 0.75-in. clear waterproofing, the effective depths are computed as follows:

For the column strip, negative moment,

$$d = 9.5 - (0.375 + 0.75 + 0.75) = 7.63 \text{ in.}$$

For the column strip, positive moment,

$$d = 6.5 - (0.312 + 0.75) = 5.44 \text{ in.}$$

For the middle strip, positive moment,

$$d = 6.5 - (0.312 + 0.625 + 0.75) = 4.81 \text{ in.}$$

For the middle strip, negative moment,

$$d = 6.5 - (0.312 + 0.75) = 5.44 \text{ in.}$$

By use of formula (7), Art. 4–5, $A_s = \dfrac{M}{f_s jd}$.

For the column strip, negative moment,

$$A_s = \frac{858,000}{20,000 \times 0.866 \times 7.63} = 6.5 \text{ sq in.}$$

Accept 15-#6 bars.

For the column strip, positive moment,

$$A_s = \frac{343,200}{20,000 \times 0.866 \times 5.44} = 3.64 \text{ sq in.}$$

Accept 12-#5 bars.

For the middle strip, positive moment,

$$A_s = \frac{257,400}{20,000 \times 0.866 \times 4.81} = 3.08 \text{ sq in.}$$

Accept 10-#5 bars.

For the middle strip, negative moment,

$$A_s = \frac{257,400}{20,000 \times 0.866 \times 5.44} = 2.72 \text{ sq in.}$$

Accept 9-#5 bars.

In determining d, the effective depths, for various sections of the slab, many designers arbitrarily deduct $1\frac{1}{2}$ in. from the total slab thickness. This constant deduction of $1\frac{1}{2}$ in. may be used safely in most cases. In view of the uncertainty in load assumptions and the fact that M_0 and its apportioning to the different strips are only approximations, the exactness that we used in establishing the effective depths in this example is hardly warranted.

Step 6. Check compressive stresses in the concrete. If the concrete compressive stresses are not to exceed f_c, 1350 psi, the resisting moments, Kbd^2 (see Art. 4–10), of the various sections must be equal to or larger than the bending moments. Note, in Art. 9–19, that b is to be taken as three quarters of the width of the strip or drop panel. Then,

column strip:

negative bending moment = 858,000 in-lb

resisting moment   = $236 \times (\frac{3}{4} \times 7 \times 12) \times 7.63^2$
                                    = 865,000 in-lb

positive bending moment = 343,200 in-lb

resisting moment   = $236 \times (\frac{3}{4} \times 10 \times 12) \times 5.44^2$
                                    = 630,000 in-lb

middle strip:

positive bending moment $= 257,400$ in-lb

resisting moment $= 236 \times (\frac{3}{4} \times 10 \times 12) \times 4.81^2$
$ = 491,000$ in-lb

negative bending moment $= 257,400$ in-lb

resisting moment $= 236(\frac{3}{4} \times 10 \times 12) \times 5.44^2$
$ = 630,000$ in-lb

Since in each instance the resisting moment is greater in magnitude than the bending moment, the compressive unit stress in the concrete is less than 1350 psi, the allowable, at all sections of the slab.

Step 7. Arrangement and lengths of reinforcing bars. For flat-slab construction, building codes specify the length of bars for the various positions in the two strips. If bent-up bars are used, the bend-up points are located. Table 9–9 shows the required lengths of the straight bars for our example.

TABLE 9–9.   MINIMUM LENGTHS OF FLAT SLAB REINFORCING BARS
SLABS WITH DROP PANELS

	Column Strip	Middle Strip
Top bars	50% 0.66L 50% 0.50L	100% 0.50L
Bottom bars	Minimum embedment in drop panel of 16 bar diameters but at least 10 in. Outside of drop $L - 6$ in.	50% $L - 6$ in. 50% 0.70L

For the positive moment in the column strips, place 12-#5 bars in the bottom of the slab. For the negative moment, place 15-#6 bars in the top. The middle strip will have 10-#5 bars in the bottom of the slab for the positive moment and 9-#5 bars in the top for the negative moment. In this example all bars are straight.

There will be no bent bars. The arrangement and lengths of bars are shown in Fig. 9–11 for one direction only. The same reinforcement is required in a direction at right angles to that which is shown.

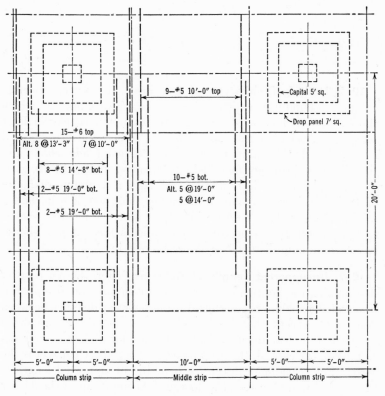

FIG. 9–11

CHAPTER 10

REINFORCED CONCRETE COLUMNS

10–1. Limiting Dimensions of Columns. Reinforced concrete columns in buildings are generally *short columns,* columns for which the unsupported length is not greater than ten times the least lateral dimension of the cross section. When the unsupported length exceeds this value, the column is termed a *long column* and the allowable loads are modified, as explained in Art. 10–10.

Principal columns in buildings shall have a minimum diameter of 12 in. or, if rectangular, a minimum thickness of 8 in. and a minimum gross area of 120 sq in. A compression member that is not continuous from story to story is called a *post.* A post should have a minimum diameter or thickness of 6 in.

10–2. Unsupported Length of Columns. For the purpose of determining the limiting cross section of columns, the *unsupported length* of the column is considered to be the clear distance between floor slabs, except that in *flat-slab construction* the unsupported length is the clear distance between the floor and the lower extremity of the capital, the drop panel, or the slab, whichever is the least. For *beam-and-slab construction,* the unsupported length is the clear distance between the floor and the underside of the deeper beam framing into the column in each direction at the next higher floor level.

The *slenderness ratio* of a column is represented by h/d, in which h is the unsupported length of the column and d is the least lateral dimension. For rectangular columns, that dimension shall be considered which produces the greatest ratio of length to depth of section.

10–3. Types of Reinforced Concrete Columns. In general, concrete columns are classified in accordance with the reinforcement that is used. See Fig. 10–1. These types are (a) *tied columns,* in which the reinforcement consists of longitudinal bars and separate lateral ties; (b) *spirally reinforced columns,* in which closely spaced spirals enclose a circular concrete core reinforced with longitudinal bars; (c) *composite columns,* having a structural steel or cast-iron

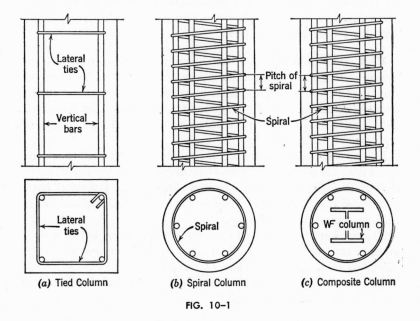

(a) Tied Column (b) Spiral Column (c) Composite Column

FIG. 10–1

column thoroughly encased in concrete reinforced with both longitudinal and spiral reinforcement; (d) *combination columns,* consisting of a structural steel column encased in concrete at least $2\frac{1}{2}$ in. thick over all metal except rivet heads. The concrete is reinforced with wire mesh encircling the column at a distance of 1 in. inside the outer concrete surface.

Tied columns and spiral columns are commonly used today. In order to conserve space, composite or combination columns may be used. The use of richer mixtures of concrete permits higher allowable unit stresses and thus permits smaller cross-sectional areas for both tied or spiral columns.

The allowable loads that may be placed on columns depend entirely upon the limitations set forth in the building code controlling construction. These requirements are far from being uniform and are frequently revised. In this text column formulas and specifications are used that are common to a number of codes and are considered to be conservative. No attempt is made to compare the various column formulas. Before making any computations for the design of a structure, the designer must consult the building regulations controlling construction in his locality and comply with the requirements set forth.

10–4. Tied Columns. A tied column has reinforcement consisting of longitudinal bars and separate lateral ties. The ratio of the effective cross-sectional area of vertical reinforcement to the gross column area, p_g, shall not be less than 0.01 nor more than 0.04. The longitudinal reinforcement shall consist of at least 4 bars of a minimum bar size of #5.

Lateral ties shall be at least $\frac{1}{4}$ in. in diameter and shall be spaced apart not over 16 bar diameters, 48 tie diameters, or the least dimension of the column. When there are more than 4 vertical bars, additional ties shall be provided so that every longitudinal bar is held firmly in its designed position.

The reinforcement for tied columns shall be protected by a covering of concrete, cast monolithically with the core, for which the thickness shall not be less than $1\frac{1}{2}$ in.

The maximum permissible axial load on *short* tied columns is given by the following formula:

$$P = 0.8 \times A_g(0.225f'_c + f_s p_g) \qquad (19)$$

in which P = the maximum permissible axial load, in pounds,

A_g = the gross area of the column, in square inches,

f'_c = the ultimate compressive strength of the concrete, in pounds per square inch,

f_s = the allowable compressive stress in vertical reinforcement, 16,000 psi for intermediate grade steel and 20,000 psi for rail or hard grade steel,

p_g = the ratio of the effective cross-sectional area of vertical reinforcement to the gross column area, A_g.

10–5. Design of a Tied Column. The designer of a reinforced concrete structure invariably makes use of safe load tables in the design of columns. When such tables are not available, the design is accomplished by assuming a trial section and computing the allowable load it will support. This allowable load is then compared with the design load to see whether or not the assumed section is sufficiently large. Since the cross section of the vertical steel may vary from 0.01 to 0.04 of the gross column area and because concrete of different strengths may be used, it is obvious that several combinations may satisfy the requirements. The following example illustrates the procedure.

Example. Let it be required to design a square tied column having an unsupported length of 8 ft 0 in. and an axial load of 115,000 lb.

SOLUTION: We shall assume that 3000-psi concrete will be used and that the vertical reinforcement will be hard grade steel for which $f_s = 20,000$ psi. See Art. 10–4.

As the unsupported length is 8 ft 0 in., a column having a least lateral dimension of 12 in. falls in the class of short columns, and its safe load may be determined by formula (19), Art. 10–4. For a trial section, let us assume the column cross section to be 12 x 12 in., with 4-#7 bars for vertical reinforcement.

One #7 bar has an area of 0.6 sq in. (Table 1–1); therefore 4 bars have an area of 4×0.6, or 2.4 sq in. The ratio of vertical reinforcement to gross area is $2.4 \div 144$ or 0.0167, the value of p_g in formula (19). Observe that this value lies between the limits of 0.01 and 0.04, as given in Art. 10–4. Then

$$A_g = 144 \qquad f'_c = 3000 \qquad f_s = 20,000 \qquad p_g = 0.0167$$

Substituting these quantities in the formula

$$P = 0.8 \times A_g(0.225f'_c + f_sp_g) \qquad \text{Formula (19), Art. 10–4}$$

$$P = 0.8 \times 144[(0.225 \times 3000) + (20,000 \times 0.0167)] = 116,230 \text{ lb}$$

or

$$P = 116,230 \text{ lb, the allowable load on the assumed section}$$

As this load is slightly greater than 115,000 lb, the design load, the assumed section, 12 x 12 in., with 4-#7 vertical bars, is acceptable.

The lateral ties will consist of #2 bars spaced 12 in. on centers to comply with the requirements given in Art. 10–4.

Problem 10–5–A. Compute the allowable axial load on a 16 x 16 in. tied column, 12 ft in length, reinforced with 4-#9 bars. The ultimate compressive strength of the concrete, f'_c, is 3000 psi, and the reinforcement is hard grade steel.

Problem 10–5–B. Design a square tied column to support an axial load of 220,000 lb, having an unsupported length of 10 ft 0 in.; 3750-psi concrete is to be used with reinforcement of hard grade steel.

10–6. Safe Load Table for Tied Columns. The preceding article explained the method of using a formula in designing a tied column. Assuming a trial section and computing its allowable load becomes a tedious method when a number of columns are to be designed. The use of Table 10–1, however, avoids the necessity of numerous trials and serves as a great time saver. Allowable loads given by use of this table are in accordance with formula (19), Art. 10–4. This formula is presented in slightly different form at the head of the table, A_s being the cross-sectional area of the vertical reinforcement. Note that the allowable loads are given in kips, units of 1000 lb. There are two parts of this table, Part 1 giving the portion of the total load carried by the concrete and Part 2 giving the load carried by the vertical bars.

The procedure for the design of columns by use of this table is as follows:

Step 1. By use of Part 1, note the load carried by the concrete for a column of a given cross section in accordance with the specification data for f'_c.

Step 2. Subtract the load carried by the concrete, found in Step 1, from the total or design load. This gives the load to be carried by the vertical bars and must lie between the minimum and maximum values given in "Load on Bars" in Part 1 of the table.

Step 3. Enter Part 2 of the table and select the number and size of bars that will give the load to be carried by the bars as determined in Step 2. Note that the selection of the bars is made to accord with the specification data for f_s, either 16,000 or 20,000 psi.

Step 4. Determine the size and spacing of the lateral ties in accordance with the data given in Art. 10–4.

To illustrate how readily this table may be used, let us design the same column given as an example in Art. 10–5.

Example. Design a square tied column having an unsupported length of 8 ft 0 in.; the axial load to be supported is 115,000 lb, 115 kips. Specification data:

$$f'_c = 3000 \text{ psi}$$

$$f_s = 20,000 \text{ psi}$$

SOLUTION: *Step 1.* Assume the column cross section to be 12 x 12 in. Referring to Part 1 of Table 10–1, we find the load to be carried by the concrete, if $f'_c = 3000$ psi, is 78 kips.

Step 2.

total axial load	=	115 kips
load carried by concrete, determined in Step 1	=	78 kips
load to be carried by the vertical bars	=	37 kips

If $f_s = 20,000$ psi, we find from the table that 23 kips and 92 kips are the minimum and maximum values that are permitted on the bars for a 12 x 12 in. cross section. As the load 37 kips lies between these limits, the 12 x 12 in. assumed section is acceptable.

Step 3. Referring to Part 2 of the table, under $f_s = 20,000$ psi, we find that 4-#7 bars will support 38 kips. As this value is slightly greater than the 37 kips found in Step 2, they will be accepted.

Step 4. For lateral ties use #2 bars spaced 12 in. on centers in conformity with the requirements given in Art. 10–4.

Example. Suppose space limitations required that a column of 10 in. in one direction be used, the data being similar to that of the previous example.

SOLUTION: Referring to Art. 10–1, we find that the minimum area permitted is 120 sq in. Therefore let us try a 10 x 12 in. cross section.

Step 1. By Part 1 of Table 10–1, the load carried on the concrete is 65 kips.

TABLE 10–1. ALLOWABLE LOADS ON TIED COLUMNS

Part 1.　P (kips) $= (0.18 f'_c A_g + 0.8 f_s A_s) \div 1000$

Column Size		Gross Area A_g	Load on Bars Min.: $0.008 f_s A_g \div 1000$ Max.: $0.032 f_s A_g \div 1000$				Load on Concrete $0.18 f'_c A_g \div 1000$				
			$f_s = 16,000$		$f_s = 20,000$		f'_c				
			Min.	Max.	Min.	Max.	2000	2500	3000	3750	5000
10	12	120	15	61	19	77	43	54	65	81	108
	14	140	18	72	22	90	50	63	76	95	126
	16	160	20	82	26	102	58	72	86	108	144
	18	180	23	92	29	115	65	81	97	122	162
12	12	144	18	74	23	92	52	65	78	97	130
	14	168	22	86	27	108	60	76	91	113	151
	16	192	25	98	31	123	69	86	104	130	173
	18	216	28	111	35	138	78	97	117	146	194
	20	240	31	123	38	154	86	108	130	162	216
14	14	196	25	100	31	125	71	88	106	132	176
	16	224	29	115	36	143	81	101	121	151	202
	18	252	32	129	40	161	91	113	136	170	227
	20	280	36	143	45	179	101	126	151	189	252
	22	308	39	158	49	197	111	139	166	208	277
16	16	256	33	131	41	164	92	115	138	173	230
	18	288	37	147	46	184	104	130	156	194	259
	20	320	41	164	51	205	115	144	173	216	288
	22	352	45	180	56	225	127	158	190	238	317
	24	384	49	197	61	246	138	173	207	259	346
18	18	324	41	166	52	207	117	146	175	219	292
	20	360	46	184	58	230	130	162	194	243	324
	22	396	51	203	63	253	143	178	214	267	356
	24	432	55	221	69	276	156	194	233	292	389
	26	468	60	240	75	300	168	211	253	316	421

Size										
20	400	51	205	64	180	144	256	216	270	360
22	440	56	225	70	198	158	282	238	297	396
24	480	61	246	77	216	173	307	259	324	432
26	520	67	266	83	234	187	333	281	351	468
28	560	72	287	90	252	202	356	302	378	504
22	484	62	248	77	218	174	310	261	327	436
24	528	68	270	84	238	190	338	285	356	475
26	572	73	293	92	257	206	366	309	386	515
28	616	79	315	99	277	222	394	333	416	554
24	576	74	295	92	259	207	369	311	389	518
26	624	80	319	100	281	225	399	337	421	562
28	672	86	344	108	302	242	430	363	454	605
26	676	87	346	108	304	243	433	365	456	608
28	728	93	373	116	328	262	466	393	491	655
28	784	100	401	125	353	282	502	423	529	706
30	900	115	461	144	405	324	576	486	608	810
32	1024	131	524	164	461	369	655	553	691	922
34	1156	148	592	185	520	416	740	624	780	1040
—	1000	128	512	160	450	360	640	540	675	900

Part 2. Load on Bars (kips) = $0.8 f_s A_s \div 1000$

Intermediate Grade: $f_s = 16{,}000$

	Number of Bars									
Bar Size	4	6	8	10	12	14	16	18	20	22
#5	16	24	32	40	48	56	63	71	79	87
#6	23	34	45	56	68	79	90	101	113	124
#7	31	46	61	77	92	108	123	138	154	169
#8	40	61	81	101	121	142	162	182	202	223
#9	51	77	102	128	154	179	205	230	256	282
#10	65	98	130	163	195	228	260	293	325	358
#11	80	120	160	200	240	280	320	360	400	440

Rail or Hard Grade: $f_s = 20{,}000$

	Number of Bars									
Bar Size	4	6	8	10	12	14	16	18	20	22
#5	20	30	40	50	60	69	79	89	99	109
#6	28	42	56	70	85	99	113	127	141	155
#7	38	58	77	96	115	134	154	173	192	211
#8	51	76	101	126	152	177	202	227	253	278
#9	64	96	128	160	192	224	256	288	320	352
#10	81	122	163	203	244	285	325	366	407	447
#11	100	150	200	250	300	349	399	449	499	549

Step 2.

total column load   = 115 kips
load carried on concrete   = 65 kips
                                       ———
load to be carried by vertical bars = 50 kips

Note that this magnitude falls between the limits of 19 and 77 kips, hence the 10 x 12 in. cross section is satisfactory.

Step 3. Accept 4-#8 bars as the vertical reinforcement, Part 2 of Table 10–1. These bars will support 51 kips and only 50 kips are required.

Step 4. The lateral ties require #2 bars spaced 10 in. on centers. See Art. 10–4.

Problem 10–6–A. Verify the allowable load computed for Problem 10–5–A by use of Table 10–1.

Problem 10–6–B. By use of Table 10–1, design a square tied column 12 ft 6 in. in length, having an axial load of 180,000 lb. Specification data:

$$f'_c = 3000 \text{ psi}$$

$$f_s = 20,000 \text{ psi}$$

Problem 10–6–C. Verify the column load designed for Problem 10–6–B by use of formula (19), Art. 10–4.

10–7. Spiral Columns. *Spiral column* is the term given to a concrete column reinforced with vertical bars and closely spaced continuous spiral hooping, as indicated in Fig. 10–1(*b*). When a concrete column is subjected to a load, there is a tendency for the concrete to expand in a direction perpendicular to the vertical axis of the column. To provide restraint against this tendency to burst and also to support laterally the vertical reinforcing bars, spiral hooping is introduced. Although spiral reinforcement is limited almost entirely to columns of circular and square cross sections, it may be employed in rectangular cross sections as well.

The ratio, p_g, of the area of the vertical reinforcement to the gross column area shall be not less than 0.01 nor more than 0.08. The minimum number of bars shall be six, and the minimum bar size shall be #5.

The maximum permissible axial load for spiral columns is found by the formula

$$P = A_g(0.225f'_c + f_s p_g) \qquad (20)$$

in which P = the maximum permissible axial load, in pounds,

A_g = the gross area of the column, in square inches,

f'_c = the ultimate compressive strength of the concrete, in pounds per square inch,

f_s = the allowable compressive unit stress in the vertical reinforcement, 16,000 psi for intermediate grade steel and 20,000 psi for rail or hard grade steel,

p_g = the ratio of the effective cross-sectional area of the vertical reinforcement to the gross column area, A_g.

The ratio of spiral reinforcement, p', shall not be less than the value given by formula (21).

$$p' = 0.45 \left(\frac{A_g}{A_c} - 1 \right) \frac{f'_c}{f'_s} \qquad (21)$$

in which p' = the ratio of volume of spiral reinforcement to the volume of the concrete core (out to out of spirals),

A_g = the gross area of the column, in square inches,

A_c = the area of the column core, in square inches,

f'_c = the ultimate compressive unit stress of concrete,

f'_s = useful limit stress of spiral reinforcement, to be taken as 40,000 psi for hot-rolled bars of intermediate grade, 50,000 psi for bars of hard grade, and 60,000 psi for cold-drawn wire.

The spiral reinforcement shall consist of evenly spaced continuous spirals held firmly in place by at least three vertical spacer bars. The center-to-center spacing of the spirals shall not exceed one sixth of the core diameter and the clear spacing between spirals shall not exceed 3 in. nor be less than $1\frac{3}{8}$ in. or $1\frac{1}{2}$ times the maximum size of the coarse aggregate.

The column reinforcement shall be protected everywhere by a covering of concrete cast monolithically with the core, for which the thickness shall not be less than $1\frac{1}{2}$ in. or as provided by fire protection or weathering provisions of the governing code.

10–8. Design of a Spiral Column. The design of a spiral column is generally accomplished by the use of tables. When tables are not available, it is necessary to assume a trial section and to compute its maximum allowable load. To illustrate the various steps required, let us take a given cross section and determine its permissible maximum load.

Example. A short spiral column has a gross diameter of 18 in., with 2 in. of protecting concrete. The vertical reinforcement consists of 10-#6 bars. Specification data:

$$f'_c = 3000 \text{ psi}$$

$$f_s = 20,000 \text{ psi}$$

The spiral reinforcement will consist of cold-drawn wire, for which $f'_s = 60,000$ psi, as given in Art. 10–7. Let it be required to determine the allowable axial load on the column.

SOLUTION: A #6 bar has an area of 0.44 sq in., Table 1–1; therefore the 10-#6 bars have an area of 10 × 0.44, or 4.4 sq in. A_g, the area of a column cross section whose diameter is 18 in., is

$$D^2 \times 0.7854 = 18 \times 18 \times 0.7854 = 254.5 \text{ sq in.}$$

Then

$$p_g = \frac{4.4}{254.5} = 0.0172$$

The maximum allowable axial load is determined by the formula

$$P = A_g(0.225f'_c + f_s p_g) \qquad \text{Formula (20), Art. 10–7}$$

Substituting the known values,

$$P = 254.5[(0.225 \times 3000) + (20,000 \times 0.0172)] = 259,330 \text{ lb}$$

the maximum permissible axial load.

To determine the spiral reinforcement, we use formula

$$p' = 0.45 \left(\frac{A_g}{A_c} - 1\right)\frac{f'_c}{f'_s} \qquad \text{Formula (21), Art. 10–7}$$

The area of the 14-in. core is $14 \times 14 \times 0.7854 = 153.9$ sq in.

Substituting in formula (21),

$$p' = 0.45 \left(\frac{254.5}{153.9} - 1 \right) \times \frac{3000}{60,000} = 0.0146$$

the ratio of spiral reinforcement to the volume of the concrete core. As a 1-in. length of core contains 153.9 cu in., a 1-in. length of core requires a volume of spiral of 0.0146 × 153.9, or 2.24 cu in. Let us assume that the spiral will be a #3 bar, the area of which is 0.11 sq in. The length of one complete turn of the spiral is the circumference of a circle whose diameter is 14 in., the diameter of the core. Hence the length of one turn is 14 × 3.1416 = 44 in., and the volume of one turn is 44 × 0.11, or 4.84 cu in. The number of inches of column length to give 4.84 cu in. of spiral is 4.84 ÷ 2.24 = 2.16, the center-to-center pitch of the spiral. Accept a #3 bar with a 2-in. pitch as the spiral reinforcement.

Problem 10–8–A. Compute the allowable axial load on a short spiral column having a gross diameter of 16 in., with 2 in. of protecting concrete. The vertical reinforcement consists of 8-#6 bars. Specification data:

$$f_s = 20,000 \text{ psi}$$

$$f'_c = 2500 \text{ psi}$$

Problem 10–8–B. What spiral reinforcement should be used for the column given in Problem 10–8–A, using cold-drawn wire?

10–9. Safe Load Tables for Spiral Columns. Tables 10–2, 10–3, and 10–4 are of great assistance in the design of spiral columns. Tables 10–2 and 10–3 are used to determine the areas of the concrete and vertical reinforcing bars in the same manner described in Art. 10–6 for tied columns. Table 10–4 is used to determine the size and pitch of spiral reinforcement. To illustrate the use of these tables, we will consider the problem illustrated in the preceding article.

Example. Let it be required to design a short spiral column having an axial load of 259 kips. Specification data:

$$f'_c = 3000 \text{ psi}$$

$$f_s = 20,000 \text{ psi}$$

TABLE 10-2. SPIRAL COLUMNS: LOAD ON GROSS SECTION *

$$P \text{ (kips)} = (0.225 f'_c A_g + f_s A_s) \div 1000$$

Square Columns

Col. Size	Gross Area A_g	$f_s=16{,}000$ Min. Load	$f_s=16{,}000$ Max. Load	$f_s=20{,}000$ Min. Load	$f_s=20{,}000$ Max. Load	f'_c 2000	2500	3000	3750	5000
14	196	31	122	39	152	88	110	132	165	221
15	225	36	150	45	187	101	127	152	190	253
16	256	41	150	51	187	115	144	173	216	288
17	289	46	175	58	218	130	163	195	244	325
18	324	52	200	65	250	146	182	219	273	365
19	361	58	200	72	250	162	203	244	305	406
20	400	64	225	80	281	180	225	270	337	450
21	441	71	225	88	281	198	248	298	372	496
22	484	77	250	97	312	218	272	327	408	544
23	529	85	275	106	343	238	298	357	446	595
24	576	92	275	115	343	259	324	389	486	648
25	625	100	300	125	374	281	352	422	527	703
26	676	108	324	135	406	304	380	456	570	760
27	729	117	324	146	406	328	410	492	615	820
28	784	125	349	157	437	353	441	529	661	882
29	841	135	349	168	437	378	473	567	710	946
30	900	144	374	180	468	405	506	608	760	1013
31	961	154	399	192	499	433	540	648	811	1081
32	1024	164	399	205	499	461	576	691	864	1151
33	1089	174	424	218	531	490	613	735	919	1225

Round Columns

Col. Size	Gross Area A_g	$f_s=16{,}000$ Min. Load	$f_s=16{,}000$ Max. Load	$f_s=20{,}000$ Min. Load	$f_s=20{,}000$ Max. Load	f'_c 2000	2500	3000	3750	5000
14	154	25	122	31	152	69	87	104	130	173
15	177	28	150	35	187	80	99	119	149	199
16	201	32	150	40	187	91	113	136	170	226
17	227	36	175	45	218	102	128	153	192	255
18	254	41	200	51	250	114	143	172	215	286
19	284	45	200	57	250	128	159	191	239	319
20	314	50	225	63	281	141	177	212	265	354
21	346	55	225	69	281	156	195	234	292	390
22	380	61	250	76	312	171	214	257	321	428
23	415	66	275	83	343	187	234	280	350	467
24	452	72	275	90	343	204	254	305	382	509
25	491	79	300	98	374	221	276	331	414	552
26	531	85	324	106	406	239	299	358	448	597
27	573	92	324	115	406	258	322	387	483	644
28	616	98	349	123	437	277	346	416	519	693
29	661	106	349	132	437	297	372	446	557	743
30	707	113	374	141	468	318	398	477	596	795
31	755	121	399	151	499	340	424	510	637	849
32	804	129	399	161	499	362	452	543	678	905
33	855	137	424	171	531	385	481	577	722	962

Note: In both sections the "Load on Concrete" columns are $0.225 f'_c A_g \div 1000$.

* Taken by permission from *Reinforced Concrete Design Handbook*, published by the American Concrete Institute.
† Minimum area of reinforcement 0.01A_g.
‡ With 1½" concrete protection and maximum number of maximum-size bars arranged in one outer ring.

Cold-drawn wire will be used for the spiral reinforcement. There will be a 2-in. concrete protection.

SOLUTION: Assume the column cross section to be circular with an 18-in. diameter. Referring to Table 10–2, we find that the load carried by the concrete is 172 kips. Then

| column load | = 259 kips |
| load carried by the concrete | = 172 kips |

| remainder of load to be carried by the vertical bars | = 87 kips |

As 87 kips, the load to be carried by the bars, falls between the limits 51 kips and 250 kips given in Table 10–2, the 18-in. column is satisfactory.

In Table 10–3 we find that 10-#6 bars will support a load of 88 kips and therefore are accepted. Note also that this table gives 12 as the maximum number of bars that may be used in one ring for a 14-in. diameter core.

In the section of Table 10–4 for cold-drawn wire with 2-in. concrete protection the spiral reinforcement for an 18-in. diameter round column is #3 ($\frac{3}{8}$ in.) spiral with a 2-in. pitch.

We find that these results agree entirely with the computations given in the example in Art. 10–8. The use of the tables, however, affords a great saving of time.

Problem 10–9–A. By use of tables, design a short spiral column to support an axial load of 390,000 lb. Specification data:

$$f_s = 20,000 \text{ psi}$$

$$f'_c = 3000 \text{ psi}$$

10–10. Long Columns. The discussion on columns thus far has been confined to *short columns*, that is, columns whose unsupported lengths are not greater than 10 times the least lateral dimension. When the ratio of unsupported length to least dimension exceeds this value, the columns are called *long columns* and the maximum allowable axial load is reduced. To compute the allowable loads on *long columns*, the following formula is used:

$$P' = P\left(1.3 - 0.03\frac{h}{\dot{t}}\right) \qquad (22)$$

TABLE 10–3. SPIRAL COLUMNS: LOADS ON BARS *

Load on Bars, A_s (kips) = $f_s A_s$ ÷ 1000   (Max. A_s = 0.08A_g)

Bar Size	6	7	8	9	10	11	12	13	14	15	16	17	18	19	20	21	22	23	24	25	26
Intermediate Grade: f_s = 16,000																					
#5	30	35	40	45	50	55	60	64	69	74	79	84	89	94	99	104	109	114	119	124	129
#6	42	49	56	63	70	77	84	92	99	106	113	120	127	134	141	148	155	162	169	176	183
#7	58	67	77	86	96	106	115	125	134	144	154	163	173	182	192	202	211	221	230	240	250
#8	76	88	101	114	126	139	152	164	177	190	202	215	228	240	253	266	278	291	303	316	329
#9	96	112	128	144	160	176	192	208	224	240	256	272	288	304	320	336	352	368	384	400	416
#10	122	142	163	183	203	224	244	264	285	305	325	346	366	386	406	427	447	467	488	508	528
#11	150	175	200	225	250	275	300	324	349	374	399	424	449	474	499	524	549	574	599	624	649
Rail or Hard Grade: f_s = 20,000																					
#5	37	43	50	56	62	68	74	81	87	93	99	105	112	118	124	130	136	143	149	155	161
#6	53	62	70	79	88	97	106	114	123	132	141	150	158	167	176	185	194	202	211	220	229
#7	72	84	96	108	120	132	144	156	168	180	192	204	216	228	240	252	264	276	288	300	312
#8	95	111	126	142	158	174	190	205	221	237	253	269	284	300	316	332	348	364	379	395	411
#9	120	140	160	180	200	220	240	260	280	300	320	340	360	380	400	420	440	460	480	500	520
#10	152	178	203	229	254	279	305	330	356	381	406	432	457	483	508	534	559	584	610	635	660
#11	187	218	250	281	312	343	374	406	437	468	499	531	562	593	624	655	686	718	749	780	811

Number of Bars

Maximum Number of Bars in Outer Ring, O, and in Inner Ring, I

d: Diameter of Core

Bar Size	Ring	10	11	12	13	14	15	16	17	18	19	20	21	22	23	24	25	26	27	28	29	30
#5	O	9	10	11	13	14	15	16	17	18	19	21	22	23	24	25	26	27	29	30	31	32
	I	4	5	7	8	9	10	11	12	13	15	16	17	18	19	20	21	23	24	25	26	27
#6	O	8	9	10	11	12	13	14	16	17	18	19	20	21	22	23	24	25	26	27	28	29
	I	—	5	6	7	8	9	10	11	12	13	14	15	16	17	18	19	20	21	22	23	24
#7	O	7	8	9	10	11	12	13	14	15	16	17	18	19	20	21	22	23	24	25	26	27
	I	—	4	5	6	7	8	9	10	11	11	12	13	14	15	16	17	18	19	20	21	22
#8	O	7	8	9	9	10	11	12	13	14	15	16	17	18	18	19	20	21	22	23	24	25
	I	—	—	4	5	6	7	8	8	9	10	11	12	13	14	15	16	17	17	18	19	20
#9	O	6	7	8	9	9	10	11	12	13	13	14	15	16	16	17	18	19	20	20	21	22
	I	—	—	—	—	—	—	6	7	7	8	9	9	10	11	12	13	13	14	15	15	16
#10	O	5	6	7	8	8	9	10	10	11	12	13	13	14	15	15	16	17	17	18	19	19
	I	—	—	—	—	—	—	—	5	6	7	8	8	9	9	10	11	12	12	13	13	14
#11	O	5	5	6	7	7	8	9	9	10	11	11	12	12	13	14	14	15	16	16	17	18
	I	—	—	—	—	—	—	—	—	5	6	6	7	7	8	9	9	10	11	11	12	12

* Reproduced by permission of the American Concrete Institute from *Reinforced Concrete Design Handbook*.

TABLE 10–4. SPIRAL COLUMNS: SIZE AND PITCH OF SPIRALS

Column Size	Core Diameter	Square Column					Round Column				
		2000	2500	3000	3750	5000	2000	2500	3000	3750	5000
Hot-Rolled 1½-In. Concrete Protection											
14	11	*	*	*	*	*	⅜–1¾	⅜–1¾	⅜–1¾	**	**
15	12	½–2	½–2	⅝–2	⅝–2	*	⅜–2	⅜–2	⅜–1¾	½–2	½–2
16	13	½–2	½–2	⅝–2	⅝–2	*	⅜–2	⅜–2	⅜–1¾	½–2	½–2
17	14	½–2¼	½–2¼	⅝–2¼	⅝–2¼	*	⅜–2¼	⅜–2¼	⅜–1¾	½–2¼	½–2
18	15	½–2½	½–2¼	⅝–2½	⅝–2¼	*	⅜–2½	⅜–2¼	⅜–1¾	½–2½	½–2
19	16	½–2½	½–2	⅝–2½	⅝–2¼	*	⅜–2½	⅜–2¼	⅜–2	½–2½	½–2
20	17	½–2¾	½–2	⅝–2¾	⅝–2¼	*	⅜–2¾	⅜–2¼	⅜–2	½–2¾	½–2
21	18	½–2½	½–2	⅝–2¾	⅝–2	*	⅜–3	⅜–2¼	⅜–2	½–2¾	½–2
22	19	½–2½	½–2	⅝–2¾	⅝–2	*	⅜–3	⅜–2¼	⅜–2	½–2¾	½–2
23	20	½–2½	½–2	⅝–2½	⅝–2	*	⅜–3	⅜–2¼	⅜–2	½–2¾	½–2
24	21	½–2½	½–2	⅝–2½	⅝–2	*	⅜–3	⅜–2¼	⅜–2	½–2¾	½–2
25	22	½–2½	½–2	⅝–2½	⅝–2	*	⅜–3	⅜–2¼	⅜–2	½–2¾	½–2
26	23	½–2¼	⅝–3	⅝–2½	⅝–2	*	⅜–3	⅜–2¼	⅜–2	½–2¾	½–2
27	24	½–2¼	⅝–3	⅝–2½	⅝–2	*	⅜–3	⅜–2¼	⅜–2	½–2¾	½–2
28	25	½–2¼	⅝–2¾	⅝–2¼	*	*	⅜–3	⅜–2¼	⅜–2	½–2¾	½–2
29	26	½–2¼	⅝–2¾	⅝–2¼	*	*	⅜–3	⅜–2¼	⅜–2	½–2¾	½–2
30	27	½–2¼	⅝–2¾	⅝–2¼	*	*	⅜–3	⅜–2¼	⅜–2	½–2¾	½–2¼
31	28	½–2¼	⅝–2¾	⅝–2¼	*	*	⅜–3	⅜–2¼	⅜–2	½–2¾	½–2¼
32	29	½–2	⅝–2¾	⅝–2¼	*	*	⅜–3	⅜–2¼	⅜–2	½–2¾	½–2¼
33	30	½–2	⅝–2½	⅝–2¼	*	*	⅜–3	⅜–2¼	⅜–2	½–3	½–2¼

Cold-Drawn 1½-In. Concrete Protection

14	11	⅜–1¾	⅜–1¾	*	*	*	¼–1¾	⅜–1¾	⅜–1¾	⅜–1¾	⅜–1¾
15	12	⅜–2	⅜–1¾	½–2	½–2	⅝–2	¼–1¾	⅜–2	⅜–2	⅜–2	⅜–1¾
16	13	⅜–2	⅜–1¾	½–2	½–2	⅝–2	¼–1¾	⅜–2	⅜–2	⅜–2	⅜–1¾
17	14	⅜–2¼	⅜–1¾	½–2¼	½–2¼	⅝–2¼	¼–1¾	⅜–2¼	⅜–2¼	⅜–2¼	⅜–1¾
18	15	⅜–2¼	⅜–1¾	½–2½	½–2¼	⅝–2½	¼–2	⅜–2½	⅜–2½	⅜–2¼	⅜–1¾
19	16	⅜–2¼	⅜–1¾	½–2½	½–2	⅝–2½	¼–2	⅜–2½	⅜–2½	⅜–2¼	⅜–1¾
20	17	⅜–2¼	⅜–1¾	½–2¾	½–2	⅝–2½	¼–2	⅜–2¾	⅜–2¾	⅜–2¼	⅜–1¾
21	18	⅜–2	⅜–1¾	½–2½	½–2	⅝–2½	¼–2	⅜–3	⅜–3	⅜–2¼	⅜–1¾
22	19	⅜–2	⅜–1¾	½–2½	½–2	⅝–2¼	¼–2	⅜–3	⅜–3	⅜–2¼	⅜–1¾
23	20	⅜–2	½–3	½–2½	½–2	⅝–2¼	¼–2	⅜–3¼	⅜–3	⅜–2¼	½–3¼
24	21	⅜–2	½–3	½–2½	½–2	⅝–2¼	¼–2	⅜–3¼	⅜–3	⅜–2¼	½–3¼
25	22	⅜–2	½–3	½–2½	½–2	⅝–2¼	¼–2	⅜–3¼	⅜–3	⅜–2¼	½–3¼
26	23	⅜–2	½–2¾	½–2¼	⅝–3	⅝–2¼	¼–2	⅜–3¼	⅜–3	⅜–2¼	½–3¼
27	24	⅜–2	½–2¾	½–2¼	⅝–3	⅝–2¼	¼–2	⅜–3¼	⅜–3	⅜–2¼	½–3¼
28	25	½–3½	½–2¾	½–2¼	⅝–2¾	⅝–2	¼–2	⅜–3¼	⅜–3	⅜–2¼	½–3¼
29	26	½–3½	½–2¾	½–2¼	⅝–2¾	⅝–2	¼–2	⅜–3¼	⅜–3	⅜–2¼	½–3¼
30	27	½–3¼	½–2¾	½–2¼	⅝–2¾	⅝–2	¼–2	⅜–3¼	⅜–3	⅜–2¼	½–3¼
31	28	½–3¼	½–2½	½–2¼	⅝–2¾	⅝–2	¼–2	⅜–3¼	⅜–3	⅜–2¼	½–3¼
32	29	½–3¼	½–2½	½–2	⅝–2¾	⅝–2	¼–2	⅜–3¼	⅜–3	⅜–2¼	½–3¼
33	30	½–3¼	½–2½	½–2	⅝–2½	⅝–2	¼–2	⅜–3¼	⅜–3	⅜–2¼	½–3¼

TABLE 10–4. SPIRAL COLUMNS: SIZE AND PITCH OF SPIRALS (*Continued*)

Column Size	Core Diameter	Square Column 2000	Square Column 2500	Square Column 3000	Square Column 3750	Square Column 5000	Round Column 2000	Round Column 2500	Round Column 3000	Round Column 3750	Round Column 5000
Hot-Rolled 2-In. Concrete Protection											
14	10	*	*	*	*	*	**	**	**	**	**
15	11	*	*	*	*	*	3/8–1 3/4	**	**	**	**
16	12	1/2–2	5/8–2	5/8–2	*	*	3/8–2	1/2–2	1/2–2	1/2–2	5/8–2
17	13	1/2–2	5/8–2	5/8–2	*	*	3/8–2	1/2–2	1/2–2	1/2–2	5/8–2
18	14	1/2–2 1/4	5/8–2 1/4	5/8–2 1/4	*	*	3/8–2	3/8–1 3/4	1/2–2 1/4	1/2–2	5/8–2 1/4
19	15	1/2–2 1/4	5/8–2 1/2	5/8–2 1/4	*	*	3/8–2	3/8–1 3/4	1/2–2 1/2	1/2–2	5/8–2 1/4
20	16	1/2–2 1/4	5/8–2 1/2	5/8–2 1/4	*	*	3/8–2	3/8–1 3/4	1/2–2 1/2	1/2–2	5/8–2 1/4
21	17	1/2–2	5/8–2 3/4	5/8–2 1/4	*	*	3/8–2	3/8–1 3/4	1/2–2 1/2	1/2–2	5/8–2 1/4
22	18	1/2–2	5/8–2 1/2	5/8–2 1/4	*	*	3/8–2	3/8–1 3/4	1/2–2 1/2	1/2–2	5/8–2 1/4
23	19	1/2–2	5/8–2 1/2	5/8–2	*	*	3/8–2	3/8–1 3/4	1/2–2 1/2	1/2–2	5/8–2 1/4
24	20	1/2–2	5/8–2 1/2	5/8–2	*	*	3/8–2	3/8–1 3/4	1/2–2 1/2	5/8–3 1/4	5/8–2 1/2
25	21	1/2–2	5/8–2 1/2	5/8–2	*	*	3/8–2	3/8–1 3/4	1/2–2 1/2	5/8–3 1/4	5/8–2 1/2
26	22	1/2–2	5/8–2 1/2	5/8–2	*	*	3/8–2 1/4	1/2–3 1/4	1/2–2 1/2	5/8–3 1/4	5/8–2 1/2
27	23	1/2–2	5/8–2 1/2	5/8–2	*	*	3/8–2 1/4	1/2–3 1/4	1/2–2 1/2	5/8–3 1/4	5/8–2 1/2
28	24	1/2–2	5/8–2 1/2	5/8–2	*	*	3/8–2 1/4	1/2–3 1/4	1/2–2 1/2	5/8–3 1/4	5/8–2 1/2
29	25	1/2–2	5/8–2 1/4	5/8–2	*	*	3/8–2 1/4	1/2–3 1/4	1/2–2 3/4	5/8–3 1/4	5/8–2 1/2
30	26	5/8–3	5/8–2 1/4	5/8–2	*	*	3/8–2 1/4	1/2–3 1/4	1/2–2 3/4	5/8–3 1/4	5/8–2 1/2
31	27	5/8–3	5/8–2 1/4	5/8–2	*	*	3/8–2 1/4	1/2–3 1/4	1/2–2 3/4	5/8–3 1/4	5/8–2 1/2
32	28	5/8–2 3/4	5/8–2 1/4	*	*	*	3/8–2 1/4	1/2–3 1/4	1/2–2 3/4	5/8–3 1/4	5/8–2 1/2
33	29	5/8–2 3/4	5/8–2 1/4	*	*	*	3/8–2 1/4	1/2–3 1/4	1/2–2 3/4	5/8–3 1/4	5/8–2 1/2

Cold-Drawn 2-In. Concrete Protection

14	10	*	*	*	*	*	**	**	**	**	**
15	11	⅜–1¾	*	*	*	*	⅜–1¾	⅜–1¾	⅜–1¾	**	**
16	12	⅜–1¾	½–2	½–2	⅝–2	⅝–2	⅜–2	⅜–2	⅜–2	½–2	½–2
17	13	⅜–1¾	½–2	½–2	⅝–2	⅝–2	⅜–2	⅜–2	⅜–2	½–2	½–2
18	14	⅜–1¾	½–2¼	½–2¼	⅝–2¼	⅝–2	⅜–2¼	⅜–2¼	⅜–2	½–2¼	½–2¼
19	15	⅜–1¾	½–2½	½–2¼	⅝–2½	⅝–2	⅜–2½	⅜–2½	⅜–2	½–2½	½–2¼
20	16	⅜–1¾	½–2½	½–2¼	⅝–2½	⅝–2	⅜–2½	⅜–2½	⅜–2	½–2½	½–2¼
21	17	⅜–1¾	½–2½	½–2	⅝–2½	⅝–2	⅜–2¾	⅜–2½	⅜–2	½–2¾	½–2¼
22	18	⅜–1¾	½–2½	½–2	⅝–2½	⅝–2	⅜–3	⅜–2½	⅜–2	½–3	½–2¼
23	19	⅜–1¾	½–2½	½–2	⅝–2½	⅝–2	⅜–3	⅜–2½	⅜–2	½–3	½–2¼
24	20	⅜–1¾	½–2½	½–2	⅝–2½	*	⅜–3¼	⅜–2½	⅜–2	½–3¼	½–2¼
25	21	½–3	½–2½	½–2	⅝–2½	*	⅜–3¼	⅜–2½	⅜–2	½–3¼	½–2¼
26	22	½–3	½–2¼	½–2	⅝–2½	*	⅜–3¼	⅜–2½	⅜–2	½–3¼	½–2¼
27	23	½–3	½–2¼	½–2	⅝–2½	*	⅜–3¼	⅜–2½	⅜–2¼	½–3¼	½–2¼
28	24	½–3	½–2¼	½–2	⅝–2½	*	⅜–3¼	⅜–2½	⅜–2¼	½–3¼	½–2¼
29	25	½–3	½–2¼	⅝–3	⅝–2¼	*	⅜–3¼	⅜–2½	⅜–2¼	½–3¼	½–2¼
30	26	½–2¾	½–2¼	⅝–3	⅝–2¼	*	⅜–3¼	⅜–2½	⅜–2¼	½–3¼	½–2¼
31	27	½–2¾	½–2¼	⅝–3	⅝–2¼	*	⅜–3¼	⅜–2½	⅜–2¼	½–3¼	½–2¼
32	28	½–2¾	½–2¼	⅝–2¾	⅝–2¼	*	⅜–3¼	⅜–2½	⅜–2¼	½–3¼	½–2¼
33	29	½–2¾	½–2¼	⅝–2¾	⅝–2¼	*	⅜–3¼	⅜–2½	⅜–2¼	½–3¼	½–2½

* No spiral available. May be designed as round column for load to be carried but built as square column with side dimension equal to diameter of round column.

** No spiral available. Design as tied column. Spirals below solid line are collapsible.

Reproduced by permission of the American Concrete Institute from *Reinforced Concrete Design Handbook.*

in which P' = the maximum permissible axial load on columns
having a length greater than 10 times the least
lateral dimension,

P = the permissible axial load on a short column, as
given by formulas (19) or (20),

h = the unsupported column length,

t = the least lateral dimension of the column.

Example. Determine the maximum allowable axial load for the
12 x 12 in. column, given in the example under Art. 10–5, having
a length of 12 ft instead of 8 ft.

SOLUTION: The length of the column is $12 \times 12 = 144$ in. The
least lateral dimension is 12 in., and $10 \times 12 = 120$ in. Therefore
this is a long column, since the length exceeds 10 times the least
lateral dimension. To find the maximum allowable load, we use
formula (22):

$$P' = P\left(1.3 - 0.03\,\frac{h}{t}\right)$$

The load that this column will support *if it is a short column* was
found to be 116,230 lb, Art. 10–5. Substituting in formula (22),

$$P' = 116{,}230\left(1.3 - 0.03\,\frac{12 \times 12}{12}\right) = 109{,}256 \text{ lb}$$

the maximum allowable axial load on the column if the length is
12 ft.

Problem 10–10–A. A 10 x 14 in. tied column, 13 ft 0 in. in length, has vertical
reinforcement consisting of 4-#6 bars. Compute the allowable axial load in
accordance with the following data:

$$f_s = 20{,}000 \text{ psi}$$

$$f'_c = 3000 \text{ psi}$$

10–11. Columns Subjected to Bending. Eccentric Loads. The
design of tied and spiral columns discussed in this chapter has been
confined to axial or concentric loads. Certain conditions of loading
and framing, however, produce bending moments in columns and
result in an unequal distribution of stresses in the column cross
section. For instance, a beam whose noncontinuous end is rigidly
connected to an exterior column produces bending stresses in the

column. Likewise, bending in interior columns results from loading due to unsymmetrical beam and girder arrangements. The two cases that may result from eccentric loading of columns are, first, a condition of unequal distribution of *compressive* stresses over the entire cross section and, second, *tensile* stresses over a portion of the cross section

The *Building Code Requirements for Reinforced Concrete* of the American Concrete Institute divides columns subjected to bending into two general classes:

1. In columns in which the load N has an eccentricity, e, greater than two thirds of the column depth, t (Fig. 10–2), it is assumed the concrete on the tension side has cracked and does not resist tension. Engineers in designing this type of eccentrically loaded column make use of plotted curves or tables.

2. Columns, in which e, the eccentricity, is no greater than two thirds of t, the column depth, may be designed on the assumption that the concrete on the tension side has not cracked and that its cross section and reinforcement must be such that

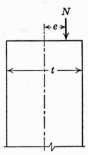

FIG. 10–2

$$\frac{f_a}{F_a} + \frac{f_b}{F_b} \qquad (23)$$

does not exceed unity.

In this formula

f_a = the nominal axial unit stress = axial load divided by A_g, the area of the member, in pounds per square inch.

F_a = the nominal allowable axial unit stress $(0.225f'_c + f_s p_g)$ for spiral columns and 0.8 times this value for tied columns, adjusted for h/t larger than 10, when necessary, in pounds per square inch.

f_b = actual bending unit stress = bending moment divided by the section modulus, $\left(\dfrac{I}{c}\right)$, of the transformed section, in pounds per square inch.

F_b = allowable bending unit stress that would be permitted if bending stress, only, existed, in pounds per square inch.

When a tied column is designed for an axial load and bending, the maximum steel ratio of 0.04 may be increased to 0.08, but the size of the column shall in no case be less than that required to withstand the axial load alone with a steel ratio of 0.04.

To design an eccentrically loaded reinforced concrete column, it is necessary first to assume a column size and a ratio of steel reinforcement. This trial column is then checked against the requirement of formula (23). The estimated size of the column may be made by computing an *equivalent axial load* for the combined axial and eccentric load. With this equivalent axial load, the size and reinforcement of the trial column may be determined in accordance with the principles and limitations previously explained for both tied and spiral columns.

The formula to be used for determining an equivalent axial load is

$$P = N + \frac{B \times M}{t} \qquad (24)$$

in which P = the equivalent axial load, in pounds,

N = the eccentric load, in pounds,

$M = N \times e$, the bending moment about the axis of the column, in inch-pounds,

t = over-all depth of the rectangular column section (see Fig. 10–2), in inches,

B = trial factor = 3 to $3\frac{1}{2}$ for tied columns and 5 to 6 for circular spiral columns, the lower values being used for columns with the minimum amount of reinforcement.

Example. Design a tied column having a 12 x 12 in. cross section and an unsupported length of 8 ft 0 in. The load on the column is 115,000 lb applied at a point 2 in. from the centroid of the section on one of the axes parallel to the sides. The concrete will have an ultimate compressive strength of $f'_c = 3000$ psi and $n = 10$. The reinforcement will be hard grade steel, $f_s = 20,000$ psi.

For this example, the eccentricity, 2 in., is smaller than two thirds of 12, or 8 in., and we may assume that the concrete on the tension side is uncracked.

SOLUTION:

1. We must first determine whether or not a 12 x 12 in. column section will support an axial load of 115,000 lb with a ratio of steel reinforcement of 0.04. In the example given in Art. 10–5 we saw that a 115,000-lb load may be supported by a 12 x 12 in. column using a steel ratio of 0.0167. Consequently, the 12 x 12 in. is acceptable thus far.

2. The next step is to compute an equivalent axial load by use of formula (24). A value of B must be assumed; let us take $B = 3$. Then,

$$P = N + \frac{B \times M}{t}$$

or

$$P = 115,000 + \frac{3 \times (115,000 \times 2)}{12} = 172,400 \text{ lb}$$

Referring to Table 10–1, we see that, for a 12 x 12 in. tied column with a maximum reinforcing ratio of 0.04,

$$\begin{aligned}
\text{load carried by the concrete} &= 78,000 \text{ lb} \\
\text{load carried by the steel} &= 92,000 \text{ lb} \\
\hline
\text{total} &= 170,000 \text{ lb}
\end{aligned}$$

As this ratio of reinforcing is much larger than the minimum amount for which $B = 3$ would be correct, a larger value of B must be used. Let $B = 3.5$. Then,

$$P = N + \frac{B \times M}{t}$$

or

$$P = 115,000 + \frac{3.5(115,000 \times 2)}{12} = 182,000 \text{ lb}$$

Thus

$$\begin{aligned}
\text{equivalent axial load} &= 182,000 \\
\text{load carried by concrete} &= 78,000
\end{aligned}$$

Subtracting,

$$\text{load to be carried by bars} = 104,000 \text{ lbs}$$

Again referring to Table 10–1, we find that 6-#10 bars will support 122,000 lb; the trial section will be a 12 x 12 in. column cross section with 6-#10 bars. The area of 1-#10 bar = 1.27 sq in., hence A_s, the area of 6 bars, = 6 × 1.27 = 7.62 sq in.

The ratio of steel reinforcement, $p_g = \dfrac{A_s}{A_g} = \dfrac{7.62}{144} = 0.0529$, A_g being the gross area of the column section. The ratio lies between 0.01 and 0.08; therefore the trial section is acceptable. See Fig. 10–3(a).

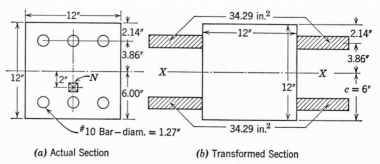

(a) Actual Section   (b) Transformed Section

FIG. 10–3

3. Determine f_a.

$$f_a = N/A_g = 115,000/144 = 799 \text{ psi}$$

the nominal axial unit stress.

4. Compute F_a.

$$F_a = (0.225f'_c + f_s p_g) \times 0.8 = [(0.225 \times 3000) + (20,000$$
$$\times 0.0529)] \times 0.8 = 1386 \text{ lb}$$

the nominal allowable axial unit stress.

5. Compute f_b.

$$f_b = \frac{M}{I} \times c$$

in which $M = N \times e$, in in-lb,

$\quad\quad\quad I$ = the moment of inertia of the transformed section, in in.^{4},

$\quad\quad\quad c$ = the distance of the extreme fiber of the cross section from the axis about which the moment of inertia is computed, in inches. In this example $c = \frac{1}{2} \times 12 = 6$ in.

Fig. 10–3(a) shows the actual cross-sectional area of the column.

Now review Art. 4–13, relating to the transformed section. The total transformed area of the six reinforcing bars is $(n - 1) \times A_s$ = $(10 - 1) \times 7.62 = 68.58$ sq in., 34.29 sq in. on each side of the horizontal axis line, as shown in Fig. 10–3(b), the transformed section.

We must now compute the moment of inertia of the transformed section with respect to the horizontal axis, $X - X$, shown in Fig. 10–3(b). Remember that #10 bars are to be used. Table 1–1 shows that the diameter of a #10 bar is 1.27 in.; $1\frac{1}{2}$ in. clear fire-proofing will be used, and the dimensions for computing the moment of inertia * are shown in Fig. 10–3(b).

The moment of inertia for the 12 x 12 in. rectangle is

$$bd^3/12 \quad \text{or} \quad I = 12 \times 12^3/12 = 1728 \text{ in.}^4$$

The moment of inertia for the wings (the hatched areas) is found by use of the transfer formula $I = I_0 + Ah^2$. But I_0 is so small, it may be ignored; hence I for the wings is

$$I = Ah^2 = 2(34.29 \times 3.86^2) = 1022 \text{ in.}^4$$

For the entire transformed section,

$$I = 1728 + 1022 = 2750 \text{ in.}^4$$

Then,

$$f_b = \frac{M}{I} \times c = \frac{115,000 \times 2}{2750} \times 6 = 501 \text{ psi}$$

the actual bending unit stress.

6. Determine F_b, the allowable bending unit stress. This is indicated, by referring to Table 4–2, as f_c, 1350 psi.

7. Checking the requirements of $\dfrac{f_a}{F_a} + \dfrac{f_b}{F_b} \leqq 1$, Formula (23),

$$\frac{799}{1386} + \frac{501}{1350} = 0.95$$

Since this quantity is less than 1, we accept a 12 x 12 in. column with 6-#10 bars, three in each face as shown in Fig. 10–3(a). The ties are #2 bars with 12 in. spacing.

---

* For moment of inertia and transferring moments of inertia, see Arts. 58, 59, and 60 of *Simplified Mechanics and Strength of Materials* by Harry Parker, John Wiley and Sons, New York.

CHAPTER 11

FOUNDATIONS

11-1. Foundations. The foundations of a building are those structural elements that support the superstructure. They are placed below grade and should extend well below the frost line. When the ground is permanently frozen to a certain depth below the surface, foundations should rest on soil below this level. The primary purpose of a footing is to spread the loads so that the allowable bearing capacity of the foundation bed is not exceeded. With the exception of bedrock, a certain amount of settlement is present for all foundation beds. It is important that the settlement be as little as possible and that, if there is settlement, it is uniform throughout the entire structure. Another essential requirement for foundations is that the lines of action of the loads, whenever possible, coincide with centers of the foundations. That is to say, the pressure on the foundation bed should be uniformly distributed. If this condition does not exist, unequal pressures result and there is a tendency toward unequal settlement.

Before determining the required dimensions of a foundation, the designer must ascertain the allowable bearing capacity of the foundation bed. In cities in which experience and tests have established the allowable strengths of various foundation soils local building codes may be consulted to determine the bearing capacities to be used in design. In the absence of such information, or for conditions in which the nature of the soil is unknown, borings or load tests should be made. For sizable structures, borings at the site should always be made. For a convenient reference, Table 11-1 is given. The allowable bearing capacities in this table are average figures compiled from a number of building codes.

The reinforcement of footings should have not less than 3 in. of concrete between it and the contact surface of the ground.

TABLE 11–1.   ALLOWABLE BEARING CAPACITIES OF VARIOUS FOUNDATION BEDS,
IN TONS PER SQUARE FOOT

Alluvial soil	$\frac{1}{2}$
Soft clay	1
Firm clay	2
Wet sand	2
Sand and clay mixed	2
Fine dry sand	3
Hard clay	4
Coarse dry sand	4
Gravel	6
Gravel and sand, well cemented	8
Hardpan or hard shale	10
Medium rock	20
Rock under caissons	25
Hard rock	80

11–2. Concrete Pedestals.   The compressive stresses in the longitudinal reinforcement at the base of a column are transferred to the pedestal or footing by dowels.   There must be at least 1 dowel for each column bar, and their sectional areas should not be less than that of the longitudinal reinforcement bars in the column. For 3000-psi concrete, or over, deformed dowels must extend up into the column and down into the pedestal or footing 20 bar diameters of intermediate or hard grade steel.   If less than 3000-psi concrete is used, these distances must be increased one third.   When the depth of the footing is insufficient to provide the required length of dowels, pedestals must be used.

The permissible compressive unit stress, f_c, over the loaded area of a pedestal or footing shall not be greater than that determined by the formula

$$f_c = f'_c \left(0.438 - 0.188 \frac{A'}{A} \right) \qquad \text{but not more than } 0.375 \, f'_c \quad (25)$$

in which f'_c = the ultimate compressive strength of concrete, in
pounds per square inch,

A' = the loaded area of the pedestal or footing at the
column base, in square inches,

A = the total area of top of pedestal or footing at the column base, in square inches.

In sloped or stepped footings A may be taken as the area of the top horizontal surface of the footing.

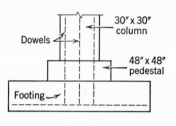

Dowels

30″ x 30″ column

48″ x 48″ pedestal

Footing

FIG. 11–1

Example. A 30 x 30 in. reinforced concrete column is supported by a 48 x 48 in. pedestal of 2500-psi concrete. See Fig. 11–1. If the column load is 600,000 lb, is the area of the pedestal large enough?

SOLUTION: Substituting the known values in the formula,

$$f_c = f'_c \left(0.438 - 0.188 \frac{A'}{A}\right) \tag{25}$$

$$f_c = 2500 \left(0.438 - 0.188 \frac{30 \times 30}{48 \times 48}\right)$$

$$f_c = 931 \text{ psi}$$

the allowable unit stress on the loaded area directly under the column. The maximum allowable $f_c = 0.375 f'_c = 0.375 \times 2500 = 938$ psi (see Table 4–2); hence the value 931 psi is acceptable.

The actual pressure is $600,000 \div (30 \times 30)$ or 666 psi. Therefore, since the actual pressure is less than the allowable, the area of the pedestal is acceptable.

Problem 11–2–A. A pedestal whose area is 36 x 36 in. supports a 24 x 24 in. column on which there is an axial load of 400,000 lb. If $f'_c = 3000$ psi, is the area of the pedestal large enough?

11–3. Wall Footings. To design a wall footing, it is convenient to consider a section of the wall 1 ft 0 in. in length. The weight of this section of the wall plus the estimated weight of the footing divided by the allowable bearing capacity of the foundation bed gives the width of the footing. Reference to Fig. 11–2 shows that the footing under the wall is an inverted beam, the upward pressure of the foundation bed corresponding to a uniformly distributed load.

Let the length of the footing be l and let a be the thickness of the wall (Fig. 11-2). Then $\dfrac{l-a}{2}$ is the projection of the footing on each side of the wall. Let w be the upward pressure of the foundation bed per foot of width. For footings supporting concrete walls, the maximum bending moment is at the face of the wall. As the projection is $\dfrac{l-a}{2}$ and w is the upward pressure per foot of width,

FIG. 11-2

$\dfrac{l-a}{2} \times w$ is the upward pressure on the projection. The lever arm of this force is one half the length of the projection, $\dfrac{l-a}{2} \times \dfrac{1}{2}$. Then

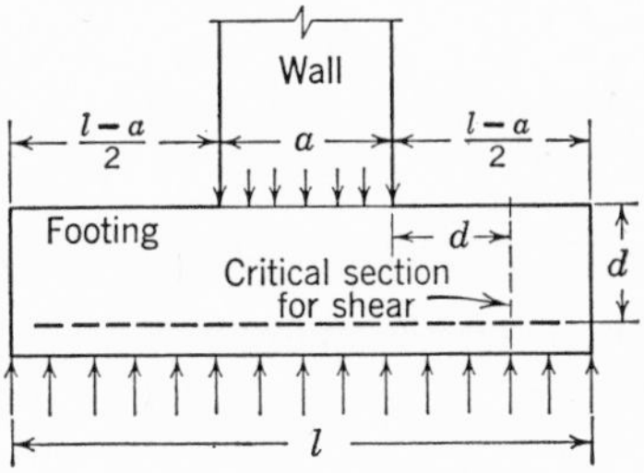

$$M = \left(\frac{l-a}{2} \times w\right) \times \left(\frac{l-a}{2} \times \frac{1}{2}\right) = \frac{w(l-a)^2}{8}$$

the value of the maximum bending moment at the face of the wall.

For footings under masonry (stone, brick, etc.) walls, the maximum bending moment is taken at a section halfway between the middle and the edge of the wall.

As in the beam problems, d is the effective depth of the reinforcing bars. In computing the vertical shearing stress, the critical section is taken at d distance from the face of the wall; see Fig. 11-2. Web reinforcement is not used in wall footings, and therefore the value of v must be within the allowable stresses for beams having no web reinforcement.

In investigating the bond stresses, the critical section for computing the vertical shear is at the face of the wall. For wall footings, the bond stress is generally quite high and therefore is an important factor in determining the size and spacing of the reinforcing bars. The usual procedure is to compute the minimum effective depth required by bending and to increase this dimension arbitrarily in order that the bond stresses may be reduced.

The main tensile reinforcing bars are invariably deformed. In addition, bars running parallel to the wall are placed in the footing to provide for stresses due to changes in temperature and to resist possible unequal settlement.

11–4. Design of a Wall Footing. The following example illustrates the various steps necessary in the design of a wall footing.

Example. A concrete wall 2 ft 0 in. in width exerts a load on the footing of 19,000 lb per linear ft. If the foundation bed is mixed sand and clay, design a reinforced concrete wall footing. Specification data:

$$f_s = 20,000 \text{ psi}$$

$$f'_c = 3000 \text{ psi}$$

$$f_c = 1350 \text{ psi}$$

$$v_c = \text{limited to } 90 \text{ psi}$$

$$u = \text{limited to } 300 \text{ psi}$$

$$n = 10$$

SOLUTION: The footing is designed as an inverted beam supporting a section of wall 1 ft 0 in. in length. Assuming that the weight of the footing is 1000 lb, the total load on the foundation bed is 19,000 + 1000, or 20,000 lb. For a foundation bed of mixed sand and clay, the allowable bearing capacity is taken as 4000 psf, Table 11–1. Then 20,000 ÷ 4000 = 5 sq ft, the area of the footing under the 1 ft 0 in. length of wall, thus making the length of the footing 5 ft 0 in. Referring to Fig. 11–2, $l = 5$ ft, $a = 2$ ft, and $\dfrac{l - a}{2} = 1.5$ ft, the length of the projection. See Fig. 11–3.

The weight of the footing does not contribute to its tendency to bend; hence 19,000 ÷ 5 = 3800 psf, which is w, the net upward pressure on the footing.

The bending moment taken at the face of the wall is

$$M = \frac{w(l - a)^2}{8} \qquad \text{(See Art. 11–3)}$$

Then

$$M = \frac{3800 \times (5 - 2)^2}{8} = 4275 \text{ ft-lb or } 51,300 \text{ in-lb}$$

The effective depth determined by bending is found by the formula

$$d = \sqrt{\frac{M}{Kb}} \qquad \text{Formula (6), Art. 4–5}$$

The width of the footing strip, b, is 12 in. From Table 4–1, $K = 236$. Then

$$d = \sqrt{\frac{51,300}{236 \times 12}} \qquad \text{or} \qquad d = 4.3 \text{ in.}$$

the minimum effective depth.

As has been noted, the bond stresses in wall footings are usually high. In order to reduce them, let us assume that d, the effective depth, is increased to 12 in. If 3 in. of insulation are added to the underside of the footing, the total depth will be $12 + 3$, or 15 in.

The critical section for shear is taken at d distance from the face of the wall. Then $V = (1.5 - 1) \times 3800 = 1900$ lb.

$$v = \frac{V}{jbd} \qquad \text{Formula (10), Art. 5–2}$$

Substituting,

$$v = \frac{1900}{0.875 \times 12 \times 12} = 15 \text{ psi}$$

acceptable, as it is less than 90 psi, the allowable shearing unit stress.

The value of V in computing the bond stress is taken at the face of the wall. Then $V = 1.5 \times 3800 = 5700$ lb. Assume for the moment that the reinforcement consists of #4 bars, their perimeters being 1.57 in. Let x be the number of bars in the 12-in. length of footing. Specification data give $u = 300$ psi.

$$u = \frac{V}{\Sigma_0 jd} \qquad \text{Formula (13), Art. 5–6}$$

Substituting,

$$300 = \frac{5700}{x \times 1.57 \times 0.875 \times 12} \qquad \text{or} \qquad x = 1.15$$

the number of bars in the 12-in. length of footing.

$$12 \div 1.15 = 10.4, \qquad \text{say } 10\tfrac{1}{2}$$

the minimum required spacing of the #4 bars.

The next step is to investigate the bars with respect to the tensile stress due to bending.

$$A_s = \frac{M}{f_s j d}$$ Formula (7), Art. 4–5

Substituting,

$$A_s = \frac{51,300}{20,000 \times 0.866 \times 12} = 0.25 \text{ sq in.}$$

Table 9–4 shows that #4 bars, $9\frac{1}{2}$ in. on centers, give this required area. We have seen that a spacing of $10\frac{1}{2}$ in. is required if the bond stress is not to exceed the allowable. Therefore we must accept #4 bars spaced $9\frac{1}{2}$ in. on centers. These bars will be deformed. Temperature stresses are provided for by running #4 bars parallel to the length of the wall, as indicated in Fig. 11–3. The

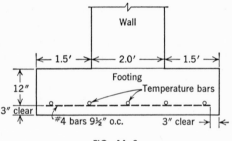

FIG. 11–3

footing as designed weighs 937.5 lb per linear ft of wall; hence the 1000-lb allowance made in computing the total load is acceptable.

The code requires 3 in. clear below the reinforcement. Then, if the total depth of the footing is 15 in., the actual effective depth will be $15 - (3 + 0.25) = 11.75$ in. The error resulting from using $d = 12$ in. is so small it may be ignored.

Problem 11–4–A. The load exerted by an 18-in. concrete wall on a reinforced concrete footing is 22,800 lb per linear ft. The foundation bed is firm clay. Design the footing in accordance with the following specification data:

$$f_s = 20,000 \text{ psi}$$

$$f'_c = 2500 \text{ psi}$$

$$f_c = 1125 \text{ psi}$$

$$v_c = \text{limited to 75 psi}$$

$$u = \text{limited to 250 psi}$$

$$n = 12$$

11-5. Independent Column Footings. The majority of independent column footings are square in plan with reinforcement consisting of two sets of bars at right angles to each other. This is known as two-way reinforcement. Four-way reinforcement consists of the addition of two diagonal bands of bars. The column may be placed directly on the footing block or it may be supported on a pedestal, the pedestal being supported by the footing block. The area of the pedestal is discussed in Art. 11-2. The compressive stress in the longitudinal reinforcement at the base of a column is transferred to the pedestal or footing by dowels, the length of which may determine the height of the pedestal.

The area of the footing is found by dividing the column load, plus the estimated weight of the footing, by the allowable bearing capacity of the foundation bed, as given in Table 11-1. The weight of independent column footings varies from 4 to 10% of the load on the column.

Two important factors in the design of reinforced concrete footings are the shear and bond stresses. A method commonly used is to assume an effective depth based on formula $d = \sqrt{\dfrac{M}{Kb}}$. This assumed depth is then used to determine the values of v and u. If they are found to exceed the allowable stresses given by the specification data, a greater depth is taken which, of course, will reduce the stresses for shear and bond.

The determination of column footing dimensions and reinforcement is not subject to precise analysis, and the loads they will support are only approximate. Building codes differ in their requirements for column footings. The American Concrete Institute's code requires that the bending moment be taken at the face of the column (or pedestal) at a section which extends completely across the footing. For the square footing shown in Fig. 11-4(a), the moment is computed by considering the load on the hatched area, cl. Let w be the upward pressure of the foundation bed in pounds per square foot, and a, c, and l, the dimensions in feet. Then, for the moment at the face of the column,

$$M = c \times l \times w \times \frac{c}{2} = \frac{wlc^2}{2} \text{ ft-lb} \quad \text{or} \quad M = 6wlc^2 \text{ in-lb}$$

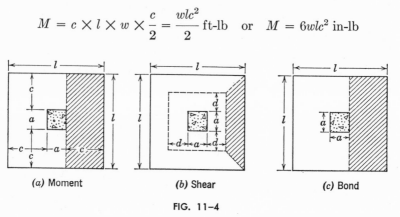

(a) Moment   (b) Shear   (c) Bond

FIG. 11–4

To allow for the two-way action in this type of footing, the total tensile reinforcement at any section must provide a resisting moment of at least 85% of the bending moment. After the bending moment has been computed, the effective depth is estimated by use of the formula $d = \sqrt{\dfrac{M}{Kb}}$. In using this formula the width, b, is taken as the entire width of the footing. It should be remembered that this formula, when used for column footings, is merely an aid in determining an effective depth. Subsequent investigation of stresses for shear and bond may require an increase in depth, these two stresses being governing factors in the design of footings.

The critical section for shear is assumed to be a vertical section at d distance from the face of the column. For a square footing, the area used in computing V, the vertical shear, is the hatched area shown in Fig. 11–4(b). This area is $\dfrac{l^2 - (a + 2d)^2}{4}$.

In computing the bond stress, the critical section is assumed to be at the face of the column. The area of the footing used in determining V is shown by the hatched area in Fig. 11–4(c). This area is $\dfrac{l(l - a)}{2}$. In computing the bond stress, the A.C.I. code permits a reduction of 15% of V, the vertical shear.

For reinforcing bars in footings, deformed bars are invariably used. The outer ends of these bars should not be less than 3 in. nor more than 6 in. from the face of the footing. A distance of 3 in. from the reinforcing bars to the bottom of the footing is considered to be a minimum thickness of protection. For footings on soil, the thickness of concrete above the reinforcement at the edge of the footing should not be less than 6 in.

11–6. Design of a Two-Way Independent Column Footing.

Example. Let it be required to design a square two-way block footing to support a 14-in. square column having a total load of 280,000 lb. The foundation bed is firm clay. Specification data:

$$f_s = 20,000 \text{ psi}$$
$$f'_c = 3000 \text{ psi}$$
$$f_c = 1350 \text{ psi}$$
$$v_c = 75 \text{ psi}$$
$$u = 240 \text{ psi}$$
$$n = 10$$

No pedestal is to be used.

SOLUTION: Estimating the weight of the footing block to be 7% of the column load, $280,000 \times 0.07 = 19,600$ lb, say 20,000 lb. Then the total load on the foundation bed is $280,000 + 20,000 = 300,000$ lb. The bearing capacity of firm clay is 4000 lb, Table 11–1; hence the required area of the footing block is $300,000 \div 4000 = 75$ sq ft. Accept, therefore, an 8 ft 8 in. square footing. See Fig. 11–5. The load producing bending in the footing is 280,000 lb; hence w, the net upward pressure of the foundation bed, is $280,000 \div 75$ or 3730 psf.

The formula used to compute the bending moment at the face of the column is $6wlc^2$ (Art. 11–5). Then, referring to Fig. 11–5,

$$M = 6 \times 3730 \times 8.67 \times 3.75^2 \times 0.85 = 2,320,000 \text{ in-lb}$$

In this equation 0.85 is the reduction factor allowed in the A.C.I. code. See Art. 11–5.

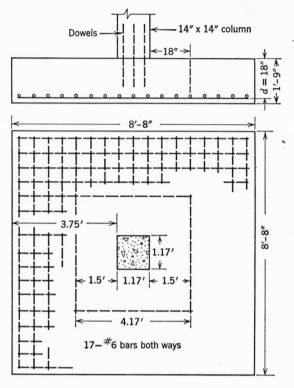

FIG. 11–5

The minimum effective depth $d = \sqrt{\dfrac{M}{Kb}}$, formula (6), Art. 4–5.

Referring to Table 4–1, $K = 236$ and $b = 8.67$ ft, or 104 in. Then

$d = \sqrt{\dfrac{2,320,000}{236 \times 104}} = 9.7$ in. This figure is only an approximation.

Accept temporarily an effective depth of 18 in. The shear and bond stresses, to be investigated later, will tell us whether or not the 18 in. is sufficiently great.

In computing the value of v, the shearing unit stress, the total vertical shear $V = \dfrac{l^2 - (a + 2d)^2}{4} \times w$

or

$$V = \frac{8.67^2 - [1.17 + (2 \times 1.5)]^2}{4} \times 3730$$

$$= 53,800 \text{ lb} \qquad \text{(See Art. 11–5)}$$

$$v = \frac{V}{jbd} \qquad\qquad \text{Formula (10), Art. 5–2}$$

Substituting,

$$v = \frac{53,800}{0.875 \times 50 \times 18} = 68.5 \text{ psi}$$

the shearing unit stress. In this equation 50 is 4.17 ft expressed in inches. The shearing stress being less than 75 psi, the allowable stress given in the specification data, it is acceptable, and thus far an effective depth of 18 in. is adequate.

To determine the area of the tensile reinforcing bars,

$$A_s = \frac{M}{f_s jd} \qquad\qquad \text{Formula (7), Art. 4–5}$$

Then

$$A_s = \frac{2,320,000}{20,000 \times 0.866 \times 18} = 7.44 \text{ sq in.}$$

Accept 17-#6 bars.

In investigating the bond stress, the value of the vertical shear

$$V = \frac{l(l - a)}{2} \times w = \frac{8.67(8.67 - 1.17)}{2} \times 3730 = 122,200 \text{ lb}$$

Taking the 15% reduction permitted by the code, $V = 122,200 \times 0.85 = 103,000$ lb.

$$u = \frac{V}{\Sigma_0 jd} \qquad\qquad \text{Formula (13), Art. 5–6}$$

Substituting,

$$u = \frac{103,000}{17 \times 2.36 \times 0.875 \times 18} = 163 \text{ psi}$$

the unit bond stress. In the foregoing equation 17 is the number of bars and 2.36 is the perimeter of a #6 bar, Table 1–1. The unit stress for bond, 163 psi, being less than 240 psi, the allowable, the 17 bars are acceptable.

The reinforcement, then, consists of two bands of 17-#6 deformed bars running at right angles with each other. The effective depth is 18 in., and 3 in. added for protection for the reinforcement gives a total depth of 1 ft 9 in. The weight of the footing, at 150 lb per cu ft, is

$$1.75 \times 8.67 \times 8.67 \times 150 = 19,600 \text{ lb}$$

Therefore the estimated weight of 20,000 lb used in determining the area of the footing was sufficiently large.

Problem 11-6-A. The column load on a two-way independent column footing is 218,000 lb. The column is 14 in. square, and the foundation bed has an allowable bearing capacity of 3000 psf. Design a square reinforced concrete footing. Specification data:

$$f_s = 20,000 \text{ psi}$$

$$f'_c = 3000 \text{ psi}$$

$$f_c = 1350 \text{ psi}$$

$$v_c = 75 \text{ psi}$$

$$u = 240 \text{ psi}$$

$$n = 10$$

11-7. Safe Load Table for Independent Column Footings. Table 11-2 is presented as an aid to the designer in determining the dimensions and necessary reinforcement for square two-way block column footings. The specification data, in accordance with which this table has been compiled, are given at the top of the table. In most cases a large and small column size are given. The footings are designed for the smallest size but may be used for the larger sizes, provided the column load is not increased. To use this table for columns having a circular cross section, enter the table having a square column of an equivalent area.

Consider a column load of 280,000 lb; the column is 14 in. square, the bearing capacity of the foundation bed is 4000 psf, and $f'_c = 3000$ psi. These are the design data given in the example worked out in the preceding article. Referring to Table 11-2, we find that the size of the footing is 8 ft 8 in. square, the total depth is 21 in., and the reinforcement consists of two bands of 17-#6 bars—the same results found by the computations

To illustrate how readily column footings may be determined by use of this table, consider the following problem.

Example. A 16-in. square column has an axial load of 250,000 lb, and the bearing capacity of the foundation bed is 6000 psf. For 2500 psi concrete with $f_s = 20,000$ psi and $f_c = 1125$ psi, what are the dimensions and reinforcement for a two-way square footing?

SOLUTION: Referring to the section of Table 11–2 which gives a soil pressure of 6000 psf, we find that a 16-in. square column having a load of 250,000 lb requires a footing 6 ft 7 in. square. The total depth of the footing is 19 in., and two bands of 17-#5 bars constitute the tensile reinforcement.

Problem 11–7–A. By use of Table 11–2, design a square two-way independent column footing to support a column load of 350,000 lb. The column is 16 in. square, and the allowable bearing capacity of the soil is 5000 psf. Specification data:

$$f_s = 20,000 \text{ psi}$$

$$f'_c = 2500 \text{ psi}$$

$$f_c = 1125 \text{ psi}$$

$$n = 12$$

11–8. Sloped Footings. The footing designed in Art. 11–6 is sometimes called a *block footing,* the upper and lower planes of the footing being parallel. A saving of material may sometimes be effected if the upper surface is composed of four inclined planes sloping away from the column. This is known as a *sloped footing.* If the slope is made too steep, double forms may be required and this may offset the saving that results from the smaller volume of concrete that is used. Sloped or *stepped footings* are permissible, provided the shear on any section outside the critical section does not exceed the allowable stresses specified. In addition, the thickness of the footing above the reinforcement at the edge of the footing shall not be less than 6 in. for footings on soil nor less than 12 in. for caps on piles. If no pedestal is used, it is customary to have the sloped planes extend from the outer edge of the footing to within 3 or 4 in. of the face of the column. In any case, the compressive unit stress on top of the footing directly under the column shall not be greater than that determined by formula (25). Art. 11–2.

TABLE 11-2. SAFE LOADS FOR SQUARE INDEPENDENT COLUMN FOOTINGS *

$f_s = 20,000$ psi $f'_c = 3000$ psi
$f'_c = 2500$ psi $n = 10$
$n = 12$ $f_c = 1350$ psi
$f_c = 1125$ psi $v = 75$ psi
$v = 75$ psi $u = 240$ psi
$u = 200$ psi

Two-way reinforcement uniformly spaced

Soil pressure—2000 psf

Col. Load, Kips	Sq. Col. Size, In.	Sq. Footing Width, Ft-In.	Sq. Footing Depth, In.	Bars Each Way $f'_c=2500$ No. Size	Bars Each Way $f'_c=3000$ No. Size
20	12	3-4	10	4-4	3-4
40	12	4-8	10	8-4	8-4
60	12	5-9	12	11-4	7-5
80	12	6-7	13	11-5	11-5
100	12	7-5	14	14-5	14-5
120	12	8-2	16	15-5	15-5
140	12	8-11	17	13-6	13-6
160	14	9-6	18	15-6	15-6
180	14	10-2	19	17-6	15-6
200	14	10-9	20	19-6	19-6
220	14	11-3	21	15-7	15-7
240	16	11-10	21	17-7	17-7
260	16	12-3	22	18-7	18-7
280	16	12-10	23	15-8	15-8
300	16	13-4	24	16-8	16-8

Soil pressure—4000 psf

Col. Load, Kips	Sq. Col. Size, In.	Sq. Footing Width, Ft-In.	Sq. Footing Depth, In.	Bars Each Way $f'_c=2500$ No. Size	Bars Each Way $f'_c=3000$ No. Size
40	12	3-3	10	7-4	6-4
80	12	4-7	12	12-4	11-4
120	12	5-8	15	16-4	10-5
160	14	6-6	16	14-5	14-5
200	14	7-4	19	12-6	12-6
240	16	8-0	20	14-6	14-6
280	16	8-8	21	17-6	17-6
320	16	9-3	23	15-7	15-7
360	16	9-11	24	17-7	17-7
400	18	10-5	25	14-8	14-8
440	18	11-0	27	12-9	12-9
480	20	11-6	27	14-9	14-9
520	20	11-11	28	15-9	15-9
560	20	12-5	30	16-9	16-9
600	22	12-10	30	17-9	17-9

Soil pressure—6000 psf

Col. Load, Kips	Sq. Col. Size, In.	Sq. Footing Width, Ft-In.	Sq. Footing Depth, In.	Bars Each Way $f'_c=2500$ No. Size	Bars Each Way $f'_c=3000$ No. Size
100	12	4-2	13	13-4	11-4
150	12	5-11	16	16-4	11-5
200	14	5-11	17	16-5	15-5
250	16	6-7	19	17-5	15-6
300	16	7-3	21	15-6	15-6
350	16	7-10	23	17-6	13-7
400	18	8-5	24	15-7	15-7
450	18	8-11	25	17-7	17-7
500	20	9-5	26	15-8	14-8
550	20	9-11	28	16-8	16-8
600	22	10-4	28	17-8	17-8
650	22	10-9	29	19-8	19-8
700	22	11-2	31	20-8	20-8
750	24	11-7	31	17-9	17-9
800	24	12-0	32	18-9	18-9

Soil pressure—3000 psf

Load					
40	12	3-9	10	8-4	7-4
60	12	4-7	11	10-4	9-4
80	12	5-4	13	12-4	12-4
100	12	6-0	14	16-4	16-4
120	12	6-7	15	13-5	13-5
140	12	7-1	16	15-5	15-5
160	14	7-7	17	12-6	12-6
180	14	8-1	18	13-6	10-7
200	14	8-7	19	11-7	11-7
220	14	9-0	20	12-7	12-7
240	16	9-5	21	13-7	13-7
260	16	9-9	21	14-7	14-7
280	16	10-2	22	12-8	12-8
300	16	10-7	23	13-8	13-8
320	16	10-11	24	13-8	13-8
340	16	11-3	25	14-8	14-8
360	16	11-7	25	15-8	15-8
380	18	11-11	25	16-8	16-8
400	18	12-3	26	13-9	13-9
420	18	12-7	27	14-9	14-9
440	18	12-11	28	15-9	15-9
460	18	13-2	28	15-9	15-9
480	20	13-6	28	16-9	16-9
500	20	13-10	29	17-9	17-9

Soil pressure—5000 psf

Load					
640	22	13-4	31	18-9	18-9
680	22	13-9	32	19-9	19-9
720	24	14-2	33	20-9	20-9
760	24	14-7	33	22-9	22-9
50	12	3-3	10	9-4	8-4
100	12	4-7	13	14-4	12-4
150	12	5-8	16	13-5	12-5
200	14	6-6	18	16-5	11-6
250	16	7-3	20	13-6	13-6
300	16	8-0	22	16-6	16-6
350	16	8-8	23	20-6	20-6
400	18	9-3	24	16-7	17-7
450	18	9-10	26	18-7	18-7
500	20	10-5	27	16-8	13-9
550	20	10-11	28	14-9	14-9
600	22	11-5	29	15-9	15-9
650	22	11-10	30	16-9	16-9
700	22	12-4	32	14-10	14-10
750	24	12-9	32	15-10	15-10
800	24	13-2	33	16-10	16-10
850	26	13-8	34	17-10	17-10
900	26	14-1	35	17-10	17-10
950	26	14-5	36	19-10	19-10
1000	26	14-10	37	19-10	19-10

Soil pressure—8000 psf

Load					
850	26	12-4	33	19-9	12-4
900	26	12-9	34	16-10	11-5
950	26	13-1	35	17-10	14-5
1000	28	13-5	35	18-10	14-5
100	12	3-7	12	14-4	12-4
150	12	4-5	15	17-4	11-5
200	14	5-1	16	20-4	14-5
250	16	5-8	18	22-4	14-5
300	16	6-3	20	19-5	13-6
350	16	6-9	22	21-5	15-6
400	18	7-3	23	24-5	13-7
450	18	7-8	24	20-6	14-7
500	20	8-1	25	21-6	16-7
550	20	8-6	26	24-6	14-8
600	22	8-11	27	19-7	15-8
700	22	9-8	29	23-7	14-9
800	24	10-3	31	19-8	15-9
900	26	10-11	32	22-8	14-10
1000	28	11-6	34	19-9	15-10
1100	30	12-1	35	21-9	16-10
1200	32	12-8	36	23-9	18-10
1300	32	13-2	38	20-10	20-10
1400	34	13-8	39	21-10	21-10
1500	34	14-2	40	23-10	23-10

* Reproduced by permission of the American Concrete Institute from *Reinforced Concrete Design Handbook*.

11–9. Design of a Two-Way Sloped Footing. The design of a sloped footing is quite similar to the design of a block footing. To illustrate the procedure let us consider the following example.

Example. A 20 x 20 in. column having a load of 300,000 lb is to be supported by a foundation bed with a bearing capacity of 3000 psf. Let it be required to design a two-way sloped footing. Specification data:

$$f_s = 20,000 \text{ psi}$$

$$f'_c = 2500 \text{ psi}$$

$$f_c = 1125 \text{ psi}$$

$$v_c = \text{limited to 75 psi}$$

$$u = \text{limited to 200 psi}$$

$$n = 12$$

SOLUTION: Let us assume that the weight of the footing is 0.09 times the column load, or $0.09 \times 300,000 = 27,000$ lb. Then the total load on the foundation bed will be $27,000 + 300,000$, or 327,000 lb. As the allowable bearing capacity of the soil is 3000 psf, $327,000 \div 3000 = 109$ sq ft, the minimum number of square feet required for the area of the footing. Accept, therefore, a footing 10 ft 6 in. square, giving an area of 110.25 sq ft.

The upward pressure of the foundation bed will be $300,000 \div 110.25$ or 2720 psf.

As a trial, let us assume that there is a flat area of footing 4 in. wide on each side of the column. This area, then, is $20 + 4 + 4$, or 28 in. square. By data the column is 20 in. square.

In accordance with the formula

$$f_c = f'_c \left(0.438 - 0.188 \frac{A'}{A} \right) \qquad \text{Formula (25), Art. 11–2}$$

$$f_c = 2500 \left(0.438 - 0.188 \frac{20 \times 20}{28 \times 28} \right) \qquad \text{or} \qquad f_c = 856 \text{ psi}$$

the allowable compressive stress directly under the column.

Note that this is less than the maximum allowable stress, 0.375 ×
2500, or 938 psi (Table 4–2), and therefore is acceptable. The
actual compressive stress is 300,000 ÷ (20 × 20), or 750 psi. As
the actual stress is less than the allowable, 856 psi, the 28 x 28 in.
flat top is acceptable.

The magnitude of the critical bending moment is found by the
equation

$$M = 6wlc^2 \times 0.85 \qquad \text{(See Art. 11–5)}$$

$$M = 6 \times 2720 \times 10.5 \times 4.42^2 \times 0.85 = 2,840,000 \text{ in-lb}$$

In this equation 0.85 is the reduction factor permitted by the A.C.I.
code. See Fig. 11–6.

In sloped footings the only portion having a maximum value of d
is that part of the footing directly below the flat top. Hence in

using the equation $d = \sqrt{\dfrac{M}{Kb}}$, we use the width of the flat top for

the dimension b, in this instance 28 in. Referring to Table 4–1,
$K = 196$. Then

$$d = \sqrt{\frac{M}{Kb}} \qquad\qquad \text{Formula (6), Art. 4–5}$$

or

$$d = \sqrt{\frac{2,840,000}{196 \times 28}} \qquad \text{or} \qquad d = 22.7 \text{ in.}$$

Accept, temporarily, $d = 23$ in. This effective depth may need to
be increased if the shear and bond stresses are greater than the
allowable.

As explained in Art. 11–8, the thickness above the reinforcement
at the edge of the footing must be at least 6 in., and this dimension
now permits us to determine the pitch of the sloped areas. To insure a minimum of 3 in. of protection for the reinforcing bars, the
distance from the underside of the footing to the center of the bars
is assumed to be 4 in. See Fig. 11–6. The actual effective depth
at the critical section for shear, d distance from the face of the column, is found to be 16.4 in., and this will be the value used for d
in the equation used to investigate the shearing unit stress.

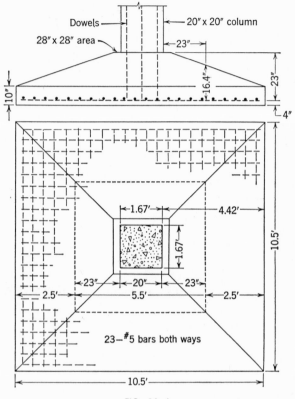

FIG. 11–6

The value of V used in determining the shearing unit stress is

$$V = \frac{l^2 - (a + 2d)^2}{4} \times w \qquad \text{(See Art. 11–5)}$$

Then

$$V = \frac{10.5^2 - [1.67 + (2 \times 1.92)]^2}{4} \times 2720 = 54,400 \text{ lb}$$

$$v = \frac{V}{jbd} \qquad \qquad \text{Formula (10), Art. 5–2}$$

Substituting,

$$v = \frac{54,400}{0.875 \times 66 \times 16.4} = 57.5 \text{ psi}$$

In the foregoing equation $66 = 20 + 23 + 23$, the value of b. The value used for d is 16.4, the actual effective depth at the critical section for shear. As 57.5 psi is less than 75 psi, the allowable shearing unit stress, the assumed depth is acceptable thus far.

To find the area of the tensile reinforcement, we use equation

$$A_s = \frac{M}{f_s jd} \qquad \text{Formula (7), Art. 4–5}$$

Substituting,

$$A_s = \frac{2,840,000}{20,000 \times 0.866 \times 23} = 7.14 \text{ sq in.}$$

This area is provided by 23-#5 bars.

To investigate the bond stress, the value to be used for V is found by the equation

$$V = \frac{l(l - a)}{2} \times w \times 0.85 \qquad \text{(See Art. 11–5)}$$

or

$$V = \frac{10.5(10.5 - 1.67)}{2} \times 2720 \times 0.85 = 107,000 \text{ lb}$$

$$u = \frac{V}{\Sigma_0 jd} \qquad \text{Formula (13), Art. 5–6}$$

Substituting,

$$u = \frac{107,000}{23 \times 1.96 \times 0.875 \times 23} = 118 \text{ psi}$$

In this equation 23 is the number of bars and 1.96 is the perimeter of a #5 bar.

As the actual bond stress has been found to be 118 psi, and by specification data the allowable value for u is 200 psi, the bond stress is acceptable. Thus it is seen that, since both the shear and bond stresses are within the stresses permitted by the specifications, the assumed effective depth is accepted and the footing will be proportioned as shown in Fig. 11–6. There will be two bands of 23-#5 bars.

Problem 11–9–A. The column load on an 18 x 18 in. column is 300,000 lb. If the allowable bearing capacity of the foundation bed is 5000 psf, design a two-way square sloped footing. Specification data:

$$f_s = 20,000 \text{ psi}$$

$$f'_c = 3000 \text{ psi}$$

$$f_c = 1350 \text{ psi}$$

$$v_c = 75 \text{ psi}$$

$$u = 240 \text{ psi}$$

$$n = 10$$

11–10. Continuous Footings. A footing problem frequently met with occurs when individual exterior column footings, concentrically loaded, are so large that they would extend beyond the building line. If the column loads and available space permit, a continuous footing may be run under the columns. This type of footing is actually an inverted continuous beam, the upward pressure of the foundation bed becoming the uniformly distributed load. The design of a continuous footing is similar to that of the usual continuous beam and the same formulas may be employed. If the foundation bed is not entirely uniform, that is, if there are certain spots somewhat more compressible than others, it is advisable to use an excess of steel reinforcement. In general, the main tensile reinforcing bars are placed at the bottom of the footing under the columns and at the top of the footing at the central portions of the spans. As a precaution against unequal settlement, reinforcing bars are sometimes placed in those parts of the footing in which compressive stresses normally occur.

11–11. Design of a Continuous Footing. To illustrate the necessary steps in the design of a continuous footing, consider the following example.

Example. The exterior wall columns of a building each carry a load of 200,000 lb. They are placed 20 ft 0 in. on centers, and their centers are 1 ft 6 in. from the building line. The columns are 24 in. square. For a bearing capacity of 4000 psf for the foundation bed, design a continuous footing. Specification data:

$f'_c = 3000$ psi

$f_s = 20,000$ psi

$f_c = 1350$ psi

$v_c =$ limited to 90 psi

$u =$ limited to 210 psi for top bars and 300 psi for others

$n = 10$

SOLUTION: The design is accomplished by considering that portion of the footing that occurs between two column centers. To determine the area of the footing, it is first necessary to approximate its weight. Assuming the footing weight between two columns to be 15% of a column load, the assumed weight is 0.15 × 200,000 = 30,000 lb. Then the total load exerted on the foundation bed, *between two column centers*, is 200,000 + 30,000 = 230,-000 lb.

$$230,000 \div 4000 = 57.5 \text{ sq ft}$$

the minimum required area of the footing. As the columns are 20 ft 0 in. on centers, 57.5 ÷ 20 = 2.875 ft, the minimum required width. Since the column centers are 1.5 ft from the building line, accept a footing width of 3 ft 0 in., thus bringing the edge of the footing on the building line, the centers of the columns falling on the center line of the footing.

As we are considering, for purpose of design, only the section of footing between two columns, the upward pressure of the foundation bed is 200,000 lb. This being an inverted *continuous beam*, the value of both the positive and negative moments is $M = \dfrac{Wl}{12}$, as explained in Art. 3–7. Then

$$M = \frac{200,000 \times 20 \times 12}{12} = 4,000,000 \text{ in-lb}$$

Determining the depth,

$$d = \sqrt{\frac{M}{Kb}} \qquad \text{Formula (6), Art. 4–5}$$

or

$$d = \sqrt{\frac{4,000,000}{236 \times 36}} = 21.8 \text{ in.}$$

This is the minimum depth permitted. In order to keep the bond and shear stresses within the allowable permitted by the specification data, d will be arbitrarily increased. Assuming the total depth to be 30 in., 4 in. for protective covering and one half a bar diameter will give an effective depth of $30 - 4$, or 26 in.

To determine the area of the tensile reinforcement,

$$A_s = \frac{M}{f_s j d} \qquad \text{Formula (7), Art. 4–5}$$

or

$$A_s = \frac{4,000,000}{20,000 \times 0.866 \times 26} = 8.9 \text{ sq in.}$$

Accept, temporarily, 10-#9 bars. See Table 1–1.

Investigating the bond stress,

$$u = \frac{V}{\Sigma_0 j d} \qquad \text{Formula (13), Art. 5–6}$$

Since the total upward pressure on one span is 200,000 lb,

$$V = 200,000 \times \tfrac{1}{2} = 100,000 \text{ lb}$$

the maximum vertical shear. Then

$$u = \frac{100,000}{10 \times 3.54 \times 0.875 \times 26} = 124 \text{ psi}$$

In this equation 10 is the number of bars and 3.54 is the perimeter of 1-#9 bar. Since 124 psi is less than 210 psi, the allowable bond stress given in the specification data for top bars, the bond stress is acceptable.

The shearing unit stress is found by the formula

$$v = \frac{V}{j b d} \qquad \text{Formula (10), Art. 5–2}$$

Then

$$v = \frac{100,000}{0.875 \times 36 \times 26} = 122 \text{ psi}$$

Since this stress is in excess of 90 psi, the value of v_c, given in the specification data, web reinforcement must be employed.

The distance from the columns in which web reinforcement is required is found by the equation

$$a = \frac{L}{2}\left(\frac{v'}{v}\right) \qquad \text{Formula (11), Art. 5–3}$$

$$v' = v - v_c \qquad \text{or} \qquad v' = 122 - 90 = 32 \text{ psi}$$

Then

$$a = \frac{20}{2}\left(\frac{32}{122}\right) = 2.62 \text{ ft}$$

the distance in which web reinforcement is needed to take the excess shearing stresses.

The spacing of the stirrups or ties is found by the formula

$$s = \frac{A_v f_v}{v' b} \qquad \text{Formula (12), Art. 5–4}$$

Assuming that $f_v = 20,000$ psi and that #4 double ties are used in place of stirrups, $A_v = 4 \times 0.2 = 0.8$. Then

$$s = \frac{0.8 \times 20,000}{32 \times 36} = 13.9 \text{ in.}$$

The maximum spacing for web reinforcement, however, is

$$s = \frac{d - m}{2} \qquad \text{(See Art. 5–4)}$$

or

$$s = \frac{26 - 4}{2} = 11 \text{ in.}$$

the maximum spacing for the ties permitted for this problem. Consequently, we shall use #4 double ties, placing the first pair 3 in. from the face of the columns and then three more pairs, toward the center of the spans, spaced 11 in. on centers. In order to hold up the top bars, in the central part of the span, additional pairs of ties are placed here, spaced 24 in. on centers, thus making a total of 13 double ties for each span.

The weight of the footing is $3 \times 2.5 \times 20 \times 150 = 22,500$ lb. This is within the 30,000 lb assumed weight; hence the allowance originally made is acceptable.

Ten #9 bars are placed in the top of the footing and spliced at the face of the column. Four continuous #9 bars are placed in the bottom, the splice occurring at the center of the span. Six additional #9 bars are placed at the bottom of the footing, under the columns, and extended to the $\frac{1}{4}$ points of the spans. This arrangement provides 10-#9 bars for both the positive and negative bending moments, as shown in Fig. 11–7.

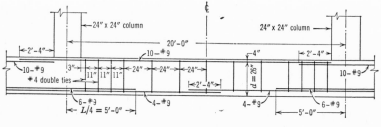

FIG. 11–7

Problem 11–11–A. The column loads on the exterior columns of a building are each 190,000 lb. The columns are 22 ft 0 in. on centers, and the centers of the columns are 1 ft 3 in. from the party line. The columns are 18 in. square, and the allowable bearing capacity of the foundation bed is 4000 psf. Design a continuous footing in accordance with the following specification data:

$$f_s = 20,000 \text{ psi}$$

$$f'_c = 2500 \text{ psi}$$

$$f_c = 1125 \text{ psi}$$

$$v_c = \text{limited to 75 psi}$$

$$u = \text{limited to 175 psi for top bars and}$$
$$\quad\quad 250 \text{ psi for bottom bars}$$

$$n = 12$$

11–12. Combined Footings. A condition that occurs frequently is a column having its face flush with a party or building line. Because the footing cannot extend beyond the building line, an independent footing is impracticable. It may also be that a continuous footing would require so great a width that the column loads would be eccentric with respect to the footing. The solution of such a problem is the construction of a single footing that supports both an exterior column and the nearest interior column. This is called a *combined footing*. Usually the two column loads are of unequal magnitudes; hence it is necessary to find the position of the resultant of the two loads and to proportion the footing so that this line of action coincides with the centroid of the footing area. The area of the combined footing is found by dividing the allowable bearing capacity of the foundation bed into the sum of the column loads plus the estimated weight of the footing. The area may be trapezoidal if required, but a rectangular shape is used wherever possible.

In order to determine the values of the shear and bending moments, shear and moment diagrams are constructed. In addition to the reinforcement running the long dimension of the footing, it must be remembered that there are bending stresses in a transverse direction. Therefore reinforcement must be added to provide for this transverse beam action.

The following example illustrates the procedure in the design of a combined footing.

11–13. Design of a Combined Footing.

Example. Let it be required to design a combined footing to support both an exterior and an interior column. The interior column is 24 x 24 in. and the exterior column is 24 x 16 in., as indicated in Fig. 11–8. They are placed 20 ft 0 in. on centers. The load on the exterior column is 260,000 lb, the interior column load is 400,000 lb, and the allowable bearing capacity of the soil is 4000 psf. The specification data are as follows:

$f'_c = 3000$ psi

$f_s = 20,000$ psi

$f_c = 1350$ psi

$v_c = $ limited to 90 psi

$u = $ limited to 210 psi for top bars and 300 psi for others

$n = 10$

SOLUTION: The sum of the column loads is $400,000 + 260,000 = 660,000$ lb. If we estimate the weight of the footing at 10% of the column loads, $0.10 \times 660,000 = 66,000$ lb. Therefore the load ex-

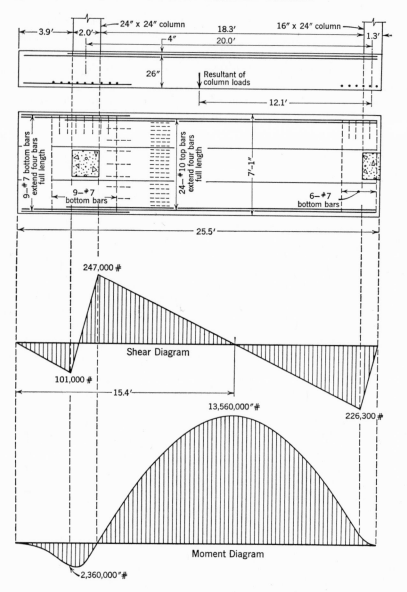

FIG. 11-8

erted on the foundation bed is $400,000 + 260,000 + 66,000 = 726,000$ lb. As the bearing capacity of the soil is 4000 psf, $726,000 \div 4000 = 181.5$ sq ft, the required minimum area of the footing.

The *resultant* of two forces is one force having the same effect as the two forces acting at their individual lines of action. The magnitude of the resultant of the two column loads is $400,000 + 260,000$, or $660,000$ lb. Its position is readily found by writing an equation of moments about the line of action of the exterior column, calling x the lever arm of the resultant. Then

$$400,000 \times 20 = 660,000 \times x$$

or

$$x = 12.1 \text{ ft} \qquad \text{(See Fig. 11–8)}$$

As the axis of the exterior column is 0.66 ft from the outer end of the footing, $12.1 + 0.66 = 12.76$ ft, the distance of the resultant from the outer end of the footing. The position of the resultant must be at the central point of the footing area; hence the length of the footing is 12.76×2 or 25.52 ft, say 25 ft 6 in. As the area of the footing is 181.5 sq ft, the width is $181.5 \div 25.5 = 7.12$ ft, say 7 ft 1 in.

The upward pressure of the foundation bed due to the column loads is 660,000 lb, and, as the length of the footing is 25.5 ft, the upward pressure on the footing is $660,000 \div 25.5$ or $25,882$ lb *per linear ft*, say 25,900 lb.

The shear diagram is shown in Fig. 11–8. To construct this diagram, it is necessary to compute the value of the shear at certain critical points only. Remember that the value of the shear at any section in the length of the footing is equal to the algebraic sum of the vertical forces on either side of the section. Or, for convenience, we may say that the value of the shear at any section is the downward forces minus the upward forces to the left of the section.[*]

Then the shear at the left side of the interior column is

$$-(25,900 \times 3.9) = -101,000 \text{ lb}$$

At the right side of the same column, the shear is

$$400,000 - (5.9 \times 25,900) = +247,000 \text{ lb}$$

At the left side of the exterior column, reading the forces to the

[*] See Arts. 66 and 67, *Simplified Mechanics and Strength of Materials.*

right, the shear is

$$(1.3 \times 25,900) - 260,000 = -226,300 \text{ lb}$$

The two points at which the shear passes through zero, and at which the bending moment has maximum values, are, first, close to the left side of the interior column and, second, at a point near the center line between the columns. To compute the exact position of the latter, call y the distance of the point of zero shear to the left end of the footing. Then

$$400,000 = 25,900 \times y \qquad \text{or} \qquad y = 15.4 \text{ ft}$$

The value of the bending moment at any section of the footing equals the algebraic sum of the moments of the forces on either side of the section.*

The value of the bending moment at the section 15.4 ft from the left end of the footing is

$$M = (400,000 \times 10.5) - \left(15.4 \times 25,900 \times \frac{15.4}{2}\right)$$

$$= 1,130,000 \text{ ft-lb} = 13,560,000 \text{ in-lb}$$

At the left side of the interior column the value of the bending moment is

$$M = -\left(3.9 \times 25,900 \times \frac{3.9}{2}\right) = -196,000 \text{ ft-lb}$$

$$= -2,360,000 \text{ in-lb}$$

The value of the bending moment is computed for other sections and the complete curve drawn as shown in Fig. 11–8.

Consider first the moment between the columns. The moment here is the maximum value, 13,560,000 in-lb, and the depth of the footing is determined in accordance with this value.

$$d = \sqrt{\frac{M}{Kb}} \qquad\qquad \text{Formula (6), Art. 4–5}$$

$$d = \sqrt{\frac{13,560,000}{236 \times 85}} = 26 \text{ in.}$$

the effective depth.

* See Arts. 71 and 72, *Simplified Mechanics and Strength of Materials.*

In this equation 236 is the value of K found in Table 4–1, and 85 is the width of the footing, 7 ft 1 in., in inches. As the tensile stresses occur at the upper part of this section of the footing, the tensile reinforcement is placed at the top of the beam, 26 in. from the bottom. A 4-in. layer of concrete is placed above these bars for protection, making a total depth of 2 ft 6 in.

$$A_s = \frac{M}{f_s jd} \qquad \text{Formula (7), Art. 4–5}$$

$$A_s = \frac{13,560,000}{20,000 \times 0.866 \times 26} = 30.1 \text{ sq in.}$$

Referring to Table 1–1, we find that 24-#10 bars provide this area. The critical section for shear is d distance to the right of the right-hand face of the interior column. Its value is

$$V = 247,000 - \left(\frac{26}{12} \times 25,900\right) = 190,900 \text{ lb}$$

$$v = \frac{V}{jbd} \qquad \text{Formula (10), Art. 5–2}$$

$$v = \frac{190,900}{0.875 \times 85 \times 26} = 99 \text{ psi}$$

As the shearing unit stress is greater than 90 psi, the allowable, web reinforcement is required.

Referring to Art. 5–3, we find that the distance from the column in which web reinforcement is required is found by the use of a modified form of formula (11), $a = L_0 \left(\dfrac{v'}{v}\right)$, in which L_0 is the distance from the point of zero shear to the point of maximum shear. In this problem $L_0 = 15.4 - 5.9$ or $L_0 = 9.5$ ft. See Fig. 11–8. Then,

$$v' = v - v_c = 99 - 90 = 9 \text{ psi}$$

and

$$a = L_0 \left(\frac{v'}{v}\right) = 9.5 \times \frac{9}{99} = 0.86 \text{ ft}$$

the distance from the face of the column in which web reinforcement is required.

Assuming that $f_v = 20,000$ psi and that the web reinforcement will consist of #3 double ties

$$s = \frac{A_v f_v}{v'b} \qquad \text{Formula (12), Art. 5–4}$$

Then

$$s = \frac{(4 \times 0.11) \times 20,000}{9 \times 85} = 11.5 \text{ in.}$$

But the maximum allowable spacing is

$$\frac{d - m}{2} \quad \text{or} \quad s = \frac{26 - 4}{2} = 11 \text{ in.} \qquad \text{(See Art. 5–4)}$$

Therefore we shall use #3 double ties, placing the first pair at 5 in. from the column and the next pair at a space of 11 in. In order that the top bars at the center of the footing between columns may be held in place, we shall use additional pairs of ties placed here with approximately 24 in. spacing. Computations for shear show that web reinforcement is not required at other sections of the footing.

To investigate the bond stress,

$$u = \frac{V}{\Sigma_0 jd} \qquad \text{Formula (13), Art. 5–6}$$

$$u = \frac{247,000}{24 \times 3.99 \times 0.875 \times 26} = 113 \text{ psi}$$

This is the unit bond stress, and, since it is less than 210 psi, the allowable, the 24-#10 bars are acceptable. Note that 3.99 in. is the perimeter of a #10 bar, Table 1–1.

The value of the moment at the left face of the interior column is 2,360,000 in-lb. This portion of the footing acts as a cantilever. The tensile forces are at the bottom of the footing, and consequently the reinforcing bars will be placed there. The depth of the footing is uniform throughout its length, and, since the moment at this section is considerably less than the maximum moment between the columns, the 26-in. effective depth will be ample. Obviously less steel will be required for this cantilever portion.

$$A_s = \frac{M}{f_s j d} \qquad \text{Formula (7), Art. 4--5}$$

$$A_s = \frac{2,360,000}{20,000 \times 0.866 \times 26} = 5.25 \text{ sq in.}$$

the required area of tensile reinforcement for these bottom bars.

$$u = \frac{V}{\Sigma_0 j d} \qquad \text{or} \qquad \Sigma_0 = \frac{V}{u j d} \qquad \text{Formula (13), Art. 5--6}$$

$$\Sigma_0 = \frac{101,000}{300 \times 0.875 \times 26} = 14.8 \text{ in.}$$

the required sum of the perimeters of the bars. Referring to Table 1–1, we find that 9-#7 bars give an area of 5.4 sq in., and the sum of their perimeters is $9 \times 2.75 = 24.8$ in. Therefore they are accepted.

The computations thus far have concerned reinforcement running parallel to the long dimension of the footing. Now let us consider the beam action in a transverse direction. Reinforcement will be needed in the areas directly below the columns. These portions of the footings act as cantilevers extending on each side of the columns.

Consider first the interior column. The transverse length of the footing is 7.1 ft, and, as the column load is 400,000 lb, the upward pressure on the footing is $400,000 \div 7.1$, or 56,300 lb *per linear ft*. The moment at the face of the column is

$$M = 56,300 \times 2.55 \times \frac{2.55}{2} \times 12 = 2,200,000 \text{ in-lb}$$

Although the width of the footing is 7.1 ft, it is impossible to determine accurately the effective dimension parallel to the long axis of the footing. Nevertheless, we are safe in assuming that this dimension is the width of the column plus the effective depth of the footing, or $24 + 26 = 50$ in., the width b. Then

$$d = \sqrt{\frac{M}{Kb}} = \sqrt{\frac{2,200,000}{236 \times 50}} = 13.6 \text{ in.}$$

The reinforcement for this portion of the beam will be in the bottom of the footing directly above and at right angles to the layer of 9-#7 bars. Since 13.6 in. is required and the actual effective depth is $26 - 1$, or 25 in., there is ample depth.

$$A_s = \frac{M}{f_s j d} = \frac{2,200,000}{20,000 \times 0.866 \times 25} = 5.08 \text{ sq in.}$$

the required area of reinforcement.

The value of the shear at the face of the column is

$$V = 2.55 \times 56,300 = 143,500 \text{ lb}$$

$$\Sigma_0 = \frac{V}{ujd} = \frac{143,500}{300 \times 0.875 \times 25} = 21.9 \text{ in.}$$

the sum of the perimeters of the bars.

Referring to Table 1-1, 9-#7 bars have an area of 5.4 sq in., and the sum of their perimeters is 24.7 in.; hence they are accepted.

The value of V used in computing the shearing unit stress is taken at d distance from the face of the column. As the face of the column is only 2.55 ft from the outer edge of the footing, the critical section for shear is approximately at the face of the footing. Therefore the shearing unit stress need not be investigated.

In a similar manner, the transverse beam action under the exterior column is considered.

$$260,000 \div 7.1 = 36,600 \text{ lb per linear ft of width}$$

the upward pressure of the foundation bed.

The moment at the face of the column is

$$M = 36,600 \times 2.55 \times \frac{2.55}{2} \times 12 = 1,430,000 \text{ in-lb}$$

This column is flush with the end of the footing, and b may be considered the width of the column plus $\frac{1}{2}$ the effective depth, or

$$b = 16 + \frac{26}{2} = 29 \text{ in.}$$

$$d = \sqrt{\frac{M}{Kb}} = \sqrt{\frac{1,430,000}{236 \times 29}} = 14.5 \text{ in.}$$

the required effective depth.

As the actual effective depth is 25 in., the depth is acceptable.

$$A_s = \frac{M}{f_s jd} = \frac{1,430,000}{20,000 \times 0.866 \times 25} = 3.3 \text{ sq in.}$$

the area of reinforcement required.

At the face of the column, $V = 36,600 \times 2.55 = 93,500$ lb.

$$\Sigma_0 = \frac{V}{ujd} = \frac{93,500}{300 \times 0.875 \times 25} = 14.3 \text{ in.}$$

the required sum of the perimeters of the reinforcing bars.

To find the size and number of bars to meet these two requirements, we refer to Table 1–1. The area of 6-#7 bars is $6 \times 0.6 = 3.6$ sq in., and the sum of their perimeters is $6 \times 2.749 = 16.5$ in.; hence they are accepted.

For the same reason previously explained, the shearing unit stress need not be investigated.

For this footing, stirrups will be required only at the right side of the interior column. The positions of the bars are shown in Fig. 11–8.

11–14. Pile Foundations. When a structure is to be erected on unreliable soil, it is frequently necessary to use pile foundations. The piles may be driven to a firm stratum, or they may depend for support upon friction between their surfaces and the soil. Pile foundations for buildings are generally driven in groups, with a minimum spacing of 2 ft 6 in. center to center of piles. A concrete cap is constructed over the piles, and in reality we have a footing block supported by isolated piles rather than by the upward uniform pressure of the foundation bed. Hence a footing supported by piles may be considered as a footing supported by a number of concentrated forces rather than by a force uniformly distributed.

The tops of the piles are embedded in the concrete cap from 4 to 6 in., and 12 in. is generally considered the minimum distance from the top of the footing cap to the reinforcing bars. It is customary to have a layer of 3 or 4 in. of concrete between the tops of the piles and the bands of reinforcing bars.

The number of piles is determined by dividing the allowable bearing capacity of one pile into the sum of the column load and the assumed weight of the footing. The design of the footing is essentially the same as that of a footing supported on soil, but, instead of an upward pressure uniformly distributed, each net pile reaction is an isolated force whose magnitude is the column load divided by the number of piles.

In Art. 11–5 it was noted that the critical section for shear, for a footing resting on soil, is at d distance from the face of the column or pedestal. For a footing supported by piles, the section is $d/2$ from the face of the column or pedestal. Any piles whose centers are at or within the section are to be excluded in computations for shear. For footings of this type, the shearing stress generally determines the depth, the footing being of uniform thickness.

11–15. Design of a Footing Supported on Piles.

Example. Let it be required to design a reinforced concrete footing supported on piles. The column is 18 in. square and exerts a load of 80,000 lb on the footing. The allowable bearing capacity of each pile is 20,000 lb. The specification data are as follows:

$$f'_c = 3000 \text{ psi}$$

$$f_c = 1350 \text{ psi}$$

$$f_s = 20,000 \text{ psi}$$

$$v_c = \text{limited to 75 psi}$$

$$u = \text{limited to 240 psi}$$

$$n = 10$$

SOLUTION: Assume that the weight of the footing is 12,000 lb. Then the total load to be supported by the piles is $80,000 + 12,000 = 92,000$ lb. Each pile has a maximum bearing capacity of 20,000 lb, so that $92,000 \div 20,000 = 4+$; hence we shall use 5 piles. The net load *per pile* will be $80,000 \div 5$, or 16,000 lb. The simplest symmetrical arrangement of 5 piles is shown in Fig. 11–9. A spacing of not more than 3 ft 0 in. center to center of piles is maintained, and there is a distance of 1 ft 3 in. from the center of the outer piles to the face of the footing. The footing will be made 6 ft 9 in. square.

The value of the bending moment at the face of the column is $M = 2 \times 16,000 \times 16.5 = 528,000$ in-lb. In this equation 16,000 lb is the upward pressure of one pile and 16.5 in. is the lever arm

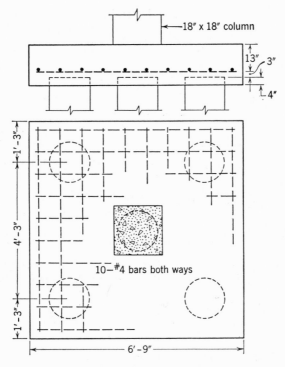

FIG. 11-9

about the face of the column. It should be noted that the pile directly below the column has no effect on the bending moment in the footing.

The value of b used in determining the depth by bending will be taken as the width of the footing, 81 in. $K = 236$ (found in Table 4-1). Then

$$d = \sqrt{\frac{M}{Kb}} = \sqrt{\frac{528,000}{236 \times 81}} = 5.3 \text{ in.}$$

However, we know that 12 in. is a minimum thickness of concrete over the reinforcement, and therefore we shall accept $d = 13$ in. to give a full 12-in. layer of concrete. We must remember that this effective depth must be investigated with respect to shear and bond stresses.

The value of V to be used in determining the shearing unit stress is two one-half piles or 16,000 lb. As the critical section for shear is at $d/2$ distance from the face of the column, b, the width of this section, is $6.5 + 18 + 6.5$, or 31 in.

$$v = \frac{V}{jbd} = \frac{16,000}{0.866 \times 31 \times 13} = 45.8 \text{ psi}$$

So far, the depth of 13 in. is acceptable, since 45.8 psi is less than 75 psi, the allowable shearing stress.

A reduction of 15% of M is permitted in computing A_s. Thus

$$A_s = \frac{M}{f_s jd} \quad \text{or} \quad A_s = \frac{0.85 \times 528,000}{20,000 \times 0.866 \times 13} = 1.99 \text{ sq in.}$$

the required area of the reinforcing bars.

$$u = \frac{V}{\Sigma_0 jd} \quad \text{or} \quad \Sigma_0 = \frac{V}{ujd} \quad \text{or}$$

$$\Sigma_0 = \frac{2 \times 16,000 \times 0.85}{240 \times 0.866 \times 13} = 10.07 \text{ in.}$$

the sum of the perimeters of the bars.

By referring to Table 1–1, it is found that 10–#4 bars provide an area of 2.00 sq in., and the sum of their perimeters is 15.7 in.; hence they are accepted. There will be two bands of bars at right angles to each other. See Fig. 11–9.

Problem 11–15–A. A 16-in. square column exerts a load of 40,000 lb on a footing supported by piles. If each pile has a bearing capacity of 20,000 lb, design the footing in accordance with the following specification data:

$$f_s = 20,000 \text{ psi}$$

$$f'_c = 3000 \text{ psi}$$

$$f_c = 1350 \text{ psi}$$

$$v_c = \text{limited to 75 psi}$$

$$u = \text{limited to 240 psi}$$

$$n = 10$$

CHAPTER 12

RETAINING WALLS

12–1. General Considerations. A *retaining wall* is a wall whose purpose is to resist the thrust of a bank of earth or other material. The three types of retaining walls are illustrated in Fig. 12–1. The *gravity wall*, Fig. 12–1(a) and (b), is constructed of such proportions that its weight alone resists the thrust of the earth. The *cantilever wall*, constructed of reinforced concrete, Fig. 12–1(c), makes use of the weight of the earth in resisting the tendency to overturn at the outer edge. The vertical slab, supported on a horizontal base, serves as a cantilever beam in resisting the earth pressure. Figure 12–1(d) illustrates the *counterfort wall*. It is similar to the canti-

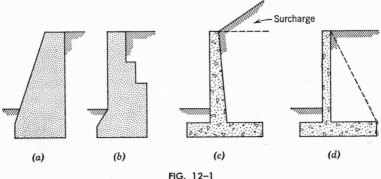

(a)   (b)   (c)   (d)

FIG. 12–1

lever wall with the exception that the vertical slab is tied to the base at regular intervals with triangular-shaped cross walls. Although not always used, the base slab for the cantilever and counterfort walls is generally extended beyond the outer face of the wall to aid in preventing overturning.

The type of retaining wall to use depends on several factors, the height, loads, foundation bed, and the existing conditions affecting construction. Low walls are invariably gravity walls constructed of brick, stone masonry, or concrete. It is usually most economical to use the counterfort wall for heights of 20 ft and over, whereas the walls of intermediate height are generally the cantilever type. The costs of labor and material are governing factors, and a selection is sometimes made as a result of designing two types and comparing their costs.

The stability of a retaining wall must be investigated with respect to the tendency (1) to slide on its base, (2) to overturn at the toe, and (3) to crush or settle unduly at the toe or outer edge. The design procedure consists in assuming the wall to be of certain dimensions and materials and then to investigate its stability with respect to the three possible failures listed above. When acceptable proportions have been established, the structural elements, base, vertical slab, etc., are further investigated with respect to the unit stresses in the concrete and reinforcement, and such modifications as may be necessary are made.

Practical considerations require that the bottom of the wall be placed below the frost line. It is also necessary to provide drainage holes at regular intervals to permit the escape of water. For concrete walls, construction joints should be made not more than 30 ft on centers.

A gravity wall should have a base whose thickness is four tenths to one half the height. If the outer face of the wall is vertical, greater stability may be obtained by increasing the thickness below grade at the toe; see Fig. 12–1(b). The weight of the wall is a factor in its ability to resist the thrust of the retained earth, but, as the earth pressure diminishes rapidly from the bottom upward, the wall thickness may also be reduced, as indicated in the same figure. Various arbitrary rules are sometimes used in proportioning retaining walls, but for economy and safety, particularly in walls 5 ft and over in height, a careful design should be made.

12–2. Earth Pressure. The primary forces to be considered in the design of a retaining wall are, first, the weight of the wall and, second, the thrust exerted by the pressure of the retained earth. Given the dimensions of the wall, its weight may be computed accurately. The thrust of the soil, however, depends upon several factors. When loose earth is deposited on a horizontal flat surface, it piles up in a mound. The angle between the horizontal and the side of the mound is known as the *angle of repose* of the material. Different materials may have different angles of repose. For average earth fill, this angle is considered to be about 33° 42', corresponding to a slope of 1.5 to 1.

When the surface of the retained earth is horizontal, as indicated in Fig. 12–2(*a*), the earth pressure may be determined by the equation

$$P = 0.286 \frac{wh^2}{2}$$

in which P = the magnitude of the pressure, in pounds,
w = the weight of the retained soil, in pounds per cubic foot,
h = the height of the column of earth, in feet.

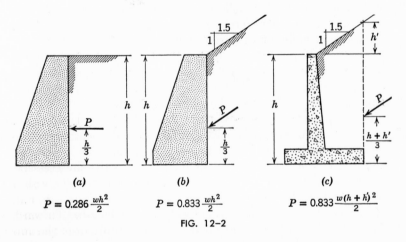

(a)	(b)	(c)
$P = 0.286 \frac{wh^2}{2}$	$P = 0.833 \frac{wh^2}{2}$	$P = 0.833 \frac{w(h + h')^2}{2}$

FIG. 12–2

When the wall is required to retain a surcharge, a slope of earth above the top of the wall, $P = 0.833 \dfrac{wh^2}{2}$. This is indicated in Fig. 12–2(*b*).

To identify a force, it is necessary that its three elements, *magnitude*, *direction*, and *line of action*, be known.[*] The magnitudes of the thrusts are established by the two foregoing formulas; their

[*] See *Simplified Design of Roof Trusses for Architects and Builders*, Chapter 1, by Harry Parker, John Wiley and Sons, New York, 2nd edition, 1953.

direction is *toward* the retaining walls, as indicated by the arrows on the forces. For the two cases illustrated in Fig. 12–2(a) and (b), the line of action of the thrust meets the wall at a point $h/3$ measured from the bottom of the retained earth. For walls of the cantilever or counterfort type with a surcharge, the line of action is at a point one third of the height of a plane passing through the heel of the wall. See Fig. 12–2(c). In each of the three cases illustrated the line of action of the thrust is assumed to be parallel to the upper surface of the retained earth.

In designing retaining walls, it is customary to consider a strip of wall 12 in. in length. Then, for instance, if the cross-sectional area of the wall is 25 sq ft, W, the weight of the wall, is the weight of 25 cu ft of material. If the wall is concrete, $W = 25 \times 150 = 3750$ lb.

12–3. Resultant of Weight of Wall and Earth Pressure. The *resultant* of two or more forces is one force that has the same effect as the two or more forces acting simultaneously. If the forces are not parallel, the resultant of two forces has its line of action passing through the intersection of the lines of action of the two given forces. The magnitude and direction of the resultant may be found graphically by constructing the parallelogram of forces.*

The graphical method of finding the resultant of the weight of the wall and the thrust of the earth affords a convenient method to use in investigating the stability of retaining walls.

In Fig. 12–3(a), P represents the thrust of the earth pressure and W is the weight of the wall. The line of action of W passes through the centroid of the wall cross section. Both P and W are forces in pounds, corresponding to a strip of wall 12 in. in length. The lines of action of P and W meet at point a, and the resultant of the two forces will pass through this point. From point a, draw, at some convenient scale of so many pounds to the inch, a line parallel to P and equal to P in length. Likewise, from point a, draw a vertical line equal to W in length. P and W then are two sides of a parallelogram; the other two sides are indicated by the dotted lines, and R, the diagonal, is the resultant of the two forces; its magnitude is found by scaling its length. When the thrust P is not horizontal, as indicated in Fig. 12–3(b), the construction is similar.

* See Chapter 1, *Simplified Design of Roof Trusses for Architects and Builders.*

The horizontal and vertical components of R, the resultant, are R_H and R_V, as indicated in Fig. 12–3(c). Since R is the resultant of the weight of the wall and the earth pressure, R_H, the horizontal component, is the force that tends to cause the wall to slide on the foundation bed. Likewise R_V, the vertical component, is the force exerting a vertical pressure on the foundation bed.

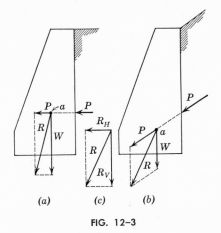

(a)   (c)   (b)

FIG. 12–3

12–4. Principle of the Middle Third. A retaining wall may be so proportioned that the resultant of its weight and the thrust of the earth intersect the base of the wall at equal distances from each side. Such a condition is illustrated in Fig. 12–4(a).

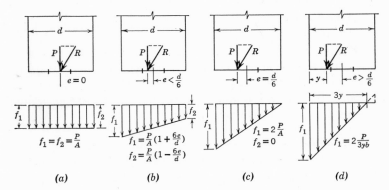

FIG. 12–4

In Fig. 12–4 let P = the vertical component of R, the resultant, d = the width of the wall, e = the distance from the center line of the wall to the point at which the resultant intersects its base, and f_1 and f_2 = the pressures on the foundation bed at the toe and heel, respectively. A = the area of that portion of the base of the wall under consideration. If, for example, the width of the wall, d, is 8 ft and a 1-ft length of wall is being investigated, $A = 8 \times 1$, or 8 sq ft. In Fig. 12–4(a) $e = 0$, and both f_1 and f_2 equal P/A; the pressure is uniformly distributed over the base, and there is a tendency for the wall to settle equally at the heel and toe. Note that the width of the wall is divided into three equal divisions, the middle and outer thirds. The point at which the resultant cuts the base is of significance in investigating the stability of the wall.

Consider Fig. 12–4(b). In this diagram the resultant cuts the base within the middle third; the distance e is less than $d/6$. The pressure on the foundation bed is not equally distributed and

$$f_1 = \frac{P}{A}\left(1 + 6\,\frac{e}{d}\right) \quad \text{and} \quad f_2 = \frac{P}{A}\left(1 - 6\,\frac{e}{d}\right)^*$$

When the resultant cuts the base at the outer edge of the middle third, that is, when $e = d/6$, as shown in Fig. 12–4(c), $f_1 = 2P/A$ and $f_2 = 0$.

Figure 12–4(d) illustrates a condition in which the resultant cuts the base outside the middle third; e is greater than $d/6$. In this case only a portion of the width of the foundation bed receives a compressive stress; it is a width of $3 \times y$. For this condition,

$f_1 = 2\,\dfrac{P}{3yb}$, b being the length of wall being investigated, 1 in., 1 ft, etc.

With the exception of the condition shown in Fig. 12–4(a), the cases shown in Fig. 12–4 are illustrations in which the pressure on the foundation bed is not uniformly distributed, and the maximum pressure, f_1, should be computed.

12–5. Stability of Retaining Walls. A retaining wall may fail in any one of three ways: (1) by overturning, (2) by undue settlement

---

* See Art. 105, *Simplified Mechanics and Strength of Materials*, by Harry Parker, John Wiley and Sons, New York, 1951.

at the toe, and (3) by sliding horizontally along its base. In addition to these three possible failures, a reinforced concrete wall may fail by rupture of any of its constituent parts, as, for instance, excessive bending stresses in the base or vertical slab.

As for overturning, the moment of the horizontal force about the toe should not exceed the moment of the vertical force about the same point. Referring to Fig. 12–5(a), $P \times x$ should not be greater than $W \times y$. It is desirable to have the resultant of thrust and weight of the wall cut the base within the middle third so that pressure is exerted over the entire foundation bed. The resisting moment divided by the overturning moment determines the factor of safety. A factor of safety of 2 is considered to be ample.

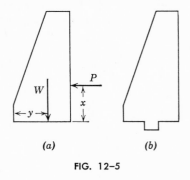

(a)   (b)

FIG. 12–5

If the pressure at the toe, indicated by f_1 in Fig. 12–4, exceeds the allowable compressive strength of the foundation bed, undue settlement or crushing of the material may result. Therefore it is necessary to compute the magnitude of f_1 to see that the allowable stress is not exceeded.

The force tending to cause a retaining wall to slide horizontally on its base is the horizontal component of the thrust, R_H in Fig. 12–3(c). The force resisting the tendency to slide is the weight of the wall multiplied by the coefficient of friction of the material composing the foundation bed. Average coefficients of friction of masonry on various foundation beds are: on wet clay, 0.3, on dry clay, 0.5, on sand, 0.4, on gravel, 0.6. The factor of safety against sliding is the resisting force divided by the force tending to cause sliding. A minimum value for the factor of safety is considered to be 1.5. When this value is exceeded, the base may be widened, thus producing a greater weight, or a key may be formed on the base, as shown in Fig. 12–5(b). Since all retaining walls extend below the frost line, the soil abutting the wall also aids in resisting the tendency to slide. This is true, however, only if the soil has not been disturbed by excavation and replaced by fill.

12–6. Design of a Gravity Retaining Wall.

Example. Let it be required to design a gravity retaining wall having a vertical exposed face extending 15 ft 0 in. above grade. The retained earth has a horizontal surface level with the top of the wall. The allowable bearing capacity of the foundation bed is 6000 psf. Assume the weight of the masonry and soil to be 150 and 100 lb per cu ft, respectively.

SOLUTION: To begin the design, we shall assume that the cross section of the wall has the dimensions shown in Fig. 12–6(a). A

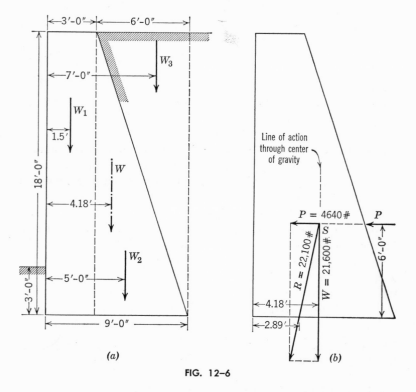

FIG. 12–6

wall of these dimensions will be investigated and modified if necessary. For convenience, we shall consider a strip of wall 12 in. in length.

The vertical weight consists of the weight of the masonry

and the triangular portion of earth marked W_3. To find the magnitude of W, the total vertical force, and a line of action passing through its center of gravity, the wall will be considered to be made up of the rectangular and triangular areas, W_1 and W_2. We shall consider the outer face of the wall as an axis about which the moments will be taken. The weights, moment arms, and moments are given in the following tabulation.

Section	Weight	Moment Arm	Moment
W_1	$3 \times 18 \times 150 = 8,100\#$	$1.5'$	$8,100 \times 1.5 = 12,150'\#$
W_2	$\dfrac{6 \times 18}{2} \times 150 = 8,100\#$	$5.0'$	$8,100 \times 5.0 = 40,500'\#$
W_3	$\dfrac{6 \times 18}{2} \times 100 = 5,400\#$	$7.0'$	$5,400 \times 7.0 = 37,800'\#$
	Total weight, $W = 21,600\#$		Sum of moments $= 90,450'\#$

Since the sum of the moments of the parts is equal to the moment of the whole, let x be the distance of the center of gravity of W, the total weight, from the left face of the wall. Then $21,600 \times x = 90,450$ ft-lb, and $x = 4.18$ ft. Thus we have determined the line of action of the total downward force.

As given in Art. 12–2, the thrust of the retained earth is found by the equation

$$P = 0.286 \frac{wh^2}{2}$$

or

$$P = 0.286 \times \frac{100 \times 18 \times 18}{2} = 4640 \text{ lb}$$

The thrust is a horizontal force that acts on the retaining wall at a point one third of its height from the base, or 6 ft from the bottom of the footing.

To find the resultant of the earth pressure and the vertical force, 21,600 lb, their lines of action are continued until they intersect at point S, Fig. 12–6(b). At this point the parallelogram of forces is constructed as explained in Art. 12–3, and the resultant is found, by scaling, to be a force of 22,100 lb. It passes through the base of the wall at a distance of 1.61 ft from the center line of the base (outside the middle third), or 2.89 ft from the outer edge. Note that the horizontal and vertical components of the resultant are 4640 and 21,600 lb, respectively.

If we investigate the wall for overturning, the overturning moment is 4640×6 or 27,840 ft-lb, and the resisting moment is 21,600 $\times 4.18$ or 90,200 ft-lb. The factor of safety for overturning is $90,200 \div 27,840$, or 3.26, acceptable; see Art. 12–5.

The distance y, 2.89 ft, is less than $d/3$, or 3 ft. This shows that the resultant cuts the base outside the middle third. The pressure f_1 at the outer edge of the wall is found by the formula

$$f_1 = 2 \times \frac{P}{3yb} \qquad \text{(Art. 12–4)}$$

Then, since we are investigating a 1-ft length of wall, $b = 1$ and

$$f_1 = 2 \times \frac{21,600}{3 \times 2.89 \times 1} \qquad \text{or} \qquad f_1 = 4990 \text{ psf}$$

This is the greatest pressure on any part of the foundation bed, and, since it is less than 6000 psf, given as data, there is no danger of crushing or undue settlement of the wall.

The horizontal force tending to cause sliding is 4640 lb. If we assume that the foundation bed is sand, the coefficient of friction is 0.4 (Art. 12–5). Then the force resisting the tendency to slide is $21,600 \times 0.4$, or 8640 lb. The factor of safety against sliding is $8640 \div 4640 = 1.86$ and is considered adequate.

As investigation has shown the assumed cross section of the wall to be safe with respect to overturning, undue settlement, and sliding, no modifications of the dimensions are required.

Problem 12–6–A. Design a gravity retaining wall having a height of 10 ft 0 in. above grade. The wall retains earth fill, the upper surface of which has a slope of 1.5 to 1; see "surcharge," Fig. 12–1(c). The bottom of the retaining wall is 3 ft 0 in. below grade, and the allowable bearing capacity of the sand foundation bed is 4000 psf.

12–7. Design of a Cantilever Retaining Wall.

Example. Let it be required to design a cantilever retaining wall having a total height of 16 ft 6 in. The wall is to retain not only the fill in back of the wall but also a surcharge with a slope of 1.5 to 1. The foundation bed is gravel having an allowable bearing capacity of 3 tons per sq ft. The wall is to be constructed of reinforced concrete in accordance with the following data:

$f'_c = 2500$ psi

$f_s = 20,000$ psi

$f_c = 1125$ psi

$v_c = $ limited to 75 psi

$u = $ limited to 175 psi for top bars and 250 psi for others

$n = 12$

SOLUTION. There are no definite rules for proportioning the elements of a wall of this type. The procedure is to select tentative dimensions, investigate the stability of such a wall, and make any modifications that may be necessary. Fig. 12–7(a) shows the assumed dimensions.

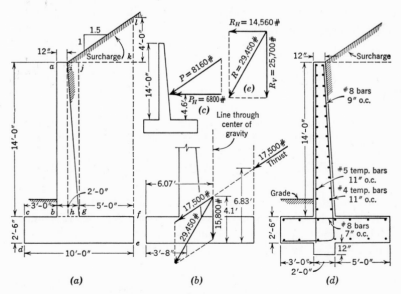

FIG. 12–7

In accordance with Art. 12-2, the magnitude of the earth pressure is found by the equation

$$P = 0.833 \frac{wh^2}{2} \quad \text{or} \quad P = 0.833 \times \frac{100 \times 20.5^2}{2} = 17,500 \text{ lb}$$

Its position is $20.5 \div 3$, or 6.83 ft above the bottom of the footing, and it has its line of action parallel to the slope of the surcharge. See Fig. 12-7(b).

To find the weight of the wall and earth directly over the base and also the line of action of this vertical force, the cross section is divided into a number of areas, as indicated in the following tabulation and shown in Fig. 12-7(a).

Section	Weight		Moment Arm	Moment	
cdef	$2.5 \times 10 \times 1 \times 150$	$= 3,750\#$	$10 \times \frac{1}{2} = 5'$	$3,750 \times 5$	$= 18,750'\#$
bhia	$14 \times 1 \times 1 \times 150$	$= 2,100\#$	$3 + \frac{1}{2} = 3.5'$	$2,100 \times 3.5$	$= 7,350'\#$
hgi	$14 \times 1 \times \frac{1}{2} \times 150$	$= 1,050\#$	$4 + \frac{1}{3} = 4.33'$	$1,050 \times 4.33$	$= 4,547'\#$
jig	$14 \times 1 \times \frac{1}{2} \times 1 \times 100$	$= 700\#$	$4 + \frac{2}{3} = 4.66'$	700×4.66	$= 3,262'\#$
gfkj	$14 \times 5 \times 1 \times 100$	$= 7,000\#$	$7.5'$	$7,000 \times 7.5$	$= 52,500'\#$
kli	$6 \times 4 \times \frac{1}{2} \times 1 \times 100$	$= 1,200\#$	$8'$	$1,200 \times 8$	$= 9,600'\#$
	Total weight, $W = 15,800\#$			Sum of moments $= 96,009'\#$	

Let x be the distance of the center of gravity of the weight W from the outer edge of the wall, line cd. Then

$$15,800 \times x = 96,009 \quad \text{and} \quad x = 6.07 \text{ ft} \qquad [\text{See Fig. } 12\text{-}7(b)]$$

Before investigating the stability of the wall for sliding and overturning, let us see if the assumed dimensions of the wall are adequate to resist bending and shear.

Consider first the vertical slab. The force tending to cause the slab to fail by bending about its base, line bg, is

$$P = 0.833 \times \frac{wh^2}{2} \quad \text{or} \quad P = 0.833 \times \frac{100 \times 14 \times 14}{2} = 8160 \text{ lb}$$

and its horizontal component is 6800 lb. This force meets the vertical slab at $14 \div 3$, or 4.66 ft above the base. See Fig. 12-7(c).

The moment of this force about the upper surface of the base, line cf, is $M = 6800 \times 4.66 \times 12 = 381,000$ in-lb.

$$d = \sqrt{\frac{M}{Kb}} \qquad \text{Formula (6), Art. 4-5}$$

For the unit stresses given as data, $K = 196$ and $j = 0.866$ (Table 4–1). Then

$$d = \sqrt{\frac{381,000}{196 \times 12}} = 12.8 \text{ in.}$$

The reinforcing rods are placed near the inner face of the wall, and, if the distance from the center of the rods is 3.5 in. to the inner face, the actual effective depth, d, will be $24 - 3.5$, or 20.5 in. As only 12.8 in. are required, the wall is sufficiently thick.

The area of the tensile reinforcing bars in the strip of vertical slab 12 in. long is found by the equation

$$A_s = \frac{M}{f_s j d} \qquad \qquad \text{Equation (7), Art. 4–5}$$

$$A_s = \frac{381,000}{20,000 \times 0.866 \times 20.5} = 1.07 \text{ sq in.}$$

Accept #8 bars spaced 9 in. on centers, Table 9–4. It should be noted that the area of the tensile reinforcement has been computed in accordance with the bending moment at the foot of the slab. The moment decreases from this point upward, and intermediate heights should be selected and the steel area and effective depths computed for those points. Obviously, if the #8 bars 9 in. on centers are continued to the top of the wall, more steel will be used than is required. Dropping one third the number of bars at the third points of the height is generally found to give a sufficient steel area.

The shear at the bottom of the vertical slab is $V = 6800$ lb. See Fig. 12–7(c).

$$v = \frac{V}{j b d} \qquad \qquad \text{Formula (10), Art. 5–2}$$

$$v = \frac{6,800}{0.875 \times 12 \times 20.5} = 31.5 \text{ psi}$$

As the shearing unit stress is less than 75 psi, given as data, stirrups are not required.

Bars spaced 9 in. on centers are equivalent to $12 \div 9$, or 1.33 bars for each 12-in. length of wall. Referring to Table 1–1, we find that the perimeter of a #8 bar is 3.14 in. Then

$$u = \frac{V}{\Sigma_0 jd} = \frac{6800}{1.33 \times 3.14 \times 0.875 \times 20.5} = 91 \text{ psi}$$

Formula (13), Art. 5–6

#8 bars are acceptable; see specification data.

The pressure exerted by the retaining wall on the foundation bed is due to two forces, the thrust of the earth, 17,500 lb, and the vertical force W, 15,800 lb. The resultant of these two forces is found graphically, as shown in Fig. 12–7(b) and explained in the example in Art. 12–6. By scaling, the resultant cuts the base 3 ft 8 in. from the outer edge, or 1 ft 4 in. from the center line of the base, and, because the base is 10 ft wide, lies within the middle third. P, the vertical component of the resultant, is found, by scaling, to be 25,700 lb, Fig. 12–7(e). Therefore there will be pressure over the entire length of the base. The pressure at point d will be

$$f_1 = \frac{P}{A}\left(1 + \frac{6e}{d}\right) = \frac{25,700}{10}\left(1 + \frac{6 \times 1.33}{10}\right) = 4640 \text{ psf}$$

See Art. 12–4. This is the maximum pressure on the foundation bed and, since it is within 6000 psf, given as data, there will be no crushing or undue settlement. The pressure exerted by the base at point e is

$$f_2 = \frac{P}{A}\left(1 - \frac{6e}{d}\right) = \frac{25,700}{10}\left(1 - \frac{6 \times 1.33}{10}\right) = 504 \text{ psf}$$

Let us now consider the possibility of the base, cdef, failing by bending about the point g, Fig. 12–7(a). The bending moment here is the difference between the moments of the upward and downward forces to the right of the point g. We know the wall will not overturn about point d, but this tendency is resisted by the weight of the earth above the projection of the base, gf. Since the moment caused by this force is the greatest moment possible about the point g, it is considered in investigating the thickness of the base.

From the above tabulation of weights and moments, the weights of the earth in sections jig, gfkj, and kli are 700 + 7000 + 1200, or a total of 8900 lb. Likewise, the sum of the moments of these weights is $3262 + 52,500 + 9600$, or 65,362 ft-lb. If we call x the distance of the center of gravity of these loads to point c, $8900 \times x = 65,362$ and $x = 7.33$ ft. Hence $7.33 - 5 = 2.33$ ft, the distance of the force 8900 lb from point g.

Another downward force on the inner projection of the footing is the vertical component of the thrust 17,500 lb; this is 9700 lb, and, if we assume that this pressure is uniformly distributed over the length gf, it acts at a point 2.5 ft from g.

The weight of the inner projection of the base is $5 \times 2.5 \times 1 \times 150 = 1875$ lb, and it acts 2.5 ft from point g.

The sum of the moments of these three forces about point g is

$$M = (8900 \times 2.33) + (9700 \times 2.5) + (1875 \times 2.5)$$

$$= 49,590 \text{ ft-lb} = 595,000 \text{ in-lb}$$

$$d = \sqrt{\frac{M}{Kb}} \qquad \text{or} \qquad d = \sqrt{\frac{595,000}{196 \times 12}} = 16.0 \text{ in.}$$

The total depth of the slab is 30 in., and, assuming that the distance from the center of the bars to the top of the slab is 3.5 in., d, the actual effective depth $= 30 - 3.5 = 26.5$ in. As only 16 in. are required, the slab is sufficiently deep.

$$A_s = \frac{M}{f_s jd} = \frac{595,000}{20,000 \times 0.866 \times 26.5} = 1.30 \text{ sq in.}$$

Accept #8 bars, 7 in. on centers (Table 9–4).

The total shear at a vertical section through point g is

$$V = 8900 + 9700 + 1875 = 20,475 \text{ lb}$$

$$v = \frac{V}{jbd} = \frac{20,475}{0.875 \times 12 \times 26.5} = 73.5 \text{ psi}$$

This is acceptable, because it is less than 75 psi.

Now let us investigate these bars for bond stress. Since they are spaced 7 in. on centers, $12 \div 7 = 1.72$, the number of bars for each 12-in. length of slab. In Table 1–1 we find that the perimeter of a #8 bar is 3.14 in. Then

$$u = \frac{V}{\Sigma_0 jd} = \frac{20,475}{1.72 \times 3.14 \times 0.875 \times 26.5} = 164 \text{ psi}$$

These bars are considered "top bars," for they are placed so that more than 12 in. of concrete is cast in the member below the bars. According to the specification data, the allowable stress for top bars is 175 psi; thus they are acceptable for bond.

The base slab may also fail by bending about the point b as a result of the upward pressure of the foundation bed on the toe. The pressure at point d was found to be 4640 psf, and at e it is 504 psf. The footing is 10 ft in width; hence the pressure directly under point b, at the face of the vertical slab, is 3400 psf. Thus the average upward pressure on the toe is $(4640 + 3400) \div 2 = 4020$ psf. As the toe is 3 ft in length, $3 \times 4020 = 12{,}060$ lb, the total upward pressure. It acts at 1.5 ft from point b. Then $M = 12{,}060 \times 1.5 \times 12 = 217{,}080$ in-lb.

$$d = \sqrt{\frac{M}{Kb}} = \sqrt{\frac{217{,}080}{196 \times 12}} = 9.6 \text{ in.}$$

As the actual effective depth is 26.5 in., this is acceptable.

$$A_s = \frac{M}{f_s jd} = \frac{217{,}080}{20{,}000 \times 0.866 \times 26.5} = 0.47 \text{ sq in.}$$

The reinforcing bars in the vertical slab, #8 bars, 9 in. on centers, are extended as indicated in Fig. 12–7(d) and afford an ample steel area.

Instead of bending the #8 bars, as shown, many designers prefer to use straight bars extending the full width at the bottom of the base slab. These bars could be #5, spaced 8 in. on centers, or #6 with a 11-in. spacing.

In addition to the tensile reinforcement, it is necessary to place horizontal temperature bars in the wall. About 0.0025 times the concrete area is considered ample for the purpose. The average thickness of the vertical slab is 1.5 ft; hence there are 1.5×144, or 216 sq in. per foot of height. $216 \times 0.0025 = 0.54$ sq in. of temperature reinforcement per foot of height. Use #5 bars near the exposed surface and #4 bars near the back of the slab. The spacing of these bars is 11 in. on centers. In order to hold the horizontal temperature bars in position near the exposed surface while the concrete is being placed, vertical spacer bars are used. These might be #3 bars, but, for such a height as given in this example, they would not be sufficiently rigid, and #4 bars should be used. These spacer bars should be spaced 24 in. on centers.

The force that tends to cause overturning about point d is the horizontal component of the thrust, 14,560 lb. As the lever arm of this force is 4.1 ft, the overturning moment is 14,560 × 4.1, or 59,700 ft-lb. The vertical component of the resultant is 25,700 lb, and, since its lever arm about the point d is 6.07 ft, the resisting moment to overturning is 25,700 × 6.07 = 156,000 ft-lb. Hence the factor of safety against overturning is 156,000 ÷ 59,700, or 2.6. Acceptable.

The force that tends to cause the wall to slide on its base is the horizontal component of the thrust, 14,560 lb. The vertical force resisting sliding is 25,700 lb. As the foundation bed is of gravel, the coefficient of friction, as given in Art. 12–5, is 0.6. The force resisting the tendency to slide is 25,700 × 0.6, or 15,420 lb. Therefore the factor of safety is 15,420 ÷ 14,560, or 1.06. The factor of safety should be at least 1.5; hence for this wall a key will be formed on the bottom of the base as shown in Fig. 12–7(*d*). The earth abutting the outer face of the wall also serves to prevent sliding.

Problem 12–7–A. Design a reinforced concrete cantilever retaining wall as an alternate solution for the wall given in Problem 12–6–A. Specification data:

$$f_s = 20,000 \text{ psi}$$

$$f'_c = 2500 \text{ psi}$$

$$f_c = 1125 \text{ psi}$$

$$v_c = \text{limited to 75 psi}$$

$$u = \text{limited to 175 psi for top bars}$$
$$\text{and 250 psi for others}$$

$$n = 12$$

CHAPTER 13

MISCELLANEOUS MEMBERS

13–1. Reinforced Concrete Stairs. A reinforced concrete stair-way may be considered an inclined slab with one-way reinforcement having steps formed on its upper surface. The usual procedure is to construct the stairway after the beams and floor slabs. When this is the case, the slab is regarded as a simple beam with a span equal to the *horizontal* distance between supports. Thus the maximum bending moment is $Wl/8$. If, however, the stair slab is placed with the supporting beams and floor slabs, negative bending moments occur at the supports and the stair slab becomes a continuous beam. As in the case of floor slabs, the stair slab is designed by considering a strip 12 in. wide for which the effective depth and tensile steel reinforcement are computed. In addition to the tensile reinforcement, transverse bars are installed to serve as temperature reinforcement, as required by the governing code.

It is considered advantageous to have relatively short span lengths. Stairways between floors are often made in two flights with an intermediate platform. The stair slab may be supported by cross beams at the ends, or the platform may be considered as part of the stair slab. In any event, a sketch of the construction is first made, and the horizontal span length between supports is determined.

The proportion of tread to riser is a matter of judgment and is usually determined by the limitations set forth in the controlling building code. Maximum and minimum dimensions for risers are about $7\frac{3}{4}$ and $6\frac{1}{2}$ in., respectively, whereas treads, exclusive of nosings, should never be less than $9\frac{1}{2}$ in. Two commonly used rules for proportioning treads and risers are (1) the sum of tread and riser should be approximately $17\frac{1}{2}$ in., and (2) their product should be between 70 and 75. For both of these rules, the tread does not include the projection of the nosing.

For the great majority of buildings, building codes require that the live load for stairways be 100 psf of horizontal area.

Let r be the height of the riser in inches and t, exclusive of the nosing, be the width of the tread in inches. Figured at 144 lb per cu ft, the weight of the steps, the hatched area in Fig. 13–1(b), is $(6 \times r)$ psf of horizontal area.

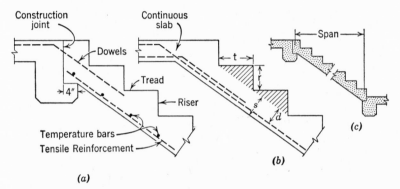

FIG. 13–1

The weight of the slab in pounds per square foot of horizontal area is $s \times \sqrt{r^2 + t^2} \times \dfrac{12.5}{t}$, in which s is the total thickness of the slab, the perpendicular distance from the bottom face of the slab to the foot of the riser. See Fig. 13–1(b).

Table 13–1 may be used to determine the thickness and required tensile reinforcement for stair slabs having 100 psf live loads. When using this table, note that $f_s = 20{,}000$ psi, $f_c = 1350$ psi, and $n = 10$. In particular, observe that the span of the stair slab is the *horizontal* span length, as shown in Fig. 13–1(c). By use of this table, no computations are necessary, but an accompanying drawing should show the position of the reinforcement and its termination.

TABLE 13–1. REINFORCED CONCRETE STAIR SLABS FOR 100 PSF LIVE LOADS

$f_s = 20,000$ psi   1″ clear protective covering
$f_c = 1350$ psi
$n = 10$

Horizontal Span of Stairs in Feet	Total Thickness of Slab in Inches	Reinforcing Steel
5	3	#3—6½″ o.c.
6	3	#3—4½″ o.c.
7	3½	#4—7″ o.c.
8	4	#4—6½″ o.c.
9	4	#4—5″ o.c.
10	4½	#5—7″ o.c.
11	5	#5—6½″ o.c.
12	5½	#5—6″ o.c.
13	5½	#5—5″ o.c.
14	6½	#6—7″ o.c.
15	7	#6—6½″ o.c.

13–2. Design of a Reinforced Concrete Stair Slab.

Example. Let it be required to design a stair slab having a live load of 100 psf and a horizontal span length of 13 ft 0 in. The risers are 7 in. in height, and the treads, exclusive of the nosings, are $10\frac{1}{2}$ in. Design data:

$$f_s = 20,000 \text{ psi}$$

$$f_c = 1350 \text{ psi}$$

$$v_c = \text{limited to } 90 \text{ psi}$$

$$u = \text{limited to } 300 \text{ psi}$$

$$n = 10$$

SOLUTION. From Table 4–1, $K = 236$ and $j = 0.866$. As given in Art. 13–1, the weight of the steps is $(6 \times r)$ lb, or $6 \times 7 = 42$ psf.

Assume that the total thickness of the slab, s, is $5\frac{1}{2}$ in.; the weight of the slab is

$$s\sqrt{r^2 + t^2} \times \frac{12.5}{t}$$

or

$$5.5\sqrt{7^2 + 10.5^2} \times \frac{12.5}{10.5} = 83 \text{ psf}$$

Then the total load $= 42 + 83 + 100 = 225$ psf.

Considering a strip of slab 12 in. wide and that the slab is simply supported at its ends,

$$M = \frac{wl^2}{8} = \frac{225 \times 13 \times 13 \times 12}{8} = 57,000 \text{ in-lb}$$

$$d = \sqrt{\frac{M}{Kb}} = \sqrt{\frac{57,000}{236 \times 12}} = 4.5 \text{ in.} \quad \text{Formula (6), Art. 4–5}$$

The required effective depth, then, is 4.5 in., and, assuming one half a bar diameter to be 0.31 in. with $\frac{3}{4}$ in. for protection, the total depth is $4.5 + 0.31 + 0.75 = 5.56$ in. Accept a total slab thickness of $5\frac{1}{2}$ in. The effective depth, d, will be $5.5 - 1.06 = 4.44$ in.

$$A_s = \frac{M}{f_s j d} \quad \text{Formula (7), Art. 4–5}$$

$$A_s = \frac{57,000}{20,000 \times 0.866 \times 4.44} = 0.74 \text{ sq in.}$$

the area of the tensile reinforcement for each 12-in. width of slab. Accept #5 bars, 5 in. on centers, Table 9–4.

The total load on the 12-in. strip is $225 \times 13 = 2920$ lb; hence

$$V = 2920 \times \frac{1}{2} = 1460 \text{ lb}$$

$$v = \frac{V}{jbd} = \frac{1460}{0.875 \times 12 \times 4.44} = 31 \text{ psi} \quad \text{Formula (10), Art. 5–2}$$

As 31 psi is within 90 psi, the allowable unit stress, the slab is sufficiently thick to resist diagonal tension stresses.

The perimeter of a #5 bar is 1.96 in., Table 1–1. At 5-in. spacing, $12 \div 5 = 2.4$, the number of bars in each 12 in. of width.

$$u = \frac{V}{\Sigma_0 jd} = \frac{1460}{2.4 \times 1.96 \times 0.875 \times 4.44} = 80 \text{ psi}$$

This stress is acceptable, since it is less than 300 psi, the allowable.

For temperature reinforcement, place #3 bars, 10 in. on centers, at right angles to the tensile reinforcement.

By referring to Table 13–1, note that the thickness of the slab and the tensile reinforcement could have been found instantly with no computations. We see that for a horizontal span of 13 ft 0 in. the required total thickness of the stair slab is $5\frac{1}{2}$ in. and the tensile reinforcement consists of #5 bars, 5 in. on centers. The design is similar to that found by computations.

Problem 13–2–A. A flight of stairs consists of thirteen $6\frac{1}{2}$-in. risers and twelve 11-in. treads. Design a reinforced concrete stair slab for a live load of 100 psf and in accordance with the following specification data:

$$f_s = 20,000 \text{ psi}$$

$$f_c = 1350 \text{ psi}$$

$$n = 10$$

13–3. Basement Walls. The minimum thickness given by some building codes for basement walls is 8 in., but 10 and 12-in. walls are commonly used. These walls should be properly waterproofed and reinforced to provide for temperature variations as well as to resist bending stresses due to the thrust of the earth.

When the wall serves as a retaining wall, it may be considered as a slab spanning from column to column or as a slab with vertical tensile reinforcement, the first and basement floor slabs serving as the two reactions for the horizontal earth pressure. As the basement height is generally less than the column spacing, the latter condition occurs most frequently.

Referring to Fig. 13–2(a), the earth pressure is considered to be a triangular loading having a maximum value at the basement floor and decreasing in magnitude toward the top of the slab. The total earth pressure is represented by P, and, as given in Art. 12–2, its magnitude is $0.286 \dfrac{wh^2}{2}$, where w = the weight of the retained earth in pounds per cubic foot and h is the height of the retained earth in feet. The direction of the resultant earth pres-

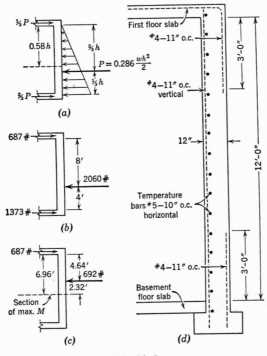

FIG. 13–2

sure is horizontal and acts at $\frac{1}{3}h$ from the bottom of the slab. The two reactions, or resisting horizontal forces, are $\frac{1}{3}P$ and $\frac{2}{3}P$, the forces resisted by the first floor and basement slabs, respectively. For this type of triangular loading, the section of the slab at which the bending moment is maximum is $0.58 \times h$ from the top of the slab. A wall of this type is in reality a vertical slab with vertical reinforcement. If the wall and the floor slabs are placed at the same time, there is restraint at the two reactions. It is customary, however, to consider the slab as simply supported, thus erring on the side of safety.

13–4. Design of a Basement Wall.

Example. Let it be required to design a 12-in. thick reinforced concrete basement wall 12 ft 0 in. in height, the basement and first floor slabs serving as supports to the horizontal earth pressure. Specification data:

$$f_s = 20{,}000 \text{ psi}$$

$$f_c = 1350 \text{ psi}$$

$$v = \text{limited to 90 psi}$$

$$u = \text{limited to 300 psi}$$

$$n = 10$$

SOLUTION. Referring to Table 4–1, we find the following formula coefficients: $K = 236$ and $j = 0.866$. The value of the total earth pressure for each linear foot of wall, assuming that the soil weighs 100 lb per cu ft, is

$$P = 0.286 \frac{wh^2}{2} = 0.286 \times \frac{100 \times 12 \times 12}{2} = 2060 \text{ lb}$$

The force resisted by the first floor slab is $\frac{1}{3} \times 2060 = 687$ lb, and the basement floor slab resists a force of $\frac{2}{3} \times 2060 = 1373$ lb. See Fig. 13–2(b).

The section of maximum bending moment in the wall slab is $0.58 \times h$ from the top, or $0.58 \times 12 = 6.96$ ft. The earth pressure *above* the section at which the bending moment is maximum is

$$0.286 \times \frac{100 \times 6.96 \times 6.96}{2} = 692 \text{ lb}$$

This is the equation $P = 0.286 \times \dfrac{wh^2}{2}$ for finding the total earth pressure, in which h is taken as the height of retained earth above the section of maximum bending moment. The position of this resultant earth pressure is $\frac{2}{3} \times 6.96$ or 4.64 ft from the top of the wall; see Fig. 13–2(c). As the value of the bending moment at any section of the slab is equal to the algebraic sum of the moments of the forces on either side of the section, the maximum bending moment is

$$M = (687 \times 6.96) - (692 \times 2.32) = 3170 \text{ ft-lb}$$

$$3170 \times 12 = 38,040 \text{ in-lb}$$

The maximum bending moment for this type of triangular loading is $M = 0.128Wl$, in which W is the triangular load and l is the span length. Thus, a simpler method of computing M for this basement wall is to apply this moment formula. Then $M = 0.128 \times 2060 \times 12 = 3170$ ft-lb, or 38,040 in-lb.

The required effective depth (thickness in this instance) is found by the equation $d = \sqrt{\dfrac{M}{Kb}}$, formula (6), Art. 4–5. Then

$$d = \sqrt{\frac{38,040}{236 \times 12}} = 3.7 \text{ in.}$$

But the wall has a total thickness of 12 in.; hence, assuming the reinforcement to consist of #4 bars, the actual effective depth, d, is $12 - 1\frac{1}{4}$, or 10.75 in., and the wall, therefore, is sufficiently thick.

$$A_s = \frac{M}{f_s jd} \qquad \text{Formula (7), Art. 4–5}$$

$$A_s = \frac{38,040}{20,000 \times 0.866 \times 10.75} = 0.204 \text{ sq in.}$$

The A.C.I. code, however, requires that the vertical reinforcement in reinforced concrete walls shall be not less than 0.0015 times the area of the reinforced section if bars are used. Hence, since the wall is 12 in. thick, the minimum A_s per foot of wall length will be $0.0015 \times 12 \times 12$, or 0.216 sq in.

Accept #4 bars, 11 in. on centers, Table 9–4. These bars, of course, will be placed near the inner side of the wall where the stresses are tensile.

To investigate the shearing stresses, $V = 1373$ lb and

$$v = \frac{V}{jbd} \qquad \text{Formula (10), Art. 5–2}$$

or

$$v = \frac{1373}{0.875 \times 12 \times 10.75} = 12 \text{ psi}$$

This indicates that web reinforcement is not required, since by Table 4–2 v may be as high as 90 psi.

Investigating the bond stress,

$$u = \frac{V}{\Sigma_0 j d} \qquad \text{Formula (13), Art. 5–6}$$

The perimeter of a #4 bar is 1.57 in., and, since there are 12 ÷ 11, or 1.09, bars in each 12-in. length of wall,

$$u = \frac{1373}{1.09 \times 1.57 \times 0.875 \times 10.75} = 85 \text{ psi}$$

the bond stress.

Since this stress is within 300 psi, the allowable, #4 bars, 11 in. on centers, are accepted for the vertical tensile reinforcement.

In addition to the vertical bars, horizontal temperature reinforcement must be used. The A.C.I. code requires that the temperature reinforcement be a minimum of 0.0025 times the area of the reinforced section of the wall. Therefore, $0.0025 \times 12 \times 12 = 0.36$ sq in., and we shall use #5 bars spaced 10 in. on centers.

To provide for possible tensile stresses in the outer portion of the wall at the basement and first floor slabs, #4 bars are provided and extended to the fourth points of height, as shown in Fig. 13–2(d).

Problem 13–4–A. A basement wall, 13 ft 0 in. in height, is supported by the basement and first floor slabs against the lateral pressure of the exterior earth fill. Design the wall in accordance with the following specification data:

$$f_s = 20,000 \text{ psi}$$

$$f'_c = 2500 \text{ psi}$$

$$f_c = 1125 \text{ psi}$$

$$v = \text{limited to 75 psi}$$

$$u = \text{limited to 250 psi}$$

$$n = 12$$

13–5. Design of an Overhanging Beam.

Example. A 10-in. wide laterally unsupported beam having a clear span of 20 ft 0 in. between the faces of the supporting columns overhangs one of the supports a distance of 8 ft 0 in. If the superimposed load is 800 lb per linear ft, design both the anchor beam and the cantilever. Specification data:

$f'_c = 3000$ psi

$f_s = 20,000$ psi

$f_c = 1350$ psi

$v_c = $ limited to 90 psi

$u = $ limited to 210 psi for top bars and 300 psi for others

$n = 10$

SOLUTION. For the stresses given as specification data, Table 4–1 shows that $K = 236$ and $j = 0.866$. Assuming that the beam weighs 200 lb per linear ft, the total load is $800 + 200 = 1000$ lb per linear ft.

The first step in the design is to construct the shear and bending moment diagrams. After these diagrams are made, we can see readily the magnitudes of the shear and moments at any of the critical sections of the beam. The load diagram is first drawn as shown in Fig. 13–3(a).

Computing the reactions,

$$20 \times R_1 = 1000 \times 28 \times 14 = 392,000 \quad \text{and} \quad R_1 = 19,600 \text{ lb}$$

$$20 \times R_2 = 1000 \times 28 \times 6 = 168,000 \quad \text{and} \quad R_2 = 8400 \text{ lb}$$

The shear diagram is drawn as shown in Fig. 13–3(b). Note that there are two points in the length of the beam at which the shear passes through zero. This indicates that there will be a maximum negative bending moment over the left support and a maximum positive bending moment at some point between R_1 and R_2. To find the position of this point, let it be x distance from R_2. Then, as the value of the shear at this point is zero,

$$0 = 8400 - 1000x \quad \text{or} \quad x = 8.4 \text{ ft}$$

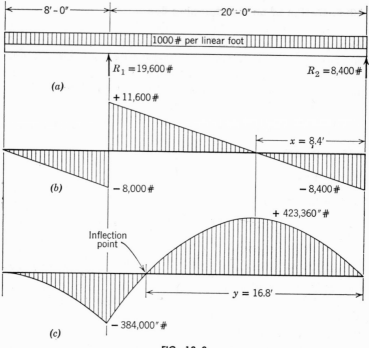

FIG. 13–3

the distance of the maximum positive bending moment from the right reaction, R_2.

The value of the maximum negative bending moment is

$$M = -(1000 \times 8 \times 4) = -32,000 \text{ ft-lb} = -384,000 \text{ in-lb}$$

The value of the maximum positive moment is

$$M = (8400 \times 8.4) - (1000 \times 8.4 \times 4.2)$$

$$= 35,280 \text{ ft-lb} = 423,360 \text{ in-lb}$$

The magnitudes of the bending moments at other sections of the beam are computed and the diagram is constructed as shown in Fig. 13–3(c).

It is seen from the diagram that the value of the bending moment is zero at a point about 3 ft to the right of R_1. This is the inflection point, the section at which the bars will be bent up, if bent bars are are used. To find this point, call it y ft to the right reaction, write the value of the bending moment and equate it to zero; thus

$$8400y - \left(1000y \times \frac{y}{2}\right) = 0$$

$$500y^2 - 8400y = 0$$

$$y = 16.8 \text{ ft}$$

To determine the depth of the beam, we shall use the maximum positive bending moment, 423,360 in-lb. Since the width of the beam is to be 10 in.,

$$d = \sqrt{\frac{M}{Kb}} = \sqrt{\frac{423,360}{236 \times 10}} = 13.4 \text{ in.}$$

Accept an effective depth of 13.5 in. The total depth will be 13.5 + 0.5 + 2 = 16 in.

The reinforcement for the maximum positive moment will be

$$A_s = \frac{M}{f_s jd} = \frac{423,360}{20,000 \times 0.866 \times 13.5} = 1.81 \text{ sq in.}$$

The reinforcement for the maximum negative moment will be

$$A_s = \frac{M}{f_s jd} = \frac{384,000}{20,000 \times 0.866 \times 13.5} = 1.64 \text{ sq in.}$$

Accept 3-#7 bars for the positive moment and 2-#7 plus 1-#6 bars for the negative moment. See Table 1–1.

The maximum shear is immediately to the right of the left reaction, $V = 11,600$ lb.

$$v = \frac{V}{jbd} = \frac{11,600}{0.875 \times 10 \times 13.5} = 98 \text{ psi} \qquad \text{Formula (10), Art. 5–2}$$

Since this value exceeds 90 psi, web reinforcement is required.

As explained in Art. 5–3, web reinforcement for a beam continuous over a support, or having no lateral support, must be provided from the support to a point beyond the inflection point a distance equal to either $\frac{1}{16}$ of the clear span or the depth of the member.

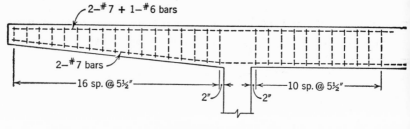

FIG. 13–4

whichever is the greater. Such reinforcement must be designed to carry at least two thirds of the total shear at the section.

Consequently, the distance in which web reinforcement is required is either

$$(20 - 16.8) + \frac{20}{16} = 3.2 + 1.25 = 4.45 \text{ ft}$$

or

$$(20 - 16.8) + \frac{16}{12} = 3.2 + 1.33 = 4.53 \text{ ft}$$

Since 4.53 ft is the greater, it will be used. Two thirds of shear stress is $\frac{2}{3} \times 98$, or 66 psi, the magnitude of v'.

Using #3 ties for web reinforcement,

$$s = \frac{A_v f_v}{v'b} = \frac{0.22 \times 20{,}000}{66 \times 10} = 6.7 \text{ in.} \quad \text{Formula (12), Art. 5–4}$$

But the maximum stirrup spacing is $\dfrac{d - m}{2}$ or $\dfrac{13.5 - 2.5}{2} = 5.5$ in.

The first stirrup is placed 2 in. from the face of the columns and the others, 5.5 in. on centers. See Fig. 13–4.

Because the left end of the beam, a cantilever, is laterally unrestrained, the same requirement applies and web reinforcement must be employed for its entire length, even though the shearing unit stress is less than 90 psi. Theoretically, no web reinforcement is required adjacent to the right support, but, since it is advisable to provide a minimum tensile reinforcement of $\frac{1}{2}$ of 1% in the top of the beam, #3 ties spaced 12 in. on centers are used to hold the tensile reinforcement in place. Then $0.005 \times 10 \times 13.5 = 0.68$ sq in.; hence we shall use 2-#6 bars with hooked ends. See Fig. 13–4.

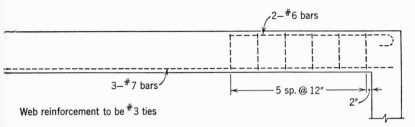

FIG. 13-4

Investigating the bond stress for the top reinforcement,

$$u = \frac{V}{\Sigma_0 jd}$$ Formula (13), Art. 5-6

Then

$$u = \frac{11,600}{[(2 \times 2.75) + 2.36] \times 0.875 \times 13.5} = 125 \text{ psi}$$

Since the bond stress is less than 210 psi, the allowable, the reinforcing bars are adequate.

The total depth of the beam determined in accordance with the maximum positive moment is 16 in. For practical reasons, this same depth will be maintained in the cantilever end of the beam at the face of the column even though the negative bending moment is smaller. The depth of the cantilever may be decreased toward the free end, as the moments decrease, or a uniform depth may be maintained. Suppose, for instance, that the total depth of the cantilever is 10 in. at the free end and 16 in. at the face of the column. Then the total depth at 4 ft 0 in. from the free end will be 13 in., making an effective depth of 10.5 in.

The negative bending moment at 4 ft 0 in. from the free end is

$$M = -(1000 \times 4 \times 2 \times 12) = -96,000 \text{ in-lb}$$

$$d = \sqrt{\frac{M}{Kb}} = \sqrt{\frac{96,000}{236 \times 10}} = 6.4 \text{ in.}$$

the required effective depth. Since, however, there is an effective depth of 10.5 in., the beam is sufficiently deep at this section. Other sections may be investigated in a similar manner.

As computed above, 3-#7 bars are used for the main tensile reinforcement between the supports and 2-#7 plus 1-#6 bars are ample for the cantilever at the face of the support. Two #6 bars with hooked ends are placed in the top of the beam at the right support. The web reinforcement consists of #3 ties placed as shown in Fig. 13-4.

Problem 13-5-A. A laterally unsupported beam 22 ft 0 in. between faces of supporting columns overhangs each end a distance of 6 ft 0 in. Design the beam for a superimposed load of 1000 lb per linear ft. Specification data:

$$f_s = 20{,}000 \text{ psi}$$

$$f'_c = 2500 \text{ psi}$$

$$f_c = 1125 \text{ psi}$$

$$v_c = \text{limited to 75 psi}$$

$$u = \text{limited to 175 psi for top bars and 250 psi for others}$$

$$n = 12$$

CHAPTER 14

PRESTRESSED CONCRETE

14–1. Prestressed Concrete. Prestressed concrete structural members are examples of an economical use of materials. Although their use is still limited in building construction, they have been used extensively in the construction of small and medium-sized bridges. The first practical application of the theory of prestressed concrete was made in France about 1928, but its first use for structural purposes in the United States was in the late 1940's. It continues to grow in favor each year.

In a book of this scope it is not feasible to discuss in detail the special materials and various construction methods employed in making a prestressed concrete structural member. However, it is shown why the conventional reinforced concrete beam is uneconomical in the use of materials and how a prestress increases the ability of a beam to resist bending stresses and to support greater loads. Illustrative examples which explain the design of prestressed beams show why such structural members are advantageous.

The concrete in the conventional reinforced concrete beam is not used economically. Such a beam is indicated in Fig. 14–1.

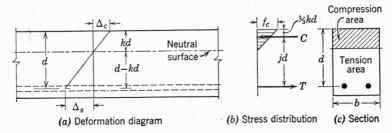

(a) Deformation diagram *(b)* Stress distribution *(c)* Section

FIG. 14–1

With respect to bending stresses, only the concrete above the neutral surface, the hatched area of the cross section, resists compressive stresses. All the concrete in the tension area is disregarded in design computations because concrete is inherently weak in resisting tension. Therefore, only about one third of the concrete resists compressive stresses, the maximum stress being at the top of the beam, with the stresses decreasing in magnitude to a zero stress at the neutral surface. Since, in the usual reinforced concrete beam the concrete cannot be used efficiently, certain forces may be applied to beams that result in a member in which all the concrete resists bending stresses. This is known as *prestressed concrete*. A prestressed concrete beam is a member so designed and constructed that all of the stresses in the concrete resulting from bending are compressive, none is tensile. How and why this condition is accomplished will be seen in the succeeding discussion.

14–2. A Block Lintel. Imagine a row of concrete blocks, laid end to end, to be used as a lintel, as shown in Fig. 14–2. Obviously

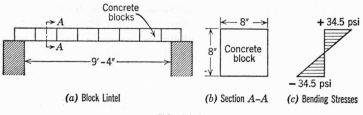

(a) Block Lintel   (b) Section A-A   (c) Bending Stresses

FIG. 14-2

a beam formed in this manner would collapse. The reason for this is readily shown by the following simple computations.

Assume that the weight of each block is 30 lb. Then the weight of the block lintel over the clear span is 7 × 30, or 210 lb. The maximum bending moment that results from this dead load is

$$M = \frac{Wl}{8} = \frac{210 \times 9.33 \times 12}{8} = 2940 \text{ in-lb}$$

The blocks are 8 in. wide and 8 in. deep, giving a cross section of 8 x 8 in. Hence the section modulus * is

* See Art. 61 of *Simplified Mechanics and Strength of Materials*, by Harry Parker, John Wiley and Sons, New York, 1951.

$$S = \frac{bd^2}{6} = \frac{8 \times 8 \times 8}{6} = 85.3 \text{ in.}^3$$

The flexure formula * is

$$\frac{M}{f} = S \quad \text{or} \quad f = \frac{M}{S} = \frac{2940}{85.3} = 34.5 \text{ psi}$$

the extreme fiber stress at both the top and bottom of the beam and the maximum compressive and tensile stresses, respectively. See Fig. 14-2(c), the stress distribution diagram. Of course, a beam formed of blocks laid end to end cannot resist tension, and such a beam could not be built.

14-3. A Prestressed Block Lintel. Figure 14-3(a) shows a similar beam made up of concrete blocks. In this case assume

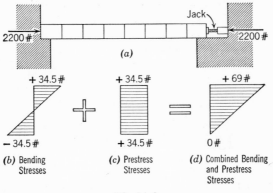

(a)

(b) Bending Stresses (c) Prestress Stresses (d) Combined Bending and Prestress Stresses

FIG. 14-3

rigid immovable masonry walls at each end of the beam with a jack inserted at the right-hand end. The jack on being operated exerts a compressive force of 2200 lb against the centroid of the 8 x 8 in. cross section, thus tending to push the assembly of blocks to the left. The force of 2200 lb exerted by the jack produces a compressive stress uniformly distributed over the 8 x 8 in. cross section. Hence $\frac{2200}{8 \times 8} = 34.5$ psi, the compressive unit stress on

* See Art. 90 of *Simplified Mechanics and Strength of Materials*.

each square inch of the cross section that results from the 2200-lb prestress.

The stress distribution diagrams are shown in Fig. 14–3(b), (c), and (d). By adding the stresses due to bending and the prestress, we see that the compressive stress at the top of the beam is 34.5 + 34.5, or 69 psi, and that the tensile stress at the bottom of the beam has disappeared, −34.5 + 34.5 = 0. There are no tensile stresses; the entire area of the cross section is in compression, and such a beam (impractical, of course) would support its own weight.

A more favorable result could be obtained if the jack were lowered to act at the lower edge of the middle third of the depth and if the prestress were reduced from 2200 to 1100 lb. See Fig. 14–4(a). Now, the prestress of 1100 lb is not distributed uni-

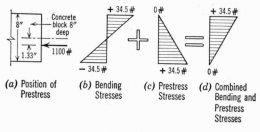

(a) Position of Prestress   (b) Bending Stresses   (c) Prestress Stresses   (d) Combined Bending and Prestress Stresses

FIG. 14–4

formly over the 8 x 8 in. cross section; the stress at the bottom of the beam is greater than at the top. By referring to Art. 12–4 and Fig. 12–4(c), we find that for a force exerted at the lower edge of the middle third the stresses at the top and bottom are $f_2 = 0$ and $f_1 = 2\dfrac{P}{A}$. Then $f_2 = 0$ and $f_1 = \dfrac{2 \times 1100}{8 \times 8} = 34.5$ psi, the stress at the bottom of the beam that results from the prestress. The stress distribution diagrams for bending and prestress stresses are shown in Fig. 14–4(b) and (c). The combined stresses are +34.5 + 0 or +34.5 psi, the stress at the top of the beam, and −34.5 + 34.5, or 0 stress at the bottom of the beam.

By applying the prestress eccentrically and reducing its magnitude by one half, the maximum compressive stress is not increased beyond the stress produced by bending alone. In practice, however, it would be difficult to construct absolutely rigid abutments, as assumed in this example. In addition, any jacks used for the prestress would have to be left in the structure permanently.

A practical method of prestressing a row of blocks to be used as a beam is indicated in Fig. 14–5. A steel bar with a head at one

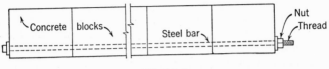

FIG. 14–5

end and with threads at the other is run through the holes in the bottom of the blocks. A nut is screwed on the threaded end. When the nut is tightened against the end block, the steel bar is put in tension and the concrete is put in compression. The purpose of the compressive prestress in the concrete is to neutralize the tensile stresses that tend to occur in the beam as a result of bending when the beam is loaded.

14–4. Steel Wire Used for Prestressed Concrete. Because of plastic flow (deformation) in both the steel and the concrete, part of the prestressing load is lost after a period of time. If the bar in Fig. 14–5 were made of the steel used for conventional reinforced concrete, the prestressing force would disappear almost completely. Therefore, for prestressed concrete, it is necessary to use special steel, a steel having a much higher ultimate strength, yield point, and allowable working stress. The average physical properties of steel wire used for prestressed concrete are shown in Table 14–1. For comparison, the properties of steel used for conventional reinforced concrete are shown in the same table.

TABLE 14–1. PHYSICAL PROPERTIES OF STEEL USED FOR PRESTRESSED CONCRETE
IN POUNDS PER SQUARE INCH

	Prestressing Steel	Conventional Reinforcing Steel (intermediate grade)
Ultimate strength	av. 250,000	70,000 to 90,000
Yield point	av. 212,000	40,000
Allowable working stress	av. 150,000	20,000

A certain portion of the prestress is also lost when the special prestress wire is used. This loss is assumed to vary between 15 and 20%, and this means that the initial prestress must be that much higher so that the prestress producing the required compression in the concrete will remain.

14–5. Concrete Used for Prestressed Concrete. In designing prestressed concrete members, we must recognize the fact that the concrete may be subjected, temporarily, to compressive stresses that are higher than the allowable stresses in the finished structure under full live loads. Also, we know that concrete does possess a certain degree of tensile strength, and, depending on the structure, a limited tensile stress may be temporarily allowed. The temporary over-stress during prestressing serves as a quality test for the materials that are used.

In general, the concretes in prestressed concrete have higher ultimate strengths than those in conventional reinforced concrete. The concretes used have ultimate strengths that lie between $f'_c = 4000$ psi and $f'_c = 6000$ psi. Concretes of even higher ultimate strength have been employed.

14–6. Design of a Conventional Reinforced Concrete Beam. The following examples compare the designs of two beams, one of the conventional reinforced concrete type and the other employing prestressed concrete. The span lengths, superimposed load, and concrete strength are the same in both cases.

Example. A simple beam has a span of 30 ft 0 in. and a superimposed uniformly distributed load of 1000 lb per linear ft. Design a conventional reinforced concrete beam in accordance with the following specification data:

$$f'_c = 3000 \ \text{psi}$$

$$f_s = 20,000 \ \text{psi}$$

$$f_c = 1350 \ \text{psi}$$

$$v_c = 90 \ \text{psi}$$

$$u = 300 \ \text{psi}$$

$$n = 10$$

SOLUTION. Referring to Table 4–1, $K = 236$ and $j = 0.866$. Assuming that the beam is 12 x 28 in., its weight per linear ft is $\frac{12 \times 28}{144} \times 150 = 350$ lb. Then 1000 (the superimposed load) + 350 = 1350 lb, the total load per linear ft.

$$W = 1350 \times 30 = 40{,}500 \text{ lb}$$

the total load on the beam.

$$M = \frac{Wl}{8} = \frac{40{,}500 \times 30 \times 12}{8} = 1{,}823{,}000 \text{ in-lb}$$

the maximum bending moment.

$$d = \sqrt{\frac{M}{Kb}} \quad \text{or} \quad d = \sqrt{\frac{1{,}823{,}000}{236 \times 12}}$$

$$= \sqrt{643} = 25.4, \quad \text{say } 25.5 \text{ in.}$$

the effective depth.

Total depth = 25.5 + 2.5 = 28 in.

$$A_s = \frac{M}{f_s jd} = \frac{1{,}823{,}000}{20{,}000 \times 0.866 \times 25.5} = 4.13 \text{ sq in.}$$

the area of the tensile reinforcement.

Referring to Table 1–1, use 3-#9 and 1-#10 bars for the longitudinal tensile reinforcement. $(3 \times 1) + 1.27 = 4.27$ sq in.

$$V = \frac{40{,}500}{2} = 20{,}250 \text{ lb}$$

the maximum vertical shear.

$$v = \frac{V}{jbd} = \frac{20{,}250}{0.875 \times 12 \times 25.5} = 76 \text{ psi}$$

Since this stress is less than 90 psi, the allowable, web reinforcement is not required.

From Table 1–1, the perimeters of #9 and #10 bars are 3.5 and 4 in., respectively. Thus

$$\Sigma_0 = (3 \times 3.5) + 4 = 14.5 \text{ in.}$$

Then

$$u = \frac{V}{\Sigma_0 jd} = \frac{20{,}250}{14.5 \times 0.866 \times 25.5} = 63 \text{ psi}$$

the bond stress, acceptable because it is less than 300 psi, the allowable.

Thus the beam will have over-all dimensions of 12 x 28 in., with 3-#9 and 1-#10 bars for the longitudinal tensile reinforcement. Web reinforcement is not required.

14–7. Design of a Prestressed Concrete Beam. The design of a prestressed beam is a problem for an experienced engineer. It is not possible, nor is it advisable, in a book of this scope to enter into the numerous problems relating to both the design and construction of a prestressed member. The following example, however, is to acquaint the reader with the principles and the procedure involved in the design of a prestressed beam and to show how this beam presents a more economical use of materials than is obtained in the conventional reinforced concrete beam. The beam designed in the previous article is now redesigned as a prestressed beam.

Example. Design a simple prestressed concrete beam having a span of 30 ft 0 in., with a superimposed load of 1000 lb per linear ft. The beam will have a width of 12 in., and $f'_c = 3000$ psi.

Allowable stresses.

Concrete at initial prestress:

compression, $f_c = 0.55 \times 3000 = 1650$ psi

tension, $f_{\text{ten}} = -3\sqrt{3000} = -165$ psi

Concrete after loss in prestress:

compression, $f_c = 0.45 \times 3000 = 1350$ psi

tension, $f_{\text{ten}} = 0$ psi

shear, $v = 90$ psi

Steel:

ultimate strength, $f_s = 250{,}000$ psi

temporary, $\quad\quad f_s = 0.80 \times 250{,}000 = 200{,}000$ psi

after losses, $\quad\quad f_s = 0.60 \times 250{,}000 = 150{,}000$ psi

Loss in prestress $= 15\%$

SOLUTION.

Nomenclature and symbols:

All compressive concrete stresses are positive $(+)$.

All tensile concrete stresses are negative $(-)$.

Concrete unit stresses are designated by the letter f with two subscripts, the first indicating the cause of the stress and the second, the location of the stress.

The subscript letters are

> d for dead load
> l for live load
> p for prestress
> pi for initial prestress
> c for combination of causes
> t for top of beam
> b for bottom of beam

Thus f_{dt} indicates the concrete unit stress due to the dead load in the top of the beam and f_{pib} indicates the concrete unit stress due to the initial prestress in the bottom of the beam.

The design of a prestressed concrete beam requires that its width and depth be assumed and, by computations, investigated to see that the dimensions are acceptable. In this illustrative example a depth of 22 in. was first assumed, but computations showed it to be too small. Next, a greater depth is taken, 22.5 in., and, since by data the width is to be 12 in.,

area, $A = 12 \times 22.5 = 270$ sq in.

section modulus, $S = \dfrac{bd^2}{6} = \dfrac{12 \times 22.5 \times 22.5}{6} = 1012$ in.^{3}

weight of beam $= \dfrac{12 \times 22.5}{144} \times 150 = 282$ lb per linear ft

W_d, dead load $= 282 \times 30 = 8460$ lb

$V_d = 8460 \times \frac{1}{2} = 4230$ lb

$$M_d = \frac{Wl}{8} = \frac{8460 \times 30 \times 12}{8} = 381,000 \text{ in-lb}$$

W_l, live load $= 30 \times 1000 = 30,000$ lb

$V_l = 30,000 \times \frac{1}{2} = 15,000$ lb

$$M_l = \frac{Wl}{8} = \frac{30,000 \times 30 \times 12}{8} = 1,350,000 \text{ in-lb}$$

Bending stresses due to dead load are $\dfrac{M}{f} = S$ or $f = \dfrac{M}{S}$.
Then

$$f_{dt} = \frac{381,000}{1012} = +376 \text{ psi}$$

$$f_{db} = \frac{381,000}{1012} = -376 \text{ psi}$$

Bending stresses due to live load are

$$f_{lt} = \frac{1,350,000}{1012} = +1332 \text{ psi}$$

$$f_{lb} = \frac{1,350,000}{1012} = -1332 \text{ psi}$$

The stresses produced by the combination of dead and live loads are

$$f_{ct} = +376 + 1332 = +1708 \text{ psi}$$

$$f_{cb} = -376 - 1332 = -1708 \text{ psi}$$

In the final structure, after loss in prestress, the stresses due to the combined action of dead load, prestress, and live load are, by data,

$$f_{ct} = +1350 \text{ psi}$$

$$f_{cb} = 0 \text{ psi}$$

Prestress must be of such magnitude that

$$f_{pt} = 1350 - 1708 = -358 \text{ psi}$$

$$f_{pb} = 0 - (-1708) = +1708 \text{ psi} \qquad \text{(See Fig. 14–6)}$$

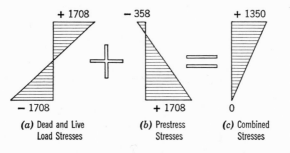

+ 1708	− 358	+ 1350
− 1708	+ 1708	0
(a) Dead and Live Load Stresses	*(b)* Prestress Stresses	*(c)* Combined Stresses

FIG. 14–6

The prestress is an eccentric load at the end of the beam.
Referring to Art. 12–4 and Fig. 12–4(*b*),

$$f_{pt} = \frac{P}{A}\left(1 - \frac{6e}{d}\right)$$

$$f_{pb} = \frac{P}{A}\left(1 + \frac{6e}{d}\right)$$

In these two equations e is the eccentricity of the prestress load and d is the depth of the member. Since the stresses -358 psi and $+1708$ psi are the final stresses (after losses) that result from P_i, the initial prestress, the initial prestress must be higher than P. Thus, with a loss of 15%, these equations become

$$f_{pit} = \frac{(1 - 0.15)P_i}{A} \times \left(1 - \frac{6e}{d}\right) = -358 \text{ psi} \qquad \text{Equation (1)}$$

$$f_{pib} = \frac{(1 - 0.15)P_i}{A} \times \left(1 + \frac{6e}{d}\right) = +1708 \text{ psi} \qquad \text{Equation (2)}$$

Adding equations (1) and (2),

$$\frac{2(1 - 0.15)P_i}{A} = +1350 \text{ psi}$$

and, for $A = 270$ sq in.,

$$P_i = \frac{1350 \times 270}{2 \times 0.85} = 215,000 \text{ lb}$$

the initial prestress. Either equation (1) or (2) may be used to compute $\frac{6e}{d}$. Taking equation (2),

$$\frac{0.85 \times 215,000}{270} \left(1 + \frac{6e}{d}\right) = +1708$$

$$\frac{6e}{d} = \frac{1708 \times 270}{0.85 \times 215,000} - 1 = 1.52$$

Then

$$e = \frac{1.52 \times 22.5}{6} = 5.7 \text{ in.}$$

the eccentricity of the prestress. Thus the stresses produced by the initial prestress of 215,000 lb are

$$f_{pit} = \frac{215,000}{270} (1 - 1.52) = -414 \text{ psi}$$

$$f_{pib} = \frac{215,000}{270} (1 + 1.52) = +2010 \text{ psi}$$

After 15% loss these stresses will be

$$\text{final } f_{pt} = 0.85 \times (-414) = -352 \text{ psi}$$

$$\text{final } f_{pb} = 0.85 \times (+2010) = +1708 \text{ psi}$$

Because of the eccentric action of the prestress, the beam tends to lift at the center of the span until the dead-load acts.

After the losses in prestress have occurred, the combined dead load and prestress stresses are $+24$ psi at the top and $+1332$ psi at the bottom of the beam, as shown in Fig. 14–7. These stresses are less than the allowable, and, thus far, the 22.5-in. depth is acceptable.

When the stresses that result from the live load are added, Fig. 14–8 shows that the stresses at the top and bottom of the beam are

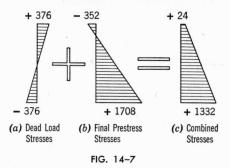

+ 376   − 352   + 24

− 376   + 1708   + 1332

(a) Dead Load Stresses   (b) Final Prestress Stresses   (c) Combined Stresses

FIG. 14–7

+1356 psi and 0 psi, respectively. The entire area of concrete is in compression. The slight overstress of 6 psi at the top of the beam is acceptable.

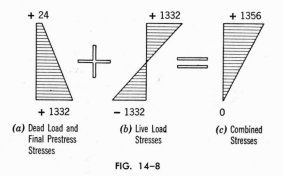

+ 24   + 1332   + 1356

+ 1332   − 1332   0

(a) Dead Load and Final Prestress Stresses   (b) Live Load Stresses   (c) Combined Stresses

FIG. 14–8

To determine the required area of steel to produce the prestress, two conditions must be fulfilled:

1. At initial prestress,

$$A_s = \frac{\text{initial prestress } P_i}{\text{allowable initial stress } f_s} = \frac{215,000}{200,000} = 1.08 \text{ sq in.}$$

2. At final prestress (after losses)

$$A_s = \frac{\text{final prestress } P}{\text{allowable final } f_s} = \frac{0.85 \times 215,000}{150,000} = 1.22 \text{ sq in.}$$

The second value governs, and the required steel area may be arranged in four strands (or cables) of seven wires each. The required area of each wire is $\dfrac{1.22}{4 \times 7}$, or 0.0436 sq in. The corresponding diameter for this area is 0.236 in. Accept 0.25-in. diameter wires.

The strands are run through longitudinal tubes set in the forms before placing the concrete. The holes in the tubes are slightly larger than the strands and as smooth as possible so that there will be a minimum of friction during the prestressing. For an exact design, the areas of the holes are deducted from the nominal area of the cross section. The section modulus of the net cross-sectional area of the beam is also computed. To protect the wires from corrosion, the interstices between the walls of the tubes and the strands are filled with cement grout after the prestressing is completed.

Thus far the design has considered the stresses at a section of the beam at the center of the span (where the maximum bending moment occurs) that result from the dead and live loads. At the ends of the beams, the stresses in the concrete are due only to shear and the prestress; the bending moments of both the dead and live loads are zero. It was seen that the stresses after losses are -352 (tension) psi and $+1708$ (compression) psi at the top and bottom of the beam, respectively. These stresses, however, are excessive; they are not acceptable and must be reduced. Since they are due to the eccentricity of the prestress load at the ends of the beam, the stresses may be reduced by reducing the degree of eccentricity. One half of the number of strands, two, is draped in the form of a parabola so that there is no eccentricity for these two strands at the ends of the beam. Since the initial prestress is 215,000 lb, each pair of strands has a prestress of 107,500 lb, as shown in Fig. 14–9.

From the properties of the parabola, the angle with the horizon-

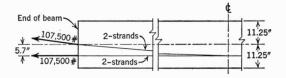

FIG. 14–9

tal at the end of the beam is computed and the vertical and horizontal components of the inclined prestress are determined. For this example, these forces are shown in Fig. 14–10.

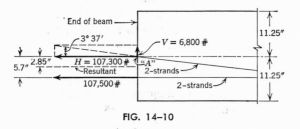

FIG. 14–10

The resultant of the two horizontal forces has a magnitude of 107,300 + 107,500, or 214,800 lb. To find its distance from the mid-depth of the beam (e, its eccentricity), write an equation of moments about the point "A," Fig. 14–10. Then

$$(107,500 \times 5.7) + (107,300 \times 0) = 214,800 \times e$$

and

$$e = 2.85 \text{ in.}$$

the eccentricity of the resultant, 214,800 lb.

To find the direct compressive stresses at the end of the beam that result from this initial prestress of 214,800 lb, we shall use the formulas given in Art. 12–4, Fig. 12–4(b). Then

$$\text{Top} \quad f_{pit} = \frac{214,800}{270}\left(1 - \frac{6 \times 2.85}{22.5}\right) = +191 \text{ psi}$$

$$\text{Bottom } f_{pib} = \frac{214,800}{270}\left(1 + \frac{6 \times 2.85}{22.5}\right) = +1400 \text{ psi}$$

Thus, we see that now (at the end of the beam) there is no tension at the top, and the stress at the bottom is less than the temporarily allowable stress of 1650 psi. After the loss in prestress these stresses become

$$\text{Top} \quad f_{pit} = +191 \times 0.85 = +162 \text{ psi}$$

$$\text{Bottom } f_{pib} = +1400 \times 0.85 = +1190 \text{ psi}$$

These two stresses are acceptable.

In addition to a reduction of stresses at the ends of the beam to values within the allowable, the draping of the steel wires produces a force acting vertically upward. This is directly opposite to the forces due to the dead and live loads. Thus the shear at the ends of the beam is reduced. Because the shear for the dead and live loads is $4230 + 15,000$ or $19,230$ lb and the upward force after loss is 6800×0.85 or 5780 lb,

$$V = 19,230 - 5780 = 13,450 \text{ lb}$$

Since the beam has a rectangular cross section, the maximum shear is at its mid-depth,*

$$v = \frac{3}{2} \times \frac{V}{A} = \frac{3}{2} \times \frac{13,450}{270} = 75 \text{ psi}$$

Acceptable.

In a conventional reinforced concrete beam the shearing stress is a measure of diagonal tension. In prestressed concrete the diagonal tension is further reduced by the presence of longitudinal stresses in the beam at the mid-depth. The resulting so-called "principal stress" may be computed with sufficient accuracy by the formula

$$f_{\text{prin}} = -\sqrt{v^2 + \left(\frac{f_m}{2}\right)^2} + \frac{f_m}{2}$$

in which f_m = the compressive stress at the mid-depth due to the prestress in psi and v = the shearing stress at the mid-depth in psi. In this example,

$$f_m = \frac{162 + 1190}{2} = 676 \text{ psi}$$

Then

$$f_{\text{prin}} = -\sqrt{75^2 + \left(\frac{676}{2}\right)^2} + \frac{676}{2} = -8 \text{ psi}$$

Acceptable.

This 30-ft-span simple beam was first designed as a conventional reinforced concrete beam. Now it has been designed as a prestressed beam. It is noted that prestressing permits a substantial reduction in depth (28 to 22.5 in.) and, consequently, in weight

* See Art. 7-5, *Simplified Mechanics and Strength of Materials.*

and cost of side forms, a reduction in the required steel area of almost one fourth of that required in the conventional beam, and also a reduction in the shearing unit stress despite the smaller dimensions of the beam. These are economies, but part of the savings may be offset by the higher price of the high strength steel wires and of the prestressing process itself.

14–8. Posttensioning and Pretensioning. In the foregoing example the prestress was applied *after* the concrete had attained sufficient strength to sustain the stresses set up by the prestress. This method of prestressing is known as *posttensioning*, sometimes called *unbonded prestressing*. The wires or cables are placed in the forms in light metal or cardboard tubes to prevent a bond between the concrete and the wires. Anchorages, through which the wires are threaded, are placed at the ends of the beams and the tensioning is applied by means of hydraulic jacks.

In *pretensioning* or *bonded prestressing* the wires or cables are placed in the empty forms and pulled to their required tensile stress by means of jacks. After this, the concrete is placed in the forms and allowed to cure. When the jacks are released, the stress in the wires is transferred to the concrete by the bond between the two materials. The design of a pretensioned member is similar to that of a posttensioned member, except that the losses in prestress may be greater for a pretensioned beam because of shrinkage and creep during the hardening of the concrete.

INDEX

TABLE 4–1. FORMULA COEFFICIENTS FOR RECTANGULAR BEAM SECTIONS

$n = 12$ ($f'_c = 2500$ psi)

f_s	f_c	K	k	j	p
18,000	875	141	0.368	0.877	0.0089
	950	161	0.388	0.871	0.0102
	1000	173	0.400	0.867	0.0111
	1125	207	0.429	0.857	0.0134
20,000	875	133	0.344	0.885	0.0075
	950	152	0.363	0.879	0.0086
	1000	164	0.375	0.875	0.0094
	1125	196	0.403	0.866	0.0113

$n = 10$ ($f'_c = 3000$ psi)

f_s	f_c	K	k	j	p
18,000	1050	169	0.368	0.877	0.0107
	1125	189	0.385	0.872	0.0120
	1200	208	0.400	0.867	0.0133
	1350	248	0.429	0.857	0.0161
20,000	1050	160	0.344	0.885	0.0090
	1125	178	0.360	0.880	0.0101
	1200	197	0.375	0.875	0.0113
	1350	236	0.403	0.866	0.0136

$n = 8$ ($f'_c = 3750$ psi)

f_s	f_c	K	k	j	p
18,000	1300	209	0.366	0.878	0.0132
	1400	234	0.384	0.872	0.0149
	1500	260	0.400	0.867	0.0167
	1688 ·	309	0.428	0.857	0.0200
20,000	1300	197	0.342	0.886	0.0111
	1400	221	0.359	0.880	0.0126
	1500	246	0.375	0.875	0.0141
	1688	294	0.403	0.866	0.0170